CATALC

OF BRITISH &

CIGARETTL …ARDS

1998 edition

FIRST CATALOGUE PRODUCED IN 1929

Cards illustrated on front cover are from the series:
John Player & Sons   Cricketers Caricatures by 'Rip' 1926
John Player & Sons   Film Stars 3rd Series 1938
Ogdens Ltd   Motor Races 1931

ISBN 0 903790 76 9

Published by
THE LONDON CIGARETTE CARD COMPANY LTD
Sutton Road, Somerton,
Somerset, England TA11 6QP

Telephone: 01458-273452
Fax: 01458-273515
International Calls: Telephone: 011 44 1458-273452
Fax: 011 44 1458-273515

HOW TO USE THE CATALOGUE

This catalogue is published in four sections. Section 1 covers the cigarette card issues of British Tobacco Manufacturers for the home market together with certain export series (indicated by 'export' in brackets). Section 2 deals with cards issued outside the United Kingdom. Section 3 covers reprinted series and section 4 illustrations.

In each section manufacturers are featured in alphabetical order, and the issues of each firm are catalogued alphabetically within suitable sub-divisions, such as, in Section 1, 'Pre-1919 Issues', 'Post-1920 Issues', 'Silks', 'Miscellaneous' and, in Section 2, 'With Brand Name', 'Without Brand Name', 'Silks', etc. Where a brand name but no maker's name is shown on the card, reference should be made to the appropriate Index of Brands. Anonymous series, that is those with printed backs but no brand or maker's name, are listed under the firms to which the issue has been attributed. Anonymous British issues are also listed at the end of Section 1.

Information is given in the columns from left to right as follows:

Size

(a) British issues and reprints series: the code letter refers to the size of the card as indicated in the chart on page x. A number 1 or 2 after the letter means that the card is slightly larger or smaller than shown.

(b) Foreign issues: the absence of a code letter indicates that the series is of standard size. A code letter 'L' defines the card as being large (about 80 × 62 mm). Other codes are 'K' = smaller than standard, 'M' = between standard and large, and 'EL' = larger than large.

Printing

(a) British issues and reprint series: the code indicates the printing on the front of the card. 'BW' = black-and-white; 'C' = coloured; 'CP' = colour photograph; 'P' = photograph; 'U' = uncoloured (monochrome).

(b) Foreign issues: the letter 'P' is used to show that a series consists of photographs.

Number in Set

This figure gives the number of cards in the series. A question mark alongside shows the exact number is unknown.

Title and Date

Where a series title is printed on the cards, this is used in the catalogue. For cards which do not exhibit a series title, an 'adopted' title is shown (indicated by an asterisk in the British section). Where a firm issued more than one series with the same title, these are distinguished by the addition of 'Set 1', 'Set 2', etc. or a code letter. The date of issue, where known, is shown in brackets, otherwise an approximate date is shown prefixed by 'C'.

Reference Code

(a) British issues: un-numbered series, series issued by more than one manufacturer, and different series of the same title issued by a single firm, have been given an 'H' or 'Ha' number cross-referencing to Handbooks Parts I and II respectively, which provide further information. In some cases it might be necessary to follow the 'H' number through to Handbook Part II and also the World Tobacco Indexes (i.e. H.189 in Handbook Part I, Ha.189 in Handbook Part II, and XI/H.189 in World Index).

(b) Foreign issues: 'RB18' followed by a number refers to the BAT and Tobacco War reference book. 'WI' and 'WII' refer to World Tobacco Index Part I and Part II respectively. A reference number following a Wills series relates to the Wills Reference Book (details of these publications will be found on page iv).

Prices

The last two columns show the London Cigarette Card Company's selling prices for odd cards and complete sets in very good condition. Where no price is shown, this does not necessarily mean that the Company are permanently unable to supply, and if you require items in this category please request a quotation enclosing a self-addressed envelope either with an International Reply Coupon or ready-stamped for posting in Britain.

HOW TO ORDER CARDS

\vailability

Ve have the world's largest stocks of cigarette cards and the chances are that we will be able to supply 'our requirements for most series at the prices shown in the catalogue. However, certain odd cards, par-icularly from rarer series, may not be available in top condition and in such cases it is helpful if you indi-ate whether cards of a lower standard are acceptable at reduced prices. If a complete set is not in stock, ve may be able to offer a part set, with one or two cards missing, at the appropriate fraction of full cata-ogue price. In some instances we can supply sets on request in fair to good condition at half catalogue rice. If in doubt, please write for a quotation, enclosing a stamped, self-addressed envelope.

:nd Numbers

Vhen ordering 'end' numbers, for example Nos. 1 and 50 of a set of fifty, please note that the following pplies. For series catalogued up to £1 per card, end cards are charged at treble price. For series catalogued rom £1 to £3 per card, end cards are charged at £3 per card. And for series catalogued at more than £3 er card there is no additional charge for end numbers.

'ostage

nland second class post is included in all prices quoted. Overseas postage is charged at cost.

Overseas payments in currencies other than Sterling are acceptable, but allow £4 for bank conversion harges.

)rdering

'lease ensure that your name and full address are clearly shown. State the maker's name and the set title equired (with 'first series', 'second series', date of issue, etc. as appropriate). For odds, please list each ndividual number wanted. Make your crossed cheque or postal order payable to The London Cigarette 'ard Company Limited and enclose with order. Notes and coins should be registered. Foreign remittances vill be credited after conversion and deduction of bank charges. We accept Access, Eurocard, Mastercard nd Visa credit cards. Quote your card number and expiry date. Please allow 14 days for delivery. Send our order to:

The London Cigarette Card Co. Ltd.
Sutton Road, Somerton, Somerset TA11 6QP, England
Telephone: Somerton (01458) 273452

nswering Machine For the convenience of customers, an answering machine is in operation to receive rders when the office is closed. Just leave your order, name and address with credit card number and xpiry date, and it will be dealt with as soon as possible. Please note that we can only deal with odds rders and general enquiries in office hours. Telephone number: (01458) 273452 (international 011 44 458 273452).

ax Machine Our fax machine is on 24 hours a day to receive orders. Just place your order stating your ame, address, credit card number and expiry date. The fax number is (01458) 273515 (international 011 4 1458 273515).

emember that your cards will look their best when displayed in one of our albums, for which please see age viii. Value Added Tax where applicable is included in all prices shown, at the current rate of 17½%.

howroom

.t our Showroom in separate premises in West Street, Somerton, some 2,500 different sets are displayed r sale, together with a large selection of framed cards, albums and books, as well as framing kits and ounting boards. For further information about the Showroom, including opening times, please see back over. Odd cards for collectors' wants lists are not stocked at the Showroom, but are available from our eadquarters in Sutton Road on Mondays to Fridays from 9.30am to 1pm and 2pm to 4.30pm.

uarantee

the unlikely event that you, the collector, are not satisfied with the cards supplied, we guarantee replace them or refund your money, provided the goods are returned within 14 days of receipt. This uarantee does not affect your statutory rights.

CARTOPHILIC REFERENCE BOOKS

Handbook Part I (1888 to 1919). 172-page reference book (no prices) listing subjects of unnumbered series, etc. Illustrated, hardback. Covers British cigarette cards issued between 1888 and 1919, cross-referenced to the catalogue (964 cards illustrated) **£12.00**

Handbook Part II (1920 to 1940). 164-page reference book (no prices) listing subjects of unnumbered series, etc. Illustrated, hardback. Covers British cigarette cards issued between 1920 and 1940, and all silk issues, cross-referenced to the catalogue (906 cards illustrated) **£12.00**

World Tobacco Card Index and Handbook Part I. 701 pages and nearly 2,000 cards illustrated **£23.50**

World Tobacco Card Index Part II. Supplement to Index I, 452 pages with approximately 3,600 cards illustrated **£15.50**

World Tobacco Card Index Part III. Supplement to Index I and II, 504 pages with more than 650 cards illustrated **£25.00**

World Tobacco Card Index Part IV. Supplement to Index I, II and III, 688 pages, illustrated . . **£18.50**

World Tobacco Card Index Part V. Supplement to Index I, II, III, IV, 552 pages with approximately 1300 cards illustrated **£18.50**

The Card Issues of Abdulla/Adkin/Anstie. 20 pages **£3.25**

The Card Issues of Ardath Tobacco. 28 pages **£3.25**

Australian and New Zealand Card Issues. Over 300 pages with 600 cards illustrated **£15.50**

The Card Issues of BAT and Tobacco War. 336 pages with nearly 3,000 cards illustrated. . . . **£12.50**

The Card Issues of Churchman. 36 pages with 29 cards illustrated **£3.25**

The Card Issues of Faulkner. 12 pages **£3.25**

The Card Issues of Gallaher. 40 pages **£3.25**

The Card Issues of Hill. 28 pages **£3.25**

The Card Issues of Lambert & Butler. 32 pages with 25 cards illustrated **£3.25**

The Card Issues of Ogdens including Guinea Gold. 244 pages with 356 cards illustrated **£12.50**

The Card Issues of Godfrey Phillips. 40 pages with 225 cards illustrated **£3.25**

The Card Issues of John Player. 44 pages with 26 cards illustrated **£3.25**

The Card Issues of Taddy. 32 pages with 30 cards illustrated **£3.25**

The Card Issues of Wills. 200 pages with 559 cards illustrated **£10.00**

Guide Book No. 1, Ty-Phoo Tea Cards. 36 pages with 68 cards illustrated **£3.25**

Guide Book No. 2, F. & J. Smith Cards. 36 pages with 79 cards illustrated **£3.25**

Guide Book No. 3, A & BC Gum Cards. 44 pages with 29 cards illustrated (2nd edition 1994). . . **£3.25**

British Trade Card Index Part I. Pre-1945 issues, 216 pages with 423 cards illustrated **£10.00**

British Trade Card Index Part II. 1945-1968 issues, 232 pages with 274 cards illustrated **£10.00**

British Trade Card Index Part III. 1968-1986 issues, 400 pages with 480 cards illustrated . . . **£12.50**

British Trade Card Index Part IV. 1986-1994 issues, 411 pages with 550 cards illustrated . . . **£20.00**

Errors and Varieties in British Trade Cards. 36 pages with 33 cards illustrated **£3.25**

Directory of British Tobacco Issuers. 36 pages with 16 cards illustrated **£3.25**

Glossary of Cartophilic Terms. 40 pages with 27 cards illustrated **£3.25**

Brooke Bond Picture Cards — The First Forty Years. 72 pages with more than 100 colour Illustrations **£6.75**

BOOKS FOR THE COLLECTOR

The Catalogue of Trade Card Issues, 1998 Edition (illustrated). This catalogue details a magnificent selection of different series issued by non-tobacco companies including Barratt and Brooke Bond from the 19th century to the present day. Contains many mint condition sets priced at only £1.75 each plus 16 pages of illustrations **£4.50**

The Catalogue of Liebig Issues, 1996 Edition. Features around 1,500 different series (all except the earliest). This book lists each title with Fada reference, number in set, date of issue and price **£3.00**

Collecting Cigarette Cards and Other Trade Issues by Dorothy Bagnall. An interesting paperback dealing with cigarette and trade cards from their origin through to the post-war period. 112 pages with 126 cards Illustrated **£5.00**

The Pinnace Collection. All 2462 footballer cards of the 1920s issued by Godfrey Phillips. Illustrated and listed alphabetically, 112 pages **£10.50**

Cigarette & Trade Cards by Gordon Howsden. Traces the history and development of cards from their beginning to the present day and includes the background of the issuing firms, thematic collecting, printing and production, grading, pricing and so on. Authoritatively written in an easy-to-read style and beautifully illustrated in colour, the book approaches the subject from a fresh angle which will appeal to seasoned collectors and newcomers alike. Cigarette & Trade Cards is not only an indispensable reference work but also a joy to read or just browse through. 152 large-format pages with 220 colour illustrations featuring 750 cards and related ephemera **£12.95**

FRAMING KITS

The frames are designed with glass on both sides so that the cards can be placed in the mount to display both fronts and backs without risk of damage.

COMPLETE EMPTY FRAMES

Complete kit includes wooden frame, mounting board, two sheets of glass, spring clips, etc., ready for wall display in the following sizes:

50 standard size cards	£35.00	25 large size cards	£35.00
25 standard size cards	£20.00	24 large size cards	£35.00
15 standard size cards	£16.00	20 large size cards	£32.00
10 standard size cards	£14.00	15 large size cards	£27.00
3 standard size cards	£6.50	12 large size cards	£20.00
1 standard size card	£6.50	6 large size cards	£14.00

1 postcard size card £6.50

MOUNTING BOARDS

Mounting boards can be purchased separately in green, black, brown or maroon as follows:

50 standard size cards	£4.25	25 large size cards	£4.25
25 standard size cards	£3.25	* 24 large size cards	£4.25
** 15 standard size cards	£2.50	* 20 large size cards	£4.25
10 standard size cards	£2.50	** 15 large size cards	£4.25
3 standard size cards	£2.00	** 12 large size cards	£3.25
1 standard size card	£2.00	6 large size cards	£2.25

1 postcard size card £2.00

* Available in black only

** Available only in green or black

POST FREE TO UK ADDRESSES, OR COLLECT FROM OUR SHOWROOM

AUCTIONS AND FAIRS

Saturday 3 January 1998	Postal Auction
Saturday 7 February 1998	Postal Auction
Saturday 7 March 1998	at Langport Arms Hotel, Langport, Somerset
Saturday 4 April 1998	Postal Auction
Saturday 2 May 1998	Postal Auction
Saturday 6 June 1998	at Eccleston Hotel, Victoria, London
Saturday 4 July 1998	Postal Auction
Saturday 1 August 1998	Postal Auction
Saturday 5 September 1998	Postal Auction
Saturday 3 October 1998	at Langport Arms Hotel, Langport, Somerset
Saturday 7 November 1998	Postal Auction
Saturday 5 December 1998	at Eccleston Hotel, Victoria, London

Viewing from 10.00a.m.

Auction begins 1.30p.m.

Auction catalogues available 4 weeks before date of sale free from the address below (automatically sent free to *Cigarette Card News* subscribers)

Also on display at the London & Somerset auctions over 2500 different sets for direct sale:

* Many hundreds of sets in mint condition from £1.50
* Selection of rare sets in top condition
* Wide range of sets in fair to good condition at half price
* Hundreds of pre-1918 odd cards and types individually priced
* The latest new issues and additions to stock
* Books, collectors' aids and albums
* Specific requirements brought for viewing if requested in advance

Free admission. Everybody welcome.

Eccleston Hotel, Victoria, London:

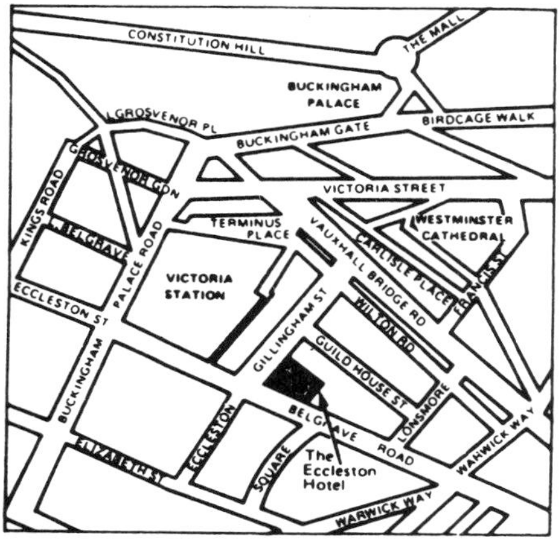

Langport Arms Hotel, Langport, Somerset:

From London: M3, A303 to junction with A37, then A372.

From the Midlands and North: M5 to junction 25, A378 to Langport.

From the South Coast: various routes to Yeovil, A37 to Ilchester, B3151 to A372 to Langport.

From the South West: M5 to junction 25, A378 to Langport.

From Bath/Bristol: use A367/A37 to junction with A303, A372 to Langport.

The Langport Arms Hotel is in the town centre adjacent to the main free car park.

THE LONDON CIGARETTE CARD COMPANY LIMITED
SUTTON ROAD, SOMERTON, SOMERSET TA11 6QP, ENGLAND
Telephone: (01458) 273452
Fax: (01458) 273515

THE CIGARETTE CARD VIDEO

On 7 January 1993, history was made when the first ever television programme devoted entirely to cigarette cards was broadcast by HTV. And now you can buy the video, called 'Miniature Masterpieces'.

Introduced by the well-known west country personality Fred Wedlock, whose grandfather played football for Bristol City and who is featured in Ogden's 1905 series of Famous Footballers, the programme concentrates on the heyday of cigarette cards. In visits to the Wills' tobacco factory and the printers Mardon Son & Hall, we meet Eric Sampson, one of the artists who were employed in the top floor studios during the 1930s, and see some of his work. Text writer, Geoff Bennett, tells us about one of his mistakes which led to the issue of a corrected card, and we observe a modern artist, Eric Bottomley, at work on the recent series of Britain's Motoring History. Charlie Watkins, retired foreman printer at Mardons, shows us how cards were printed by chromolithography and letterpress. We see cards from many different periods — the Boer War, World War I, the 1920s and '30s, through to the famous Air Raid Precautions series, among the last to be printed by Mardons before their Caxton Works was destroyed in the blitz.

The cameras visit the London Cigarette Card Company in Somerton, and Frank Doggett demonstrates some of the more unusual cartophilic items such as silks, cards in metal frames and a record cigarette card which somehow the sound engineers actually manage to play. The film sound track cleverly uses music and historic recordings to recreate the essence of the period.

This fascinating tape was made by the production company Forum Television and plays for approximately 25 minutes. It is now available exclusively from the London Cigarette Card Company. For the technically minded, the tape is on the PAL standard (625 lines) and is suitable for playing in Great Britain and Europe (except France), Australia, New Zealand, South Africa and many other countries around the world, but not in the USA and Canada which are on the NTSC system. If in doubt, overseas collectors should seek advice. Normal copyright rules apply.

This is a unique opportunity to obtain a fascinating film which really does do justice to the subject — you will be impressed.

Price £10.50

SPECIAL ITEMS
for COLLECTORS

* **Numbered printed wants lists**
  30 adhesive labels, Nd 1-50 . . . . **75p**
  30 non-adhesive labels, Nd 1-200 . . . . **75p**

* **'Glascine' wrapping strips:**
  200 pieces for standard size cards (123 × 68 mm) **£2.80**
  200 pieces for large size cards (175 × 83mm) **£3.20**
  200 pieces for extra large size cards (228 × 83mm) **£3.50**

CARD SIZES (Applies to British issues only)

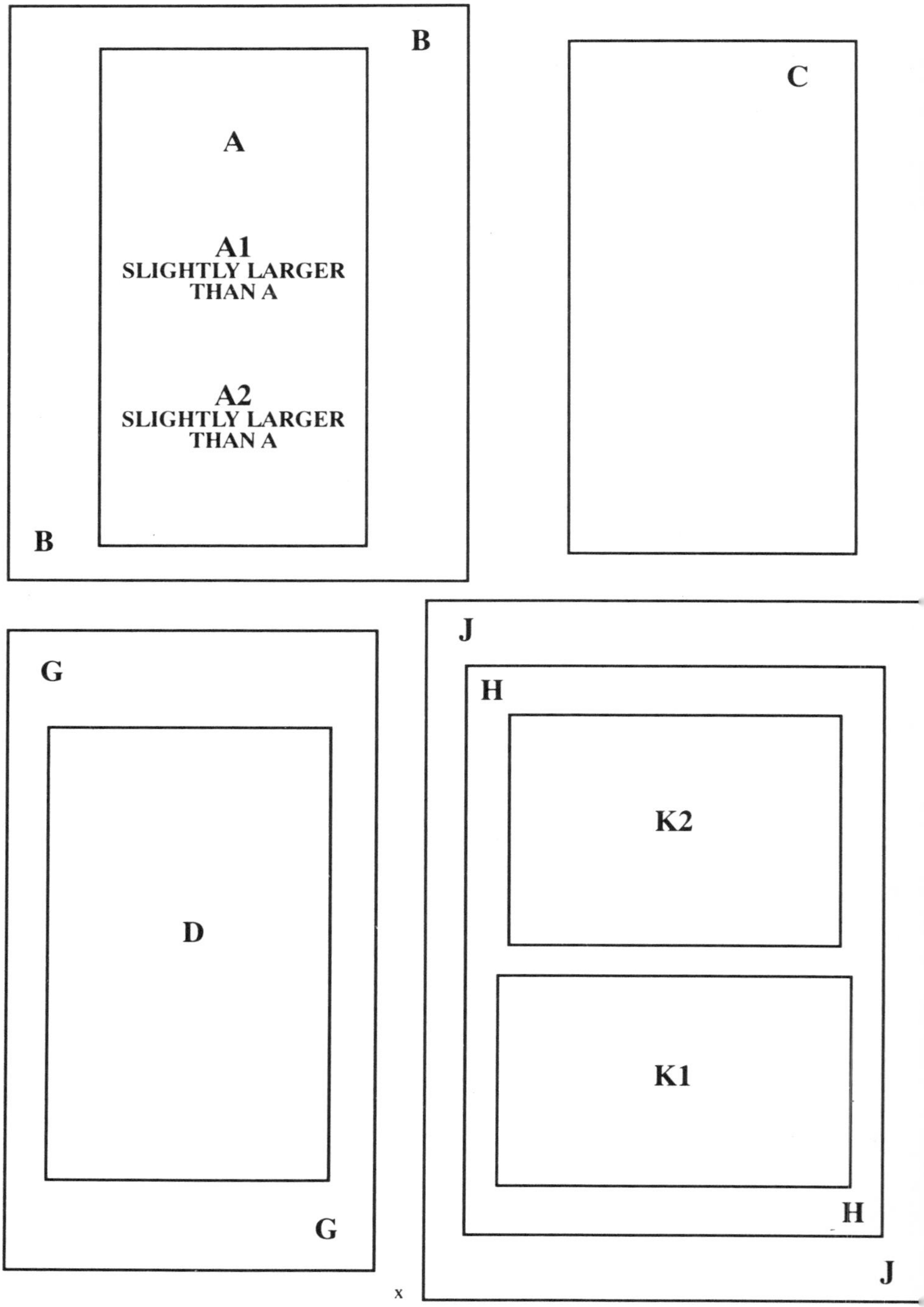

SECTION I

BRITISH CIGARETTE CARDS

INDEX OF BRANDS

The following is a list of the cases so far known where cards appear without the name of issuer, but inscribed with a brand name or other indication which is the collector's only clue to the identity of the issuer.

A INDEX OF BRANDS and initials found on British issues of cards or silks

Leon de Cuba Cigars — see Eldons
Levant Favourites — see B. Morris
Life Ray Cigarettes — see Carreras
Lucana Cigarettes — see Sandorides

Manikin Cigars — see Freeman
Matossian's Cigarettes — see Henley & Watkins
Max Cigarettes — see A. & M. Wix
Mayblossom Cigarettes — see Lambert & Butler
Mills — see Amalgamated

New Orleans Tobacco — see J. & T. Hodge

Oracle Cigarettes — see Tetley

Pibroch Virginia — see Fryer
Pick-Me-Up Cigarettes — see Drapkin & Millhoff
Pinnace — see Godfrey Phillips
Pioneer Cigarettes — see Richmond Cavendish
Polo Mild Cigarettes — see Murray
Private Seal Tobacco — see Godfrey Phillips

QV Cigars — see Webster

RS — see Robert Sinclair
Reina Regenta Cigars — see B. Morris
De Reszke Cigarettes — see Millhoff and Godfrey Phillips
Ringers Cigarettes — see Edwards, Ringer & Bigg
Roseland Cigarettes — see Glass

Senior Service Cigarettes — see Pattreiouex
Spinet Cigarettes or The Spinet House — see Hill
The Spotlight Tobaccos — see Hill
Star of the World Cigarettes — see JLS
State Express Cigarettes — see Ardath
Summit — see International Tobacco Co.
Sunripe Cigarettes — see Hill
Sunspot Cigarettes — see Theman
Sweet Alva Cigarettes — see Drapkin

TSS — see Tobacco Supply Syndicate
Tatley's Cigarettes — see Walker's Tobacco Co.
Three Bells Cigarettes — see J. & F. Bell
Tipsy Loo Cigarettes — see H.C. Lloyd
Topsy Cigarettes — see Richards & Ward
Trawler, Critic and King Lud Cigarettes — see Pattreiouex
Turf Cigarettes — see Carreras

WTC — see Walker's Tobacco Co.

B INDEX OF INSCRIPTIONS found on British issues of cards

'The Cigarettes with which these Picture Cards are issued are manufactured in England and are Guaranteed Pure' — see Hill
'England expects that Every Man will do his duty — By Purchasing these Cigarettes you are supporting British labour' — issuers unknown, see Anonymous
'Issued with these Famous Cigarettes' — see Teofani
'Issued with these Fine Cigarettes' — see Teofani
'Issued with these High Grade Cigarettes' — see Teofani
'Issued with these Well-known Cigarettes' — see Teofani
'Issued with these World Famous Cigarettes' — see Teofani
'Presented with these well-known choice cigarettes' — see Teofani
'Smoke these cigarettes always' — see Teofani
'These Cigarettes are Guaranteed Best British Manufacture' — see Hill.

C INDEX OF OTHER INDICATIONS found on British Tobacco issues

THE B.I. Co. — see Burnstein Isaacs
Chantler & Co., Bury — see Lea
'Eagle, Cork' — see Lambkin
Agnes D. Eld, Dudley — see Lea
L. & Y. Tobacco Co. — see Lancs. and Yorks. Tobacco Manufacturing Co.
Orient Line Steamships — see Singleton & Cole
PO Box 5764, Johannesburg — see A. & M. Wix
S.C. Peacock Sales Co. — see Lea

ABDULLA & CO. LTD, LONDON

20 page Reference Book (combined with Adkin & Anstie) available — £3.25

Size	*Print-ing*	*Number in set*		*Handbook reference*	*Price per card*	*Complete set*
A	***EXPORT ISSUES POST-1920***					
A	BW	50	Beauties of To-Day (1938)	Ha.514	£3.60	—
A	C	25	British Butterflies (1935)	Ha.517-1	£1.00	£25.00
A	P	52	Cinema Stars Set 1 (c1933)	Ha.515-1B	£3.60	—
A2	U	30	Cinema Stars Set 2 (c1933)	Ha.515-2	£3.60	—
A2	U	30	Cinema Stars Set 3 (c1933)	Ha.515-3	£3.60	—
A2	U	32	Cinema Stars Set 4 (c1933)	Ha.515-4	£2.20	£70.00
A2	C	32	Cinema Stars Set 5 (c1933)	Ha.515-5	£2.20	£70.00
A2	C	30	Cinema Stars Set 6 (c1933)	Ha.515-6	£3.60	—
D	C	25	Feathered Friends (1935)	Ha.516	£1.00	£25.00
A2	C	50	Film Favourites (1934)	Ha.517-2	£3.60	—
A	C	50	Film Stars (1934)		£8.00	—
—	C	24	*Film Stars (128 × 89mm) (c1934)	Ha.517-3	£8.00	—
A	C	25	Old Favourites (1936) (Flowers)	Ha.517-4	80p	£20.00
A	C	40	Screen Stars (1939):			
			A Normal Abdulla back		£1.25	£50.00
			B 'Issued by the Successors to ...' back		£1.80	—
A2	C	50	Stage and Cinema Beauties (1935)	Ha.517-5	£3.60	—
A	U	30	Stars of the Stage and Screen (c1934)		£3.60	—
B	***MISCELLANEOUS***					
		? 4	Bridge Rule Cards (various sizes) (c1935)		£16.00	—
—	C	2	Commanders of the Allies (127 × 67mm) (c1915)		£60.00	—
	BW	3	Great War Gift Packings Cards (1916)		£50.00	—
A	U	18	Message Cards (letters of the alphabet) (c1936)		£11.00	—
K2	U	18	Message Cards (letters of the alphabet) (c1936)		£11.00	—

ADCOCK & SON, Norwich

POST-1920 ISSUE

A1	U	12	Ancient Norwich (1928)		—	£85.00
			11/12 Ancient Norwich (No. 6 missing)		£3.00	£33.00

ADKIN & SONS, London

20 page reference book (combined with Abdulla & Anstie) available — £3.25

A	***PRE-1919 ISSUES***					
D	BW	25	*Actresses — French. Nd. 126-150 (c1898)	H.1	£140.00	—
A	C	15	*Beauties 'PAC' (c1898)	H.2	£180.00	—
A2	C	12	Character Sketches:	H.3		
			A Black printing on back (1901)		£7.00	£85.00
			B Green printing on back (1902)		£7.00	£85.00
A2	C	12	A Living Picture (c1901):	H.5		
			A 'Adkin & Sons' at top back			
			(i) crimson		£7.00	£85.00
			(ii) scarlet		£7.00	£85.00
			B 'These cards are ...' at top back		£7.00	£85.00
A	BW	25	Notabilities (1915)	H.6	£5.00	£125.00
A1	C	12	Pretty Girl Series (Actresses) (c1897)	H.7	£50.00	—
A2	C	12	*Pretty Girl Series 'RASH' (1897):	H.8		
			A Calendar back		£50.00	—
			B Advertisements back		£30.00	—
			C Figure and verse back		£30.00	—
D	C	12	A Royal Favourite (1900)	H.9	£12.00	£145.00

ADKIN & SONS, London *(continued)*

Size	*Print-ing*	*Number in set*		*Handbook reference*	*Price per card*	*Complete set*
A	BW		Soldiers of the Queen (1899-1900):	H.10		
			A Series of 50:			
		25	(a) Nos. 1-25 '... and exclusively with'		£27.00	—
		50	(b) Nos. 1-50 and variety '... and issued with ...'		£4.50	£225.00
		59	B Series of 60, plus No. 61 (Nos 28, 33 not issued)		£4.50	—
A	BW	31	*Soldiers of the Queen and Portraits (1901)	H.11	£5.00	£160.00
A	C	30	Sporting Cups and Trophies (1914)		£15.00	—
A	BW	25	War Trophies (1917)		£5.00	£125.00
B	***POST-1920 ISSUES***					
A	C	50	Butterflies and Moths (1924)	H.80	£1.80	£90.00
A	C	50	Wild Animals of the World (1922)	H.77	£1.60	£80.00
C	***MISCELLANEOUS***					
—	C	12	Character Sketches (premium issue) (c1901)		£80.00	—
—	C	? 4	*Games — by Tom Browne, postcard back (135 × 85mm) (c1900)	H.4	£150.00	—
—	C	12	A Living Picture (premium issue) (c1900)		£80.00	—

H.J. AINSWORTH, Harrogate

PRE-1919 ISSUE

D	C	30	*Army Pictures, Cartoons, etc (1916)	H.12	£75.00	—

ALBERGE & BROMET, London

PRE-1919 ISSUES

A	C	25	*Boer War and General Interest (c1900):	H.13		
			A 'Bridal Bouquet' and 'El Benecio' wording on green leaf design back		£85.00	—
			B 'La Optima' and 'Federation' wording on green leaf design back		£85.00	—
			C 'Bridal Bouquet' and 'El Benecio' wording on brown leaf design back		£85.00	—
Dl	C	40	*Naval and Military Phrases (c1904):	H.14		
			A 'Bridal Bouquet' and 'El Benecio'		£80.00	—
			B 'La Optima' and 'Federation'		£80.00	—
Dl	C	30	*Proverbs (c1903)	H.15	£80.00	—

PHILLIP ALLMAN & CO. LTD, London

POST-1940 ISSUES

A	C	50	Coronation Series (1953)		60p	£30.00
			Pin-up Girls (1953):			
A1	C		A First 12 subjects:			
		12	Ai Unnumbered, 'For men only'		£2.75	£33.00
		12	Aii Numbered, 'Ask for Allman always'		£2.75	£33.00
		12	Aiii Unnumbered, 'Ask for Allman always'		£2.75	£33.00
A1	C	12	B Second 12 subjects		£3.25	—
A1	C	24	C Inscribed '1st series of 24'		£6.00	—
—	C	24	D Large size (75 × 68mm)		£3.25	—

AMALGAMATED TOBACCO CORPORATION LTD ('Mills' Cigarettes)

A POST-1940 ISSUES

—	C	25	Famous British Ships 'Series No. 1' (75 × 48mm) (1952)		15p	£3.00
—	C	25	Famous British Ships 'Series No. 2' (75 × 48mm) (1952)		15p	£3.00

AMALGAMATED TOBACCO CORPORATION LTD ('Mills' Cigarettes) *(continued)*

Size	*Print-ing*	*Number in set*		*Handbook reference*	*Price per card*	*Complete set*
—	C	50	History of Aviation (75 × 48mm) (1952):			
			A Nos. 1 to 16, 18 to 25 and 27		£1.70	—
			B Nos. 17, 26 and 28 to 50		16p	£4.00
A	C	25	Kings of England (1954)		£1.40	£35.00
A	C	25	Propelled Weapons (1953)		15p	£3.00
B EXPORT ISSUES						
A	C	25	Aircraft of the World (1958)		25p	£7.50
A	C	25	Animals of the Countryside (1957)		15p	£3.50
A	C	25	Aquarium Fish (1961)		15p	£3.50
A	C	25	Army Badges — Past and Present (1961)		60p	£15.00
A	C	25	British Coins and Costumes (1958)		24p	£6.00
A	C	25	British Locomotives (1961)		28p	£7.00
A	C	25	British Uniforms of the 19th Century (1957)		70p	£17.50
A	C	25	Butterflies and Moths (1957)		15p	£3.25
A	C	25	Cacti (1961)		32p	£8.00
A	C	25	Castles of Britain (1961)		£1.00	£25.00
A	C	25	Coins of the World (1961)		15p	£3.00
A	C	25	Communications (1961)		80p	£20.00
A	C	25	Dogs (1958)		60p	£15.00
A	C	25	Evolution of the Royal Navy (1957)		60p	£15.00
A	C	25	Football Clubs and Badges (1961)		£1.00	£25.00
A	C	25	Freshwater Fish (1958)		24p	£6.00
A	C	25	Guerriers à Travers les Ages (French text) (1961)		70p	£17.50
A	C	25	Historical Buildings (1959)		70p	£17.50
A	C	25	Histoire de l'Aviation, 1st series (French text) (1961)		20p	£5.00
A	C	25	Histoire de l'Aviation, 2nd series (French text) (1962)		50p	£12.50
A	C	25	Holiday Resorts (1957)		15p	£2.75
A	C	25	Interesting Hobbies (1959)		40p	£10.00
A	C	25	Into Space (1958)		24p	£6.00
A	C	25	Les Autos Moderns (French text) (1961)		40p	£10.00
A	C	25	Medals of the World (1959)		20p	£5.00
A	C	25	Merchant Ships of the World (1961)		40p	£10.00
A	C	25	Merveilles Modernes (French text) (1961)		40p	£10.00
A	C	25	Miniature Cars and Scooters (1959)		£1.00	£25.00
A	C	25	Nature (1958)		15p	£2.75
A	C	25	Naval Battles (1959)		30p	£7.50
A	C	25	Ports of the World (1957)		15p	£2.75
A	C	25	Ships of the Royal Navy (1961)		30p	£7.50
A	C	25	Sports and Games (1958)		£1.00	£25.00
A	C	25	Tropical Birds (1959)		£1.00	—
A	C	25	Weapons of Defence (1961)		60p	£15.00
A	C	25	Wild Animals (1958)		20p	£5.00
A	C	25	The Wild West (1960)		80p	£20.00
A	C	25	World Locomotives (1959)		60p	£15.00

THE ANGLO-AMERICAN CIGARETTE MAKING CO. LTD, London

PRE-1919 ISSUE

A	C	20	Russo-Japanese War Series (1906)	Ha.100	£180.00	—

THE ANGLO CIGARETTE MANUFACTURING CO., London

A PRE-1919 ISSUES

A	C	36	Tariff Reform Series (1909)	H.16	£25.00	—

E. & W. ANSTIE, Devizes

Size	Printing	Number in set		Handbook reference	Price per card	Complete set
			20 page reference book (combined with Abdulla & Adkin) available — £3.25			
A	***PRE-1919 ISSUES***					
A	C	16	*British Empire Series (1904)	H.17	£11.00	£175.00
—	C	8	Puzzles (26 × 70mm) (1902)	H.18	£110.00	—
—	C	5	Royal Mail (70 × 50mm) (1899)	H.19	£200.00	—
B	***POST-1920 ISSUES***					
A2	C	25	Aesop's Fables (1934)	Ha.518	£2.00	£50.00
A	BW	40	Nature Notes (1939)		£10.00	—
A	U	50	People of Africa (1926)		£3.00	£150.00
A	U	50	People of Asia (1926)		£3.00	£150.00
A	U	50	People of Europe (1925)		£3.00	£150.00
A2	BW	40	Places of Interest (1939):			
			A Varnished front		75p	£30.00
			B Unvarnished front		£1.50	£60.00
A	C	50	*Racing Series (1922):			
			1-25 — Racing Colours		£4.00	—
			26-50 — Horses, Jockeys, Race-courses, etc		£5.00	—
A	C	50	Scout Series (1923)		£2.40	£120.00
A2	C		Sectional Series:	Ha.519		
		10	Clifton Suspension Bridge (1938)		£2.50	£25.00
		10	Stonehenge (1936)		£2.50	£25.00
		10	The Victory (1936)		£2.50	£25.00
		20	Wells Cathedral (1935)		£1.75	£35.00
		20	Wiltshire Downs (1935)		£1.75	£35.00
		10	Windsor Castle (1937)		£1.70	£17.00
A2	BW	40	Wessex (1938)		£1.25	£50.00
A	U	50	The World's Wonders (1924)		£1.50	£75.00
C	***SILKS.***		Anonymous unbacked woven silks. Width sizes only are quoted as the silks were prepared in ribbon form and length sizes are thus arbitrary.			
—	C	? 9	**Flags, large (width 95mm) (c1915)*	Ha.495-1	£9.00	—
—	C	40	**Flags, small (width 42mm) (c1915)*	Ha.495-1	£1.30	—
—	C	? 83	**Regimental Badges (width 32mm) (c1915)*	Ha.495-3	From £1.20	—
—	C		**Royal Standard and Portraits (c1915):*	Ha.495-2		
		1	*Royal Standard (width 61mm)*		—	£15.00
		1	*King George V:*			
			(a) Large (width 71 mm), black frame		—	£70.00
			(b) Large (width 71mm), gold frame		—	£60.00
			(c) Small (width 15mm)		—	£70.00
		1	*Queen Mary:*			
			(a) Large (width 71 mm)		—	£60.00
			(b) Small (width 35mm)		—	£75.00
		1	*Lord French (width 71mm)*		—	£85.00
		1	*Lord Kitchener (width 71mm)*		—	£20.00

H. ARCHER & CO., London

PRE-1919 ISSUES

C	C		*Actresses — Selection from 'FROGA A and B' (c1900):	H.20		
		? 20	A 'Golden Returns' back		£50.00	—
		? 13	B 'M.F.H.' back		£60.00	—
C			*Beauties — 'CHOAB' (c1900):	H.21		
	U	50	A 'Bound to Win' front		£25.00	—
	C	? 5	B 'Golden Returns' back		£65.00	—
	C	? 4	C 'M.F.H.' back		£65.00	—
C	C	20	*Prince of Wales Series (c1912)	H.22	£25.00	—

ARDATH TOBACCO CO. LTD, London

28 page reference book available — £3.25

Size	*Printing*	*Number in set*		*Handbook reference*	*Price per card*	*Complete set*
A			***PRE-1919 ISSUES***. All export			
—	U	30	Boucher Series (77 × 62mm) (c1915)		£2.60	—
A1	U	40	Franz Hals Series, Dutch back (c1916)		£15.00	—
—	U	30	Gainsborough Series (77 × 62mm) (c1915)		£2.60	—
A1	U	50	Great War Series (c1916)		£5.00	—
A1	U	50	Great War Series 'B' (c1916)		£5.00	—
A1	U	50	Great War Series 'C' (c1916)		£5.00	—
			Hollandsche Oude Meesters, Dutch back (70 × 60mm) (c1916):			
—	U	25	A First 25 subjects		£15.00	—
—	U	25	B Second 25 subjects		£15.00	—
—	U	30	Raphael Series (77 × 62mm) (c1915)		£2.60	—
—	U		Rembrandt Series (1914):			
		30	A Large size (77 × 62 mm), English back		£3.50	—
		40	B Large size (77 × 62mm), Dutch back		£16.00	—
		30	C Extra-large size (101 × 62mm)		£5.00	—
—	U	30	Rubens Series (77 × 61 mm) (c1915):			
			A English 'State Express' back		£2.60	—
			B English 'Winfred' back		£15.00	—
			C Dutch back		£15.00	—
			D New Zealand 'State Express' back		£15.00	—
—	U	30	Valasquez Series (c1915):			
			A Large size (77 × 62mm)		£3.50	—
			B Extra-large size (101 × 62mm)		£5.00	—
B			***POST-1920 NON-PHOTOGRAPHIC ISSUES***			
A1	C	50	*Animals at the Zoo (export) (c1924):	Ha.520		
			A Back with descriptive text		£2.20	—
			B Back without description, 'Double Ace' issue		£15.00	—
A	C	96	Ardath Modern School Atlas (export) (c1935)		£1.30	—
A	C	25	Big Game Hunting (export) (c1930):			
			A Back in blue		£3.00	—
			B Back in black		£12.00	—
A	U	50	Britain's Defenders (1936)		70p	£35.00
	U	50	British Born Film Stars (export) (1934):			
A2			A Small size, back white semi-glossy		£1.40	—
A2			B Small size, back cream matt		£1.40	—
—			C Medium size (67 × 53mm)		£2.30	—
	U		Camera Studies (c1939):			
—		36	A Small size (70 × 44mm)		£1.00	£36.00
—		45	B Large size (79 × 57mm)		£1.00	£45.00
—	C	25	Champion Dogs (95 × 67mm) (1934)		£1.20	£30.00
A	C	50	Cricket, Tennis and Golf Celebrities (1935):			
			A Home issue, grey back		£1.20	£60.00
			B Export issue, brownish-grey back, text revised		£1.80	£90.00
—	U	25	Dog Studies (95 × 68mm) (1938)		£3.00	£75.00
A	C	25	Eastern Proverbs (export) (c1930)	Ha.521	£1.40	£35.00
A	C	48	Empire Flying-Boat (sectional) (1938)		£1.50	£75.00
A	C	50	Empire Personalities (1937)		60p	£30.00
A	C	50	Famous Film Stars (1934)		80p	£40.00
A	C	50	Famous Footballers (1934)		£1.00	£50.00
A	C	25	Famous Scots (1935)		£1.00	£25.00
—	C	25	Fighting and Civil Aircraft (96 × 68mm) (1936)		£1.60	£40.00
A	C	50	Figures of Speech (1936)		70p	£35.00
A	C	50	Film, Stage and Radio Stars (1935)		80p	£40.00

ARDATH TOBACCO CO. LTD, London *(continued)*

Size	*Print-ing*	*Number in set*		*Handbook reference*	*Price per card*	*Complete set*
—	C	25	Film, Stage and Radio Stars (96 × 68mm) (1935)		£1.20	£30.00
—	C	50	From Screen and Stage (96 × 65mm) (1936)		80p	£40.00
A	U	50	Life in the Services (1938):			
			A Home issue, adhesive		70p	£35.00
			B Export issue, non-adhesive		£1.20	£60.00
A	C	50	National Fitness (1938):			
			A Home issue, adhesive		50p	£25.00
			B Export issue, non-adhesive		80p	£40.00
A	U	50	Our Empire (export) (c1937)	Ha.522	£1.20	£60.00
A	C		Proverbs (c1936):			
		25	A Home issue Nos 1-25		80p	£20.00
		25	B Export issue Nos 26-50		£1.80	—
	U	100	Scenes from Big Films (export) (1935):			
A			A Small size, white back		£1.60	—
A			B Small size, cream back		£1.60	—
—			C Medium Size (67 × 52mm)		£3.50	—
A	C	50	Silver Jubilee (1935)		70p	£35.00
A	C	50	Speed — Land, Sea and Air (1935):			
			A Home issue, 'Issued with State Express'		£1.20	£60.00
			B Export issue, Ardath name at base		£1.60	—
—	C	25	Speed — Land, Sea and Air (95 × 68mm) (1938)		£1.00	£25.00
A	C	50	Sports Champions (1935):			
			A Home issue, 'State Express' at base		90p	£45.00
			B Export issue, 'Ardath' at base		£1.60	£80.00
A	C	50	Stamps — Rare and Interesting (1939)		£1.20	£60.00
A	C	50	Swimming, Diving and Life-Saving (1937) (export)	Ha.523	£1.40	—
A	C	50	Tennis (1937) (export)	Ha.524	£1.50	—
A	C	48	Trooping the Colour (sectional) (1939)		£1.80	£90.00
A	C	50	Who is This? (1936) (Film Stars)		£1.80	£90.00
—	BW	24	World Views (No. 13 not issued) (95 × 68mm) (1937)		32p	£8.00
A	C	50	Your Birthday Tells Your Fortune (1937)		60p	£30.00

C POST-1920 PHOTOGRAPHIC ISSUES

A2	P	54	Beautiful English Women (1928) (export)		£3.00	—
A2	P	35	Hand Shadows (c1930) (export)		£18.00	—
A2	CP	50	New Zealand Views (1928) (export)		£2.50	—
H	P		Photocards — Numbered Series (1936)*:			
		110	'A' — Football Clubs of Lancashire		£1.00	£110.00
		110	'B' — Football Clubs of North East Counties		£1.00	£110.00
		110	'C' — Football Clubs of Yorkshire		£1.00	£110.00
		165	'D' — Football Clubs of Scotland		85p	£140.00
		110	'E' — Football Clubs of Midlands		£1.00	£110.00
		110	'F' — Football Clubs of London and Southern Counties		85p	£95.00
		99	'Z' — General Interest (Sports):			
			Nos. 111-165		40p	£22.00
			Nos. 166-209 (Cricket etc)		40p	£18.00
		11	'A.s' (1), 'C.s' (2-3), 'E.s' (4-10), 'F.s' (11) — Football Clubs (supplementary)		£3.00	£33.00
H	P		Photocards — 'A Continuous Series of Topical Interest' (1937):	Ha.525		
		22	Group A — Racehorses and Sports		65p	£14.00
		22	Group B — Coronation and Sports		—	£35.00
			21 Different (minus Walter Neusel)		70p	£14.00
		22	Group C — Lancashire Personalities		—	£42.00
			21 Different (minus Gracie Fields)		£1.00	£21.00
		22	Group D — Sports and Miscellaneous		£1.00	£22.00

ARDATH TOBACCO CO. LTD, London *(continued)*

Size	*Print-ing*	*Number in set*		*Handbook reference*	*Price per card*	*Complete set*
		22	Group E — Film Stars and Sports		£1.00	£22.00
		22	Group F — Film Stars and Sportsmen		£1.00	£22.00
		66	'G.S.' — Miscellaneous subjects (export)		£1.80	—
H	P		Photocards — 'A Continuous Series of General interest', with album offer (1938):	Ha.526		
		11	Group G — Australian Cricketers		£18.00	—
		22	Group H — Film, Radio and Sporting Stars		£1.00	£22.00
		22	Group I — Film Stars and Miscellaneous		£1.20	£26.00
	P		Photocards — 'A Continuous Series of General Interest', without album offer — uncoloured (1938):	Ha.527		
H		22	Group J — Film Stars and General Interest		70p	£15.00
H		22	Group K — Film, Radio and Sporting Stars:			
			1 With 'Kings' Clause		£1.00	£22.00
			2 Without 'Kings' Clause (export)		£1.20	£26.00
H		44	Group L — Film Stars and Miscellaneous		60p	£26.00
		45	Group M — Film Stars and Miscellaneous:			
C			1 Small size		80p	£36.00
—			2 Large size (80 × 69 mm), with 'Kings' Clause		80p	£36.00
—			3 Large size (80 × 69mm), without 'Kings' Clause		80p	£36.00
	P	45	Group N — Film, Stage and Radio Stars:			
C			1 Small size		80p	£36.00
—			2 Large size (80 × 69mm)		80p	£36.00
H	CP		Photocards — 'A Continuous Series of General Interest', without album offer — Hand coloured (export) (1938):	Ha.528		
		22	Group 1 — Views of the World		80p	£17.50
		22	Group 2 — Views of the World		80p	£17.50
		22	Group 3 — Views of the World		80p	£17.50
			Real Photographs:			
	P	45	Group O — 'A Continuous Series of General Interest' — Films, Stage and Radio Stars (1939)	Ha.529	70p	£32.00
C	P	45	'1st Series of 45' — Film and Stage Stars (1939)		90p	£40.00
C	P	54	'2nd Series of 54' — Film and Stage Stars (1939)		90p	£50.00
2	P	18	'First Series' — Views (1937)		£2.20	—
2	P	18	'Second Series' — Film and Stage Stars (1937)		£2.20	—
2	P	18	'Third Series' — Views (1937)		£2.20	—
2	P	18	'Fourth Series' — Film and Stage Stars (1937)		£2.20	—
2	P	18	'Fifth Series' — Views (1938)		£2.20	—
2	P	18	'Sixth Series' — Film and Stage Stars (1938)		£2.20	—
H	P	44	'Series One' 'G.P.1' — Film Stars (export) (1939)		80p	£35.00
H	P	44	'Series Two' 'G.P.2' — Film Stars (export) (1939)		25p	£11.00
H	P	44	'Series Three' 'G.P.3' — Film Stars (export) (1939)		£2.20	—
H	CP	44	'Series Three' 'C.V.3' — Views (export) (1939)		80p	£35.00
H	CP	44	'Series Four' 'C.V.4' — Views (export) (1939)		23p	£10.00
2	P	36	'Series Seven' — Film and Stage Stars (1938)		90p	—
2	P	54	'Series Eight' — Film and Stage Stars (1938)		60p	£32.00
	P	54	'Series Nine' — Film and Stage Stars (1938):			
H			A Medium size		60p	£32.00
2			B Extra-large size		60p	£32.00
	P	54	'Series Ten' — Film and Stage Stars (1939):			
—			A Large size (80 × 69mm)		60p	£32.00
2			B Extra-large size		60p	£32.00
	P	54	'Series Eleven' — Film and Stage Stars (1939):			
—			A Large size (80 × 69mm)		60p	£32.00
2			B Extra-large size		90p	—

ARDATH TOBACCO CO. LTD, London *(continued)*

Size	*Print-ing*	*Number in set*		*Handbook reference*	*Price per card*	*Complete set*
—	P	54	'Series Twelve' — Film and Stage Stars (80 × 69mm) (1939)		60p	£32.00
—	P	54	'Series Thirteen' — Film and Stage Stars (80 × 69mm) (1939)		60p	£32.00
	P	36	'Of Famous Landmarks' (1939):			
—			A Large size (80 × 69 mm), titled 'Real Photographs'		£2.50	—
	J2		B Extra-large size, titled 'Real Photographs of Famous Landmarks'		£1.50	£55.00
	P	36	'Of Modern Aircraft' (1939):			
—			A Large size (80 × 69mm		£2.50	—
J2			B Extra-large size		£1.50	£55.00
D	***MISCELLANEOUS***					
—	C	30	Girls of All Nations (78 × 66mm) (c1916)		£15.00	—
		25	Historic Grand Slams (folders) (101 × 70mm) (c1935)		£20.00	—
J2	U	48	How to Recognise the Service Ranks (holed for binding) (c1939)		£3.20	—
			Industrial Propaganda Cards (c1942):			
H1	U	2	A Black fronts		£4.00	£8.00
H1	C	4	B Coloured fronts		£5.00	£20.00
J2	BW	11	C White fronts		£3.60	£40.00
J2	U	150	Information Slips (holed for binding) (1938)		£2.25	—
			Ministry of Information Cards (1941-3):			
J2	U	5	A Calendar — 'It all depends on me'		£2.50	£12.50
			B Greeting Card — 'It all depends on me'		£5.00	—
—	C	24	C 'It all depends on me' (80 × 63mm)		£1.25	£30.00
—	C	1	D Union Jack Folder (59 × 41mm)		—	£10.00
—	C	1	E 'On the Cotton Front' (80 × 63mm)		—	£2.00
—	BW	1	F 'On the Kitchen Front' (70 × 55mm)		—	£2.00
J2	U	? 4	Wonderful Handicraft (c1935)		£18.00	—

THE ASSOCIATED TOBACCO MANUFACTURERS LTD

POST-1920 ISSUES

C2	C	25	Cinema Stars (export) (c1926):	Ha.530		
			A 'Issued with Bond Street Turkish Cigarettes'		£25.00	—
			B 'Issued with John Bull Virginia Cigarettes'		£25.00	—
			C 'Issued with Club Virginia Cigarettes'		£25.00	—
			D 'Issued with Heliopolis Turkish Cigarettes'		£25.00	—
			E 'Issued with Sports Turkish Cigarettes'		£25.00	—

A. ATKINSON, London

PRE-1919 ISSUE

D	C	30	*Army Pictures, Cartoons, etc (c1916)	H.12	£75.00	—

AVISS BROTHERS LTD, London

PRE-1919 ISSUE

D1	C	40	*Naval and Military Phrases (c1904)	H.14	£75.00	—

J.A. BAILEY, Swansea

PRE-1919 ISSUE

D1	C	40	*Naval and Military Phrases (c1904)	H.14	£130.00	—

A. BAKER & CO. LTD, London

Size	Printing	Number in set		Handbook reference	Price per card	Complete set
PRE-1919 ISSUES						
A	BW	20	*Actresses — 'BLARM'(c1900):	H.23		
			A Long design back (64mm)		£25.00	—
			B Design altered and shortened (58mm)		£25.00	—
A	BW	10	*Actresses — 'HAGGA' (c1900)	H.24	£25.00	£250.00
	BW		*Actresses 'Baker's 3-sizes' (c1900):	H.25		
A		25	Small cards		£25.00	—
		25	Medium cards (56 × 75mm)		£35.00	—
		? 9	Extra large cards (67 × 127mm)		£180.00	—
C	BW	? 41	*Baker's Tobacconists' Shops (c1901):	H.26		
			A 'Try our 3½d Tobaccos' back		£150.00	—
			B 'Cigar, Cigarette, etc. Manufacturers' back		£100.00	—
C	C	25	Beauties of All Nations (c1900):	H.27		
			A 'Albert Baker & Co. (1898) ...' back		£14.00	£350.00
			B 'A. Baker & Co. ...' back		£9.00	£225.00
C	BW	16	*British Royal Family (c1902)	H.28	£40.00	—
A1	BW	20	Cricketers Series (1901)	H.29	£250.00	—
A1	C	25	*Star Girls (c1898)	H.30	£130.00	—

BAYLEY & HOLDSWORTH

PRE-1919 ISSUE

A	C	26	*International Signalling Code (c1910)		£140.00	—

E. C. BEESTON, Wales

PRE-1919 ISSUE

D	C	30	*Army Pictures, Cartoons etc (c1916)	H.12	£75.00	—

BELFAST SHIPS STORES CO. LTD, Belfast

PRE-1919 ISSUE

	C	1	*Dickens' Characters (79 × 40mm) (c1895)	H.31	£200.00	—

J. & F. BELL LTD, Glasgow

PRE-1919 ISSUES

A	BW	10	*Actresses — 'HAGGA' ('Three Bells Cigarettes) (c1900)	H.24	£70.00	—
C	C	25	*Beauties — Tobacco Leaf Back (c1898):	H.32		
			A 'Bell's Scotia Cigarettes' back		£90.00	—
			B 'Three Bells Cigarettes' back		£90.00	—
A	C	25	Colonial Series (c1901)		£35.00	—
A	BW	30	*Footballers (c1902)		£45.00	—
A	C	25	Scottish Clan Series No. 1 (c1903)	H.33	£12.00	£300.00

B. BELLWOOD, BRADFORD

PRE-1919 ISSUE

C	C	18	Motor Cycle Series (c1912)	Ha.469	£80.00	—

RICHARD BENSON LTD, Bristol

POST 1920 ISSUE

	U	24	Old Bristol Series:			
—			A Original issue (80 × 70mm) (c1925)		£3.00	£75.00
—			B Reprint (88 × 78-83mm) (1946)		£2.00	£50.00

BENSON & HEDGES, London

Size	Printing	Number in set		Handbook reference	Price per card	Complete set
POST-1940 ISSUE						
A2	C	1	Advertisement Card, The Original Shop (1973)		—	£2.00

FELIX BERLYN, Manchester

PRE-1919 ISSUE						
	C	25	Golfing Series (Humorous) (c1910):			
A1			A Small size		£300.00	—
—			B Post card size (139 × 87mm)		£400.00	—

BERRY, London

PRE-1919 ISSUE						
D	U	? 1	London Views (c1905)	H.34	£130.00	—

BEWLAY & CO. LTD, London

PRE-1919 ISSUES						
D1	U		Bewlay's War Series (Generals, etc) (c1915):	Ha.477		
		12	A 'Caps the Lot' Smoking Mixture		£11.00	—
		6	B Try Bewlay's 'Caps the Lot' Mixture		£11.00	—
		6	C Try Bewlay's 'Modern Man' Mixture		£11.00	—
D1	U	25	Bewlay's War Series (Photogravure War Pictures) (c1915):	H.35		
			A 'Modern Man' Mixtures etc		£11.00	—
			B 'Modern Man' Cigarettes		£11.00	—
			C 'Two Great Favourites'		£11.00	—
A	C	? 6	*Comic Advertisement Cards (1909)	H.36	£200.00	—

W.O. BIGG & CO., Bristol

PRE-1919 ISSUES						
A	C	37	*Flags of All Nations (c1904):	H.37		
			A 'Statue of Liberty' back, 4d oz		£7.00	—
			B As A:— (a) altered to 4½d by hand		£7.00	—
			(b) 4½d red seal over 4d		£7.50	—
			C Panel design 'New York' Mixture		£7.50	—
A	C	50	Life on Board a Man of War (c1905)	H.38	£9.00	£450.00

JAS. BIGGS & SONS, London

PRE-1919 ISSUES						
C	C	26	*Actresses — 'FROGA A' 'Two Roses' in white (c1900)	H.20	£35.00	—
C	C	25	*Actresses — 'FROGA A & B' 'Two Roses' in black (c1900)	H.20	£55.00	—
A	C		*Beauties, with frameline — 'CHOAB' (c1900):	H.21		
		25	A Blue typeset back		£65.00	—
		? 8	B Overprinted in black on Bradford cards		£60.00	—
C	C		*Beauties, no framelines — selection 'BOCCA' (c1900):	H.39		
		25	A Blue back		£65.00	—
		25	B Black back		£65.00	—
C	C	30	*Colonial Troops (c1901)	H.40	£30.00	—
C	C	30	*Flags and Flags with Soldiers (c1903)	H.41	£25.00	—
A1	C	25	*Star Girls (c1900)	H.30	£150.00	—

J. S. BILLINGHAM, Northampton

Size	*Printing*	*Number in set*		*Handbook reference*	*Price per card*	*Complete set*
PRE-1919 ISSUE						
D	C	30	*Army Pictures, Cartoons etc (c1916)	H.12	£75.00	—

R. BINNS, Halifax

POST-1920 ISSUE						
A	U	? 6	*Halifax Footballers (c1924)	Ha.531	£90.00	—

BLANKS CIGARETTES

POST-1920 ISSUE						
A	C	50	Keystrokes in Break-Building (c1935)		£175.00	—

THE BOCNAL TOBACCO CO., London

POST-1920 ISSUES						
A2	U	25	Luminous Silhouettes of Beauty and Charm (1938)		£2.00	£50.00
A2	C	25	Proverbs Up-to-Date (1938)		£2.00	£50.00

ALEXANDER BOGUSLAVSKY LTD, London

POST-1920 ISSUES						
—	C	12	Big Events on the Turf (133 × 70mm) (1924)		£35.00	—
A2	C	25	Conan Doyle Characters (1923):			
			A Back in black, white board		£6.00	—
			B Back in grey, cream board		£6.00	—
			C Back in green		£6.00	—
A2	C	25	Mythological Gods and Goddesses (1924)		£1.60	£40.00
A	C	25	*Sports Records, Nd. 1-25 (1925)		£1.40	£35.00
A	C	25	Sports Records, Nd. 26-50 (1925)		£1.40	£35.00
	C	25	Winners on the Turf (1925):			
A			A Small size, captions 'sans serif'		£3.00	£75.00
A			B Small size, captions with 'serif'		£4.00	—
B			C Large size		£5.00	—

R. & E. BOYD LTD, London

POST-1920 ISSUES						
—	U	25	Places of Interest (c1938):			
			A Size 67 × 35mm		£40.00	—
			B Size 71 × 55mm		£40.00	—
—	U	25	Wild Birds at Home (75 × 57mm) (c1938)	Ha.626	£40.00	—

WM. BRADFORD, Liverpool

PRE-1919 ISSUES						
C	C	50	*Beauties 'CHOAB' (c1900)	H.21	£27.00	—
D	U	? 7	Beauties — 'Jersey Lily Cigarettes' (c1900)	Ha.488	£170.00	—
D2	BW	20	Boer War Cartoons (c1901)	H.42	£85.00	—

T. BRANKSTON & CO., London

PRE-1919 ISSUES						
C	C	30	*Colonial Troops (c1901):	H.40		
			A Golf Club Mixture		£30.00	—
			B Red Virginia		£30.00	—
			C Sweet as the Rose		£30.00	—
A2	C	12	*Pretty Girl Series 'RASH' (c1900)	H.8	£150.00	—

BRIGHAM & CO., Reading

Size	*Printing*	*Number in set*		*Handbook reference*	*Price per card*	*Complete set*
PRE-1919 ISSUES						
B	U	16	Down the Thames from Henley to Windsor (c1912)		£90.00	—
A	U	16	Reading Football Players (c1912)		£140.00	—
—	BW	3	Tobacco Growing in Hampshire (89 × 79mm) (1915)		£13.00	£40.00

BRITANNIA ANONYMOUS SOCIETY

PRE-1919 ISSUE						
—	C	? 19	*Beauties and Scenes (60 × 40mm) (c1914)	Ha.532	£75.00	—

BRITISH & COLONIAL TOBACCO CO., London

PRE-1919 ISSUE						
A1	C	25	*Armies of the World (c1900)	H.43	£100.00	—

J.M. BROWN, Derby

PRE-1919 ISSUE						
D	C	30	*Army Pictures, Cartoons etc (c1916)	H.12	£75.00	—

JOHN BRUMFIT, London

POST-1920 ISSUE						
A	C	50	The Public Schools' Ties Series (Old Boys) (1925)		£3.00	£150.00

G.A. BULLOUGH, Castleford

PRE-1919 ISSUE						
D	C	30	*Army Pictures, Cartoons etc (c1916)	H.12	£75.00	—

BURSTEIN, ISAACS & CO., London

(The BI-CO Company, B.I. & Co. Ltd)

POST-1920 ISSUES						
D	BW	25	Famous Prize-Fighters, Nd. 1-25 (1923)		£5.00	—
D	BW	25	Famous Prize-Fighters, Nd. 26-50 (1924)		£5.00	—
D	P	28	London View Series (1922)		£4.00	—

BYRTWOOD & CO., Bristol

PRE-1919 ISSUE						
A2	U	25	*Pretty Girl Series — 'BAGG' (c1900)	H.45	£120.00	—

CABANA CIGAR CO., London

PRE-1919 ISSUE						
—	BW	1	Advertisement Card — 'Little Manturios' (63 × 49mm) (1905)		—	£180.00

PERCY E. CADLE & CO. LTD, Cardiff

PRE-1919 ISSUES						
A1	BW	20	*Actresses 'BLARM' (c1900)	H.23	£30.00	—
C	U	26	*Actresses — 'FROGA A' (c1900):	H.20		
			A Printed Back		£35.00	—
			B Rubber — Stamped Back		£125.00	—
C	C	26	*Actresses — 'FROGA B' (c1900)	H.20	£45.00	—
C	BW	12	*Boer War and Boxer Rebellion Sketches (c1901)	H.46	£40.00	—
C	BW	10	*Boer War Generals — 'FLAC' (c1901)	H.47	£60.00	—
A	BW	20	*Footballers (c1904)	H.4	£35.00	—

CARRERAS LTD, London

Size	Printing	Number in set		Handbook reference	Price per card	Complete set
A	***PRE-1919 ISSUES***					
—	C		*Flags of the Allies (shaped) (c1915):	H.49		
		1	1 Grouped Flags:			
			A 'All Arms' Cigarettes		£40.00	—
			B 'Black Cat' Cigarettes		£40.00	—
		5	2 Allies Flags:			
			A 'Black Cat' Cigarettes		£40.00	—
			B 'Life Ray' Cigarettes		£75.00	—
A	C	140	Raemaeker's War Cartoons (1916):			
			A 'Black Cat' Cigarettes		£1.10	£155.00
			B Carreras Cigarettes		£3.50	—
A	C	50	The Science of Boxing (c1916):			
			A 'Black Cat' back		£2.50	£125.00
			B 'Carreras Ltd' back		£3.50	—
A	C	80	Types of London (1919)		£1.25	£100.00
A	C	50	Women on War Work (c1916)		£6.00	£300.00
B	***POST-1920 ISSUES.*** Mostly home issues, export only issues indicated.					
A	CP	24	Actresses and Their Pets (1926) (export)		£4.00	—
	C	48	Alice in Wonderland (1930):			
A			A Small size, rounded corners		£1.35	£65.00
A			B Small size, square corners		£2.80	—
B2			C Large size		£1.60	£80.00
		1	D Instruction Booklet		—	£15.00
A	C	50	Amusing Tricks and How to Do Them (1937)		70p	£35.00
	C		Battle of Waterloo (1934):	Ha.533		
C		1	1 Paper insert, with instructions		—	£8.00
—		15	*2 Soldiers and Guns, large size (67 × 70mm)		£3.00	—
A			*3 Soldiers and Guns, small size:			
		10	Soldiers — Officers' Uniforms		£1.50	—
		12	Soldiers and Guns		£1.50	—
C1	C	50	Believe it or Not (1934)		50p	£25.00
A	C	50	Birds of the Countryside (1939)		80p	£40.00
A	C	50	Britain's Defences (1938)		60p	£30.00
	C	25	British Costumes (1927):			
C2			A Small size		£1.20	£30.00
B2			B Large size		£1.20	£30.00
A	P	27	British Prime Ministers (1928) (export)		£1.20	£32.00
A1	C	1	Calendar for 1934		—	£20.00
A	C	50	Celebrities of British History (1935):			
			A Brown on cream back (two shades of ink)		90p	£45.00
			B Pale brown on bluish black		90p	£45.00
A	C	25	Christie Comedy Girls (1928) (export)		£1.60	£40.00
A	U		Cricketers (1934):			
		30	A 'A Series of Cricketers'		£2.80	£85.00
		50	B 'A Series of 50 Cricketers':			
			1 Front in brown and white		£3.00	£150.00
			2 Front in black and white		£35.00	—
A	BW	50	Dogs and Friend (1936)		28p	£14.00
A	C	50	Do You Know? (1939)		22p	£11.00
A	C	50	Famous Airmen and Airwomen (1936)		£1.40	£70.00
	C		Famous Escapes (1926):			
A		25	A Small size		£1.20	£30.00
B2		25	B Large size		£1.20	£30.00
—		10	C Extra-large size (133 × 70mm)		£2.20	£22.00
A2	C	96	Famous Film Stars (1935)	Ha.534	£1.00	£95.00

Size	*Printing*	*Number in set*		*Handbook reference*	*Price per card*	*Complete set*
A	C		Famous Footballers (1935):			
		48	A Set of 48		£1.00	£50.00
		24	B Nos. 25-48 redrawn		£1.40	£35.00
A	C	25	Famous Men (1927) (export)		£1.20	£30.00
B2	P	24	Famous Naval Men (1929) (export)		£1.20	£30.00
B2	P	12	Famous Soldiers (1928) (export)		£5.00	£60.00
A	P	27	Famous Women (1929) (export)		£1.20	£32.00
A	C	25	Figures of Fiction (1924)		£1.60	£40.00
	P	54	Film and Stage Beauties (1939):			
A2			A Small size		40p	£22.00
—			B Medium size (70 × 60mm):			
			(a) Without full point after 'Carreras Ltd'		50p	£27.00
			(b) With full point after 'Carreras Ltd.		50p	£27.00
	P	36	Film and Stage Beauties:			
B1			A Large size (1939)		75p	£27.00
J2			B Extra-large size (1938)		£1.00	£36.00
A	C	50	Film Favourites (1938)		£1.00	£50.00
A	P	54	Film Stars — 'A Series of 54' (1937)		75p	£40.00
	P	54	Film Stars (1938):			
A			A Small size, 'Second Series of 54'		50p	£27.00
—			B Medium size (68 × 60mm), 'A Series of 54'		75p	£40.00
J2	P		Film Stars (export):			
		36	'A Series of 36' (c1935)		£2.50	—
		36	'Second Series of 36' (c1936)		£2.50	—
		36	'Third Series of 36' (c1937)		£2.50	—
		36	'Fourth Series of 36' (c1938)		£2.50	—
A2	C	50	Film Stars, by Florence Desmond (1936)		80p	£40.00
—		72	Film Stars, oval (70 × 30mm) (1934):			
	P		A Inscribed 'Real Photos'		£2.00	—
	U		B Without 'Real Photos'		£1.25	£90.00
A	C	50	Flowers (1936)		50p	£25.00
A2	C	75	*Footballers (1934):			
			A 'Carreras Cigarettes' on front 27mm long		£1.20	£90.00
			B 'Carreras Cigarettes' on front 26mm long		£1.20	£90.00
	C	36	'Fortune Telling' (1926):			
A			A Small size:			
			1 Card inset		44p	£16.00
			2a Head inset, black framelines		30p	£11.00
			2b Head inset, brown framelines		75p	£27.00
B2			B Large size:			
			1 Card inset		30p	£11.00
			2 Head inset		44p	£16.00
		1	Instruction Booklet		—	£8.00
	P		Glamour Girls of Stage and Films (1939):			
A2		54	A Small size		40p	£22.00
—		54	B Medium size (70 × 60mm)		40p	£22.00
—		36	C Large size (76 × 70mm)		£1.00	£36.00
J2		36	D Extra-large size		£1.25	£45.00
	C	50	'Gran-Pop' by Lawson Wood (1934):			
C1			A Small size		32p	£16.00
B			B Large size		35p	£17.50
	C	52	Greyhound Racing Game (1926):			
A			A Small size		25p	£12.50
B2			B Large size		25p	£12.50
		1	C Instruction Booklet		—	£8.00

Size	*Print-ing*	*Number in set*		*Handbook reference*	*Price per card*	*Complete set*
	C	48	Happy Family (1925):			
A1			A Small size		32p	£16.00
B2			B Large size		30p	£15.00
A	C	25	Highwaymen (1924)		£2.00	£50.00
A	C	50	History of Army Uniforms (1937)		£1.00	£50.00
A	C	50	History of Naval Uniforms (1937)		90p	£45.00
	C		Horses and Hounds (1926)			
A		25	A Small size		£1.60	£40.00
B2		20	B Large size		£1.60	£32.00
—		10	C Extra-large size (133 × 70mm)		£2.80	£28.00
	C	50	Kings and Queens of England (1935):			
A			A Small size		£1.30	£65.00
B2			B Large size		£2.00	£100.00
A	U	50	A 'Kodak' at the Zoo 'Series of Fifty' (1924)		60p	£30.00
A	U	50	A 'Kodak' at the Zoo '2nd Series' (1925)		60p	£30.00
A	P	27	Malayan Industries (1929) (export)		40p	£11.00
	P	24	Malayan Scenes (1928):			
A			A Small size		£1.50	£36.00
—			B Medium size (70 × 60mm)		60p	£15.00
—	C	53	*Miniature Playing Cards (44 × 32mm) (c1935)		18p	£9.00
	C	50	The 'Nose' Game (1927):			
A			A Small size		40p	£20.00
B2			B Large size		32p	£16.00
		1	C Instruction Booklet		—	£8.00
	C	50	Notable MPs (1929):			
A			A Small size		80p	£40.00
—			B Medium size (69 × 60mm)		50p	£25.00
A	P	25	Notable Ships — Past and Present (1929) (export)		£1.20	£30.00
	C		Old Staffordshire Figures (1926):			
A		24	A Small size		£1.25	£30.00
—		12	B Extra-large size (134 × 71mm)		£2.50	£30.00
B	C	24	Old Staffordshire Figures (different subjects) (1926)		£1.50	£36.00
	C	24	Orchids (1925):			
A			A Small size		£1.00	£25.00
B			B Large size		£1.00	£25.00
—			C Extra-large size (133 × 70mm)		£3.00	£75.00
A	C		Our Navy (1937):	Ha.536		
		20	A Thick card, selected numbers		90p	£18.00
		50	B Thin card		90p	£45.00
C1	C	50	Palmistry (1933)		40p	£20.00
A	P	27	Paramount Stars (1929) (export)		£1.00	£27.00
A	C	25	Picture Puzzle Series (1923)		£1.40	£35.00
—	C	53	Playing Cards (68 × 42mm) (c1925)	Ha.535-1A	£1.20	—
	C		*Playing Cards and Dominoes (1929):	Ha.535-IB		
C		52	A Small size — (a) Numbered		30p	£15.00
			(b) Unnumbered		30p	£15.00
—		26	B Large size (77 × 69mm):			
			(a) Numbered		40p	£10.00
			(b) Unnumbered		40p	£10.00
A	C	48	Popular Footballers (1936):			
			A White back		80p	£40.00
			B Cream back		80p	£40.00
—	C		Popular Personalities, oval (70 × 30mm) (1935):	Ha.629		
		72	1 Normal issue		65p	£45.00
		10	2 Replaced subjects (Nos. 1-10) for issue in Eire		£20.00	—

CARRERAS LTD, London *(continued)*

Size	Printing	Number in set		Handbook reference	Price per card	Complete set
	C		Races — Historic and Modern (1927):			
A		25	A Small size		£2.00	£50.00
B		25	B Large size		£2.00	£50.00
—		12	C Extra-large size (133 × 69mm)		£4.00	£50.00
	C		Regalia Series (1925):			
A		25	A Small size		50p	£12.50
B		20	B Large size		60p	£12.00
—		10	C Extra-large size (135 × 71mm)		£2.00	£20.00
—	C	50	'Round the World' Scenic Models (folders) (83 × 73mm) (c1930)		60p	£30.00
	C		School Emblems (1929):			
A		50	A Small size		80p	£40.00
B		40	B Large size		75p	£30.00
—		20	C Extra-large size (134 × 76mm)		£2.00	£40.00
C1	C	48	Tapestry Reproductions of Famous Paintings (sectional) (1938)		60p	£30.00
A	C	50	Tools — And How to Use Them (1935)		80p	£40.00
A	P	27	Views of London (1929) (export)		30p	£8.00
A	P	27	Views of the World (1927) (export)		75p	£20.00
A	C	25	Wild Flower Art Series (1923)		£1.00	£25.00
C	***POST-1940 TURF SLIDE ISSUES***					
A	U	50	British Aircraft (1953)		90p	£45.00
A	U	50	British Fish (1954)		40p	£20.00
A	U	50	British Railway Locomotives (1952)		£1.20	£60.00
A	U	50	Celebrities of British History (1951)		£1.20	£60.00
A	U	50	Famous British Fliers (1956)		£2.50	—
A	U	50	Famous Cricketers (1950)		£4.00	—
A	U	50	Famous Dog Breeds (1952)		£1.40	£70.00
A	U	50	Famous Film Stars (1949)		£1.60	£80.00
A	U	50	Famous Footballers (1951)		£2.50	—
A	U	50	Film Favourites (1948)		£2.50	—
A	U	50	Film Stars (1947)		£1.80	—
A	U	50	Footballers (1948)		£2.50	—
A	U	50	Olympics (1948)		£2.50	—
A	U	50	Radio Celebrities (1950)		£1.20	£60.00
A	U	50	Sports Series (1949)		£2.00	—
A	U	50	Zoo Animals (1955)		40p	£20.00
(N.B. These prices are for the full slides. If only the cut slides are required these will be half Catalogue price.)						
D	***POST-1940 ISSUES***					
A	C	50	British Birds (1976)		15p	£3.75
A	C	50	Flowers All the Year Round (1977)		20p	£10.00
A	C	50	Kings and Queens of England (1977)		20p	£10.00
A	C	50	Military Uniforms (1976)		15p	£3.75
A	C	50	Palmistry (1980)		£1.00	—
A	C	50	Sport Fish (1978)		15p	£3.75
A	C	50	Vintage Cars (1976):			
			A With word 'Filter' in white oval:			
			i Thin card, bright red oblong at top		18p	£9.00
			ii Thick card, bright red oblong at top		15p	£7.50
			iii Thin card, dull red oblong at top		30p	—
			B Without word 'Filter' in white oval		15p	£4.50
E	***MISCELLANEOUS PRE-1919 ISSUES***					
D1	BW	5	The Black Cat Handy French-English Dictionary (Booklets) (1915)		£20.00	—
D1	BW	200	The Black Cat Library (Booklets) (c1910)		£9.00	—
—	—	?	*Lace Motifs* (c1915) (various sizes)		From £8.00	—

CARRERAS LTD, London *(continued)*

Size	Printing	Number in set		Handbook reference	Price per card	Complete set
F	***MISCELLANEOUS POST-1940 ISSUES***					
A	C	60	Flags of All Nations (unissued) (c1960)		33p	£20.00
—	C		Guards Series (68 × 50mm):			
		4	A Military Mug Series (1971)		80p	—
		8	B Order Up the Guards (1970)		80p	—
		16	C Send for the Guards (1969)		80p	—
—	C	7	Millionaire Competition Folders (68 × 30mm) (1971)		£1.50	£10.00
A	U	50	Radio & Television Favourites (unissued) (c1965)		£8.00	—
G	***SILKS***					
—	C	12	Miscellaneous Series Cabinet size (1915)		£160.00	—

CARRICK & CO., Hull

PRE-1919 ISSUE						
D	C	12	*Military Terms (1901)	H.50	£50.00	—

P. J. CARROLL & CO. LTD, Dundalk, Glasgow and Liverpool

A	***PRE-1919 ISSUES***					
D	C	25	British Naval Series (c1915)	H.51	£35.00	—
A	P	20	County Louth G.R.A. Team and Officials (1913)		£22.00	—
D	BW	25	*Derby Winners (1914-15):	H.52		
			A Back in black		£80.00	—
			B Back in green		£80.00	—
B	***POST-1920 ISSUES***					
D	C	25	Ship Series (1937)		£5.00	£125.00
D	U	24	Sweet Afton Jig-Saw Puzzles (1935)		£15.00	—
C	***MISCELLANEOUS***					
D	C	25	Birds (prepared but not issued) (c1940)	Ha.537	65p	£16.00

THE CASKET TOBACCO & CIGARETTE CO. LTD, Manchester

PRE-1919 ISSUES						
A2	U	? 2	Cricket Fixture Cards, Coupon back (1905-06)		£250.00	—
A2	U	1	Cyclists Lighting-up Table (1909)		—	£200.00
A2	U	? 11	*Football Fixture Cards, Coupon back (1905-11)	H.53	£180.00	—
A2	BW	? 2	Road Maps (c1910)	H.54	£200.00	—

S. CAVANDER & CO., London and Portsea

PRE-1919 ISSUE						
D	BW	? 3	*Beauties — selection from 'Plums' (1898)	H.186	£180.00	—

CAVANDERS LTD, London and Glasgow

POST-1920 ISSUES						
A	C	25	Ancient Chinese (1926)		£1.00	£25.00
A	C	25	Ancient Egypt (1928)		£1.00	£25.00
B	C	25	Ancient Egypt (different subjects) (1928)		£1.00	£25.00
A	P	36	Animal Studies (1936)		40p	£14.00
	CP	50	Beauty Spots of Great Britain (1927):			
A			A Small size		25p	£12.50
—			B Medium size (76 × 52mm)		25p	£12.50
	CP		Camera Studies (1926):			
A		54	A Small size		20p	£10.00
—		56	B Medium size (77 × 51mm)		25p	£12.50
A	C	30	Cinema Stars — Set 6 (1934)	Ha.515	£1.10	£33.00

CAVANDERS LTD, London *(continued)*

Size	Print-ing	Number in set		Handbook reference	Price per card	Complete set
—	CP	30	The Colonial Series (77 × 51mm) (1925):			
			A Small caption, under lmm high		40p	£12.00
			B Larger caption, over lmm high		40p	£12.00
—	C	25	Coloured Stereoscopic (77 × 51mm) (1931)		50p	£25.00
D	C	25	Feathered Friends or Foreign Birds (1926):	Ha.516		
			A Titled 'Feathered Friends'		£2.00	—
			B Titled 'Foreign Birds'		£1.40	£35.00
—	C	25§	Glorious Britain (76 × 51mm) (1930)		40p	£20.00
			The Homeland Series (1924-26):	Ha.539		
A			Small size:			
	CP	50	A Back in blue		80p	£40.00
	CP	50	B Back in black, glossy front		80p	£40.00
	CP	54	C Back in black, matt front		30p	£15.00
			Medium size (77 × 51mm):			
	CP	50	D Back inscribed 'Hand Coloured Real Photos'		18p	£9.00
	CP	56	E As D, with 'Reprinted ...' at base		32p	£17.50
	CP	56	F As D, but words 'Hand Coloured' dropped		32p	£17.50
	P	56	G As D, but words 'Hand Coloured' dropped		32p	£17.50
A	C	25	Little Friends (1924)	Ha.540	£1.00	£25.00
—	C	25	The Nation's Treasures (77 × 51mm) (1925)		50p	£12.50
	P		Peeps into Many Lands — 'A Series of ...' (1927):			
D		36§	A Small size		35p	£25.00
—		36§	B Medium size (75 × 50mm)		40p	£30.00
—		36	C Extra-large size (113 × 68mm)		£1.80	—
	P	36§	Peeps into Many Lands — 'Second Series ...' (1928):			
D			A Small size		50p	£36.00
—			B Medium size (75 × 50mm)		50p	£36.00
	P	24§	Peeps into Many Lands — 'Third Series ...' (1929):			
D			A Small size		32p	£16.00
			B Medium size (75 × 50mm)		70p	£35.00
—			C As B, but inscribed 'Reprinted by Special Request'		70p	£35.00
	P	24§	Peeps into Prehistoric Times — 'Fourth Series ...' (1930):			
D			A Small size		40p	£20.00
—			B Medium size (75 × 50mm)		50p	£25.00
—	P		*Photographs (54 × 38mm) (1924):	Ha.541		
		30	1 Animal Studies		£1.30	£40.00
		3	2 Royal Family		£3.30	—
—	C	48	Regimental Standards (76 × 70mm) (c1924)	Ha.502-7	£10.00	—
C	C	25	Reproductions of Celebrated Oil Paintings (1925)	Ha.542	£1.00	£25.00
	CP	108	River Valleys (1926):			
A			A Small size		29p	£30.00
—			B Medium size (75 × 50mm)		30p	£32.00
A	C	25	School Badges (1928):	Ha.543		
			A Back in dark blue		£1.00	£25.00
			B Back in light blue		£1.00	£25.00
—	CP	30	Wordsworth's Country (76 × 51mm) (1926)		60p	£18.00

§ Stereoscopic series, consisting of a Right and a Left card for each number, a complete series is thus **double** the number shown.

R.S. CHALLIS & CO. LTD, London

POST-1920 ISSUES

D1	C	50	Comic Animals (1936)		60p	£30.00
A	BW	44	Flickits (Greyhound Racing Flickers) (1936)	Ha.589-1	£35.00	—

R.S. CHALLIS & CO. LTD, London *(continued)*

Size	*Print-ing*	*Number in set*		*Handbook reference*	*Price per card*	*Complete set*
)1	U	36	Wild Birds at Home (1935):	Ha.626		
			A Inscribed 'Issued with Baldric Cigarettes'		60p	£22.00
			B Above wording blocked out in black		£1.25	£45.00

I. CHAPMAN & Co.

PRE-1919 ISSUE

)	C	30	*Army Pictures, Cartoons, etc (c1916)	H.12	£75.00	—

CHARLESWORTH & AUSTIN LTD, London

PRE-1919 ISSUES

	U	50	*Beauties — 'BOCCA' (c1900)	H.39	£24.00	—
	BW	16	*British Royal Family (1902)	H.28	£45.00	—
	C	30	Colonial Troops (c1900):	H.40		
			A Black back		£30.00	—
			B Brown back		£30.00	—
1	BW	20	Cricketers Series (1901)	H.29	£250.00	—
	C	30	*Flags and Flags with Soldiers (c1903)	H.41	£27.00	—

CHESTERFIELD CIGARETTES

POST-1940 ISSUE

–	C	6	Chesterfield Collection (76 × 45mm) (1979)		£1.25	—
–	C	6	Cocktails (76 × 45mm) 1980		40p	£2.50

CHEW & CO., Bradford

PRE-1919 ISSUE

	C	30	*Army, Pictures, Cartoons etc (c1916)	Ha.12	£75.00	—

W.A. & A.C. CHURCHMAN, Ipswich

6 page reference book available — £3.25

PRE-1919 ISSUES

	C	26	*Actresses — 'FROGA A' (c1900)	H.20	£28.00	—
	C	? 19	*Actresses — 'FROGA B' (c1900)	H.20	£35.00	—
	U	? 24	*Actresses, 'For the Pipe' back (c1900)	H.55	£55.00	—
	C	25	Army Badges of Rank (1916)	H.56	£5.00	£125.00
	C	12	*Beauties — 'CERF' (1904)	H.57	£50.00	—
	U	25	*Beauties — 'FECKSA'(c1902)	H.58	£85.00	—
			*Beauties — 'CHOAB' (c1900):	H.21		
–	C	3	I Circular cards, 55mm diameter		£400.00	—
	C	25	II Five different backs		£120.00	—
	C	25	*Beauties — 'GRACC' (c1900)	H.59	£70.00	—
	C	50	Birds and Eggs (1906)	H.60	£6.00	£300.00
	BW	20	*Boer War Cartoons (c1901)	H.42	£90.00	—
		20	*Boer War Generals' — 'CLAM' (c1901):	H.61		
2	BW		A Black front		£35.00	—
	U		B Brown front		£35.00	—
	C	50	Boy Scouts (1916)	H.62	£5.50	£275.00
	C	50	Boy Scouts, 2nd series (1916)	H.62	£5.50	£275.00
	C	50	Boy Scouts, 3rd series (1916):	H.62		
			A Brown back		£5.50	£275.00
			B Blue back		£9.00	—
	P	41	*Celebrities — Boer War Period (c1901)	H.63	£17.00	—
	C	38	Dogs and Fowls (1908)	H.64	£6.00	—

W.A. & A.C. CHURCHMAN, Ipswich *(continued)*

Size	*Print-ing*	*Number in set*		*Handbook reference*	*Price per card*	*Complete set*
A		50	East Suffolk Churches:			
	BW		A Black front, cream back (1912)		£2.00	£100.00
	BW		B Black front, white back (1912)		£2.00	£100.00
	U		C Sepia front (1917)		£2.00	£100.00
A	C	50	Fish and Bait (1914)	H.65	£5.00	£250.00
A	C	50	Fishes of the World (1911):	H.66	—	£250.00
			30 cards as re-issued 1924		£1.65	£50.00
			20 cards not re-issued		£10.00	—
A	C	50	Flags and Funnels of Leading Steamship Lines (1912)	H.67	£6.00	—
A	C	50	Football Club Colours (1909)	H.68	£8.00	£400.00
A	U	50	*Footballers — Photogravure Portraits (c1910)		£22.00	—
A	C	50	Footballers — Action Pictures & Inset (1914)		£11.00	£550.00
C	C	40	*Home and Colonial Regiments (1902):	H.69		
			20 Caption in blue		£40.00	—
			20 Caption in brown		£40.00	—
A	C	50	Interesting Buildings (1905)	H.70	£6.00	£300.00
A	C	50	*Medals (1910)	H.71	£6.00	£300.00
A	C	50	*Phil May Sketches (1912):	H.72		
			A 'Churchman's Gold Flake Cigarettes'		£6.00	£300.00
			B 'Churchman's Cigarettes'		£7.00	—
A	C	50	*Regimental Colours and Cap Badges (1911)	H.73	£6.00	£300.00
A	C	50	Sectional Cycling Map (1913)	H.74	£6.00	£300.00
A	C	50	Silhouettes of Warships (1915)		£7.00	—
A	C	50	A Tour Round the World (1911)	H.75	£6.00	£300.00
A1	C	25	*Types of British and Colonial Troops (c1900)	H.76	£45.00	—
A	C	50	Wild Animals of the World (1907)	H.77	£6.00	£300.00
B	***POST-1920 ISSUES***					
—	C	48	Air-Raid Precautions (68 × 53mm) (1938)	Ha.544	30p	£15.00
A	U	50	Association Footballers (1938)		50p	£25.00
A	U	50	Association Footballers, 2nd series (1939)		80p	£40.00
A	C	25	Boxing (1922)	H.311	£5.00	—
A	U	50	Boxing Personalities (1938)		£1.80	£90.00
A	U	25	British Film Stars (1934)		£1.60	£40.00
A	C	55	Can You Beat Bogey at St Andrews? (1933):			
			A Without overprint		£2.75	—
			B Overprinted in red 'Exchangeable'		£2.75	—
	U		Cathedrals and Churches (1924):	Ha.545		
A		25	A Small size		£1.80	£45.00
J		12	B Extra-large size		£9.00	—
A	C	50	Celebrated Gateways (1925)		£2.00	£100.00
A	C	25	Civic Insignia and Plate (1926)		£1.80	£45.00
A	C	50	Contract Bridge (1935)		40p	£20.00
A	C	50	Cricketers (1936)		£3.00	—
	C		Curious Dwellings:			
A		25	A Small size (1926)		£1.80	£45.00
B		12	B Large size (1925)		£4.00	—
A	C	25	Curious Signs (1925)		£1.80	£45.00
	C		Eastern Proverbs:	Ha.521		
			A Small size:			
A		25	1 'A Series of 25' (1931)		80p	£20.00
A		25	2 '2nd Series of 25' (1932)		80p	£20.00
			B Large size:			
B		12	1 'A Series of 12' (1931)		£3.30	—
B		12	2 '2nd Series of 12' (1933)		£1.75	£21.00
B		12	3 '3rd Series of 12' (1933)		£1.25	£15.00
B		12	4 '4th Series of 12' (1934)		£1.25	£15.00

W.A. & A.C. CHURCHMAN, Ipswich *(continued)*

Size	*Print-ing*	*Number in set*		*Handbook reference*	*Price per card*	*Complete set*
A	C	50	Empire Railways (1931)		£2.00	£100.00
A	C	25	Famous Cricket Colours (1928)		£3.60	£90.00
	U		Famous Golfers:			
A		50	A Small size (1927)		£9.00	—
			B Large size:			
B		12	1 'A Series of 12' (1927)		£20.00	—
B		12	2 '2nd Series of 12' (1928)		£20.00	—
	C		Famous Railway Trains:			
A		25	A Small size (1929)		£2.60	£65.00
			B Large size:			
B		12	1 'Series of 12' (1928)		£4.50	£55.00
B		12	2 '2nd Series of 12' (1929)		£4.50	£55.00
A	C	52	'Frisky' (1935)		£3.50	—
A	C	50	History and Development of the British Empire (1934)		£1.20	£60.00
—	U	48	Holidays in Britain (Views and Maps) (68 × 53 mm) (1937)		30p	£15.00
—	C	48	Holidays in Britain (views only) (68 × 53mm) (1938)		30p	£15.00
A	C	25	The Houses of Parliament and Their Story (1931)		£1.60	£40.00
	C		Howlers:			
A		40	A Small size (1937)		20p	£8.00
B		16	B Large size (1936)		50p	£8.00
A	C	25	The Inns of Court (1922)		£2.20	£55.00
A	C	25	Interesting Door-Knockers (1928)		£2.20	£55.00
A	C	25	Interesting Experiments (1929)		£1.20	£30.00
A	C	50	'In Town To-night' (1938)		20p	£10.00
B	C	12	Italian Art Exhibition, 1930 (1931)		£1.50	£18.00
B	C	12	Italian Art Exhibition, 1930 — '2nd Series' (1931)		£1.50	£18.00
	C		The King's Coronation (1937):			
A		50	A Small size		18p	£9.00
B		15	B Large size		80p	£12.00
A	U	50	Kings of Speed (1939)		60p	£30.00
	C		Landmarks in Railway Progress:			
A		50	A Small size (1931)		£2.50	£125.00
			B Large size:			
B		12	1 '1st Series of 12' (1932)		£4.80	£55.00
B		12	2 '2nd Series of 12' (1932)		£4.80	£55.00
	U		Lawn Tennis (1928):	Ha.546		
A		50	A Small size		£2.50	£125.00
B		12	B Large size		£8.00	—
	C		Legends of Britain (1936):			
A		50	A Small size		80p	£40.00
B		12	B Large size		£1.50	£18.00
	C		Life in a Liner (1930):			
A		25	A Small size		£1.20	£30.00
B		12	B Large size		£2.50	£30.00
	C		Men of the Moment in Sport:			
A		50	A Small size (1928)		£3.00	£150.00
			B Large size:			
B		12	1 '1st Series of 12' (1929)		£7.00	—
B		12	2 '2nd Series of 12' (1929)		£7.00	—
—	C	48	Modern Wonders (68 × 53mm) (1938)		32p	£16.00
A	C	25	Musical Instruments (1924)	Ha.547	£2.60	£65.00
	C		Nature's Architects (1930):			
A		25	A Small size		£1.20	£30.00
B		12	B Large size		£2.25	£27.00
—	U	48	The Navy at Work (68 × 53mm) (1937)		25p	£12.00

W.A. & A.C. CHURCHMAN, Ipswich *(continued)*

Size	*Printing*	*Number in set*		*Handbook reference*	*Price per card*	*Complete set*
A	C	25	Pipes of the World (1927)		£2.40	£60.00
	C		Prominent Golfers (1931):			
A		50	A Small size		£8.00	—
B		12	B Large size		£20.00	—
	C		The 'Queen Mary' (1936):			
A		50	A Small size		£1.20	£60.00
B		16	B Large size		£2.00	£32.00
A	C	50	Racing Greyhounds (1934)		£2.40	£120.00
—	C	48	The RAF at Work (68 × 53mm) (1938)		80p	£40.00
	C		Railway Working	Ha.548		
			A Small size:			
A		25	1 'Series of 25' (1926)		£3.00	£75.00
A		25	2 '2nd Series of 25' (1927)		£2.40	£60.00
			B Large size:			
B		12	1 'Series of 12' (1926)		£8.00	—
B		13	2 '2nd Series, 13' (1927)		£8.00	—
B		12	3 '3rd Series, 12' (1927)		£8.00	—
A	BW	50	Rivers and Broads (1922):			
			A Titled 'Rivers & Broads'		£5.00	—
			B Titled 'Rivers & Broads of Norfolk & Suffolk'		£5.00	—
A	C	50	Rugby Internationals (1935)		£1.40	£70.00
A	C	50	Sporting Celebrities (1931)		£2.20	£110.00
	C		Sporting Trophies (1927):			
A		25	A Small size		£2.20	£55.00
B		12	B Large size		£4.50	—
A	C	25	Sports and Games in Many Lands (1929)		£3.00	£75.00
	C		The Story of London (1934):			
A		50	A Small size		£1.20	£60.00
B		12	B Large size		£2.50	£30.00
	C		The Story of Navigation:			
A		50	A Small size (1937)		22p	£11.00
B		12	B Large size (1935)		£1.25	£15.00
A	C		3 Jovial Golfers in search of the perfect course (1934):			
		36	A Home issue		£3.25	—
		72	B Irish issue, with green over-printing		£6.00	—
	C		Treasure Trove:			
A		50	A Small size (1937)		20p	£10.00
B		12	B Large size (1935)		£1.25	£15.00
	C		Warriors of All Nations:			
A		25	A Small size (1929)		£2.40	£60.00
			B Large size:			
B		12	1 'A Series of 12' (1929)		£3.75	£45.00
B		12	2 '2nd Series of 12' (1931)		£3.75	£45.00
	C		Well-known Ties (1934):			
A		50	A Small size		80p	£40.00
			B Large size:			
B		12	1 'A Series of 12'		£1.75	£21.00
B		12	2 '2nd Series of 12'		£1.75	£21.00
A	C	50	Well-known Ties, '2nd Series' (1935)		70p	£35.00
A	U	25	Wembley Exhibition (1924)		£2.00	£50.00
A	U	50	West Suffolk Churches (1919)		£1.60	£80.00
—	C	48	Wings Over the Empire (68 × 53mm) (1939)		30p	£15.00
	C		Wonderful Railway Travel (1937):			
A		50	A Small size		35p	£17.50
B		12	B Large size		£1.25	£15.00

W.A. & A.C. CHURCHMAN, Ipswich *(continued)*

Size	Printing	Number in set		Handbook reference	Price per card	Complete set
			MISCELLANEOUS			
—	BW	1	Christmas Greetings Card (68 × 53mm) (1938)		—	£1.50
—	U	55	Olympic Winners Through The Years (Package Designs, 30 small, 25 large) (1960)		£1.50	—
—	C	48	Pioneers (68 × 53mm) (Prepared but not issued) (c1940)		—	—
—	U	40	The World of Sport (Package Designs, 30 small, 10 large) (1961)		£1.50	—
A	C	50	World Wonders Old and New (prepared but not issued) (c1940)		35p	£17.50

WM. CLARKE & SON, Dublin

PRE-1919 ISSUES

Size	Printing	Number in set		Handbook reference	Price per card	Complete set
A	C	25	Army Life (1915)	H.78	£10.00	£250.00
A1	BW	16	*Boer War Celebrities — 'CAG' (c1901)	H.79	£22.00	—
A	C	50	Butterflies and Moths (1912)	H.80	£7.00	£350.00
A	BW	30	Cricketer Series (1901)		£120.00	—
A1	BW	66	Football Series (1902)	H.81	£15.00	—
A	C	25	Marine Series (1907)		£11.00	£275.00
A	C	50	Royal Mail (1914)	H.82	£9.00	£450.00
	C	50	Sporting Terms (38 × 58mm) (c1900):	H.83		
			14 Cricket Terms		£35.00	—
			12 Cycling Terms		£35.00	—
			12 Football Terms		£35.00	—
			12 Golf Terms		£35.00	—
—	C	? 20	*Tobacco Leaf Girls (shaped) (c1898)	H.84	£375.00	—
—	C	25	Well-known Sayings (71 × 32mm) (c1900)	H.85	£20.00	£500.00

.H. CLURE, Keighley

PRE-1919 ISSUES

Size	Printing	Number in set		Handbook reference	Price per card	Complete set
	C	30	*Army Pictures, Cartoons, etc (c1900)	H.12	£75.00	—
	U	50	War Portraits (1916)	H.86	£65.00	—

. LOMAX COCKAYNE, Sheffield

PRE-1919 ISSUE

Size	Printing	Number in set		Handbook reference	Price per card	Complete set
	U	50	War Portraits (1916)	H.86	£65.00	—

COHEN WEENEN & CO. LTD, London

PRE-1919 ISSUES

Size	Printing	Number in set		Handbook reference	Price per card	Complete set
-	P	40	*Actresses, Footballers and Jockeys (26 × 61mm) (c1901)	H.87	£40.00	—
1	U	26	*Actresses — 'FROGA A' (c1900)	H.20	£55.00	—
	C	25	*Beauties — selection from 'BOCCA' (c1900)	H.39	£70.00	—
1	C	25	*Beauties — 'GRACC' (c1900)	H.59	£80.00	—
2	BW	25	*Boxers (c1912):			
			A Black back		£11.00	—
			B Green back		£9.00	£225.00
			C *Without Maker's Name*		£14.00	—
	BW		*Celebrities — Black and white (1901):	H.88		
		65	A 'Sweet Crop, over 250 ...' back		£4.50	—
		? 19	B 'Sweet Crop, over 500 ...' back		£9.50	—

COHEN WEENEN & CO. LTD, London *(continued)*

Size	*Print-ing*	*Number in set*		*Handbook reference*	*Price per card*	*Complete set*
A	C		*Celebrities — Coloured (1901):	H.89		
		45	I 1-45 Boer War Generals etc. 'Sweet Crop, over 100 ...' back:		—	£180.00
			A Toned back		£4.00	—
			B White back		£4.00	—
			C *Plain Back*		£8.00	—
		121	II 1-121 Including Royalty, etc. 'Sweet Crop, over 250 ...' back:			
			1-45 as in I		£8.00	—
			46-121 additional subjects		£4.00	£300.00
—	C		*Celebrities — 'GAINSBOROUGH I' (1901):	H.90		
—		? 16	A In metal frames (46 × 67mm)		£100.00	—
D2		39	B 'Sweet Crop, over 250 ...' back		£35.00	—
D		30	C 'Sweet Crop, over 400 ...' back		£11.00	£330.00
		2	D *1902 Calendar Back gilt border to front*		£100.00	—
D1		39	*E Plain Back*		£12.00	£475.00
—	P	? 172	*Celebrities — 'GAINSBOROUGH II' (c1901):	H.91		
			A In metal frames (46 × 67mm)		£15.00	—
			B Without frames showing Frame Marks		£5.00	—
			C Without Frames no Frame Marks (as issued)		£10.00	—
A2	C	20	*Cricketers, Footballers, Jockeys (c1900):	H.92		
			A Caption in brown		£16.00	£320.00
			B Caption in grey-black		£16.00	£320.00
D	C	40	Fiscal Phrases (c1905):	H.93		
			A 'Copyright Regd.' on front		£10.00	£400.00
			B Without 'Copyright Regd.'		£10.00	£400.00
A2	C	60	Football Captains, 1907-8 — Series No. 5	H.94	£10.00	£600.00
A2	BW	100	*Heroes of Sport (c1898)	H.95	£60.00	—
A	C	40	*Home and Colonial Regiments (c1901):	H.69		
			A 'Sweet Crop, over 100 ...' back:			
			20 Caption in blue		£8.00	£160.00
			20 Caption in brown		£8.00	£160.00
			B 'Sweet Crop, over 250 ...' back:			
			20 Caption in blue		£10.00	—
			20 Caption in brown		£10.00	—
A2	C	20	*Interesting Buildings and Views (1902)	H.96	£9.00	£180.00
K2	C	52	*Miniature Playing Cards — Bandmaster Cigarettes (c1910)		£4.00	—
D2	C		*Nations (c1902):	H.97		
		20	A Blue back		£11.00	£220.00
		20	*B Plain back — gilt border*		£100.00	—
		1	*C* 1902 Calender back		£100.00	—
D	C	40	Naval and Military Phrases (c1904):	H.14		
			A Red back, 'Series No. 1'		£16.00	£640.00
			B 'Sweet Crop, over 250 ...' back		£26.00	—
D2	C	50	Owners, Jockeys, Footballers, Cricketers — Series No. 2 (c1906)	H.98	£11.00	£550.00
D2	C	20	Owners, Jockeys, Footballers, Cricketers — Series No. 3 (c1907)	H.99	£11.00	£220.00
D	C	30	*Proverbs, 'Sweet Crop, over 400 ...' back (c1905)	H.15	£14.00	—
A	C	20	Russo-Japanese War Series (1904)	H.100	£14.00	—
A	BW	25	*Silhouettes of Celebrities (c1905)	H.101	£12.00	£300.00
D1	C	50	Star Artistes — Series No. 4 (c1905):	H.102		
			20 With stage background		£10.00	£200.00
			30 No stage, plain background		£9.00	£270.00

OHEN WEENEN & CO. LTD, London *(continued)*

ize	Print-ing	Number in set		Handbook reference	Price per card	Complete set
)	C	50	V.C. Heroes (of World War I), Nd. 51-100 (1915):			
			51-75 — dull greyish card		£8.00	£200.00
			Without Maker's Name on back		£11.00	—
			76-100 — glossy white card		£8.00	£200.00
)	U	50	*War Series (World War I) (1915):	H.103		
			1-25 Admirals and Warships:			
			A Thick card		£8.00	£200.00
			B Thin card		£8.00	£200.00
			26-50 Leaders of the War:			
			A Maker's Name on back		£8.00	£200.00
			B *Without Maker's Name on back*		£11.00	—
1	C	30	Wonders of the World — 'Series No. 6' (c1908)	H.104	£6.50	£200.00
	POST-1920 ISSUES					
2	U	25	*Cricketers (1926)		£11.00	—
2	C	20	Nations (1923)	H.97	£4.50	£90.00
1	C	30	Wonders of the World (1923)	H.104	£2.70	£80.00
	SILKS					
–	C	16	*Victoria Cross Heroes II (72 × 70mm) (paper-backed) (c1915)	Ha.504-2	£37.00	—

. H. COLLINS, Mansfield

OST-1920 ISSUES

1	U	25	Homes of England (1924)		£6.00	£150.00
	C	25	Sports and Pastimes — Series I (1923)	H.225	£6.00	£150.00

. COLTON Jun., Retford

RE-1919 ISSUES

	C	30	*Army Pictures, Cartoons, etc (c1916)	H.12	£75.00	—
	U	50	War Portraits (1916)	H.86	£65.00	—

. W. CONQUEST, London

RE-1919 ISSUE

	C	*30	Army Pictures, Cartoons etc (c1916)	H12	£75.00	—

HE CONTINENTAL CIGARETTE FACTORY, London

OST-1920 ISSUES

	C	25	Charming Portraits (c1925):	Ha.549		
			A Back in blue, with firm's name		£5.00	—
			B Back in blue, inscribed 'Club Mixture Tobacco'		£6.00	—
			C Back in brown, inscribed 'Club Mixture Tobacco'		£7.00	—
			*D *Plain back*		£5.00	—

OOPER & CO'S STORES LTD, London

RE-1919 ISSUES

	BW	25	*Boer War Celebrities — 'STEW' (c1901):	H.105		
			A 'Alpha Mixture' back		£100.00	—
			B 'Gladys Cigars' back		£100.00	—

O-OPERATIVE WHOLESALE SOCIETY LTD, Manchester

PRE-1919 ISSUES

2	C	? 5	*Advertisement Cards (c1915)	H.106	£260.00	—
	C	25	Boy Scout Series (c1915)		£26.00	—

CO-OPERATIVE WHOLESALE SOCIETY LTD, Manchester *(continued)*

Size	*Print-ing*	*Number in set*		*Handbook reference*	*Price per card*	*Complete set*
A	C	50	British Sport Series§ (c1914)	H.112	£26.00	—
A	C	28	*Co-operative Buildings and Works (c1914)	H.107	£12.00	£325.0
A	C	25	Parrot Series (1910)		£28.00	—
A	C	18	War Series (c1915)		£25.00	—

§Note: Cards advertise non-tobacco products, but are believed to have been packed with cigarettes and/ tobacco.

B POST-1920 ISSUES

A	C	24	African Types (1936)		50p	£12.0
—	U	50	Beauty Spots of Britain (76 × 51mm) (1936)		25p	£12.5
A2	C	50	Boy Scout Badges (1939)		80p	£40.0
A	C	48	British and Foreign Birds (1938)		60p	£30.0
D	C	25	*Cooking Recipes (1923)		£2.20	£55.0
A	C	24	English Roses (1924)		£3.50	£85.0
A	C	50	Famous Bridges (48 + 2 added) (1937)		70p	£35.0
A	C	48	Famous Buildings (1935)		60p	£30.0
A2	C	25	How to Do It (1924):	Ha.550		
			A 'Anglian Mixture' back		£2.20	—
			B 'Equity Tobacco' back		£2.20	—
			C 'Jaycee Brown Flake' back		£2.20	—
			D 'Raydex Gold Leaf' back		£2.20	—
A	C	48	Musical Instruments (1934)		£3.20	£160.0
A	C	48	Poultry (1927)		£5.00	£250.0
A	C	48	Railway Engines (1936)		£2.80	£140.0
A	C	24	Sailing Craft (1935)		£1.40	£35.0
A2	C	48	Wayside Flowers, brown back (1923)		£1.70	£85.0
A2	C	48	Wayside Flowers, grey back (1928)		70p	£35.0
A2	C	48	Wayside Woodland Trees (1924)		£2.20	£110.0

C POST-1940 ISSUE

A	C	24	Western Stars (1957)		40p	£10.0

COPE BROS & CO. LTD, Liverpool

A PRE-1919 ISSUES

	BW	20	*Actresses — 'BLARM' (c1900):	H.23		
A1			A Plain backs. Name panel ¼" from border		£35.00	—
A1			B Black design back. Name ¼" from border		£35.00	—
D			C Black design back. Name panel ⅟₁₆" from border		£35.00	—
A	U	? 6	*Actresses — 'COPEIS' (c1900)	H.108	£110.00	—
A	U	26	*Actresses 'FROGA A' (c1900)	H.20	£85.00	—
D1	P	50	*Actresses and Beauties (c1900)	H.109	£12.00	—
KI	P	? 46	*Beauties, Actors and Actresses (c1900)	H.110	£22.00	—
A	C	52	*Beauties — P.C. inset (c1898)	H.111	£42.00	—
A	C	15	*Beauties 'PAC' (c1898)	H.2	£70.00	—
A1	C	50	Boats of the World (c1910)		£10.00	£500.0
D2	BW	126	Boxers (c1915):			
			1-25 Boxers		£10.00	£250.0
			26-50 Boxers		£9.00	£225.0
			51-75 Boxers		£9.00	£225.0
			76-100 Boxers		£14.00	£350.0
			101-125 Army Boxers		£10.00	£250.0
			126 'New World Champion'		—	£32.0
A1	C	35	*Boy Scouts and Girl Guides (c1910)	H.132	£10.00	£350.0
D	BW	25	British Admirals (c1915)	H.103	£11.00	£275.0
A2	C	50	British Warriors (c1912):			
			A Black on white backs		£7.00	£350.0
			B Grey on toned backs		£8.00	£400.0

COPE BROS & CO. LTD, Liverpool *(continued)*

Size	*Print-ing*	*Number in set*		*Handbook reference*	*Price per card*	*Complete set*
A	C	50	Characters from Scott (c1900):			
			A Wide card		£10.00	£500.00
			B Narrow card — officially cut		£10.00	—
	U	115	Chinese Series (c1903):	H.113		
A1			Nos 1-20		£11.00	—
A1			Nos-21-40		£11.00	—
			Nos 41-65:			
D			A Thick brown card		£11.00	—
Al			B Re-drawn, smaller format		£11.00	—
A2			Nos 66-115		£11.00	—
A	C	50	Cope's Golfers (1900):			
			A Wide card		£70.00	—
			B Narrow card — officially cut		£70.00	—
A	C	50	Dickens' Gallery (1900)		£9.00	£450.00
A	C	50	Dogs of the World (by Cecil Aldin) (c1910)		£9.00	£450.00
A	C	25	Eminent British Regiments Officers' Uniforms (c1908):		—	£250.00
			A Yellow-brown back		£10.00	—
			B Claret back		£10.00	—
A2	C	30	*Flags of Nations (c1903):	H.114		
			A 'Bond of Union' back		£11.00	£330.00
			B *Plain back*		£9.00	—
D	C	24	*Flags, Arms and Types of Nations (c1904):	H.115		
			A Numbered		£7.00	£175.00
			B Unnumbered		£40.00	—
—	U	20	*Kenilworth Phrases (80 × 70mm) (c1910)	H.116	£150.00	—
A2	C	50	Music Hall Artistes (c1910):			
			A Inscribed 'Series of 50'		£35.00	—
			B Without the above		£9.00	£450.00
A	U	472	Noted Footballers — 'Clips Cigarettes' (c1910):	Ha.474		
			1 Unnumbered — Wee Jock Simpson		—	£38.00
			120 Series of 120:			
			A Greenish-blue frame		£9.00	—
			B Bright blue frame		£9.00	—
			162 Series of 282:			
			A Greenish-blue frame		£9.00	—
			B Bright blue frame		£9.00	—
			471 Series of 500. Bright blue frame		£9.00	—
D	P	195	Noted Footballers — 'Solace Cigarettes' (c1910)		£9.00	—
A	C	24	*Occupations for Women (1897)	H.117	£90.00	—
A	C	52	*Playing Cards 'Rulers' as Court Cards. Blue backs (c1902):	H.118		
			A Rounded Corners		£16.00	—
			B Square Corners		£12.00	—
—	C	24	Photo Albums for the Million (c1902):	H.119		
			12 Buff cover (25 × 39mm)		£16.00	—
			12 Green cover (25 × 39mm)		£16.00	—
A	C	50	Shakespeare Gallery (c1900):			
			A Wide card		£9.00	£450.00
			B Narrow card — officially cut		£9.00	—
A1	C	25	*Uniforms of Soldiers and Sailors (c1900):	H.120		
			A Circular Medallion back, wide card		£28.00	—
			B Square Medallion back, wide card		£50.00	—
			C Square Medallion back, narrow card, officially cut		£22.00	—
D	BW		VC and DSO Naval and Flying Heroes:			
		50	Unnumbered (1916)	H.121	£6.00	£300.00
		25	Numbered 51-75 (1917)		£7.00	£175.00

COPE BROS & CO. LTD, Liverpool *(continued)*

Size	Print-ing	Number in set		Handbook reference	Price per card	Complete set
D	BW	20	*War Pictures (1915)	H.122	£9.00	£180.00
D	BW	25	*War Series (War Leaders and Warships) (c1915)	H.103	£12.00	—
A1	C	25	Wild Animals and Birds (c1908)		£16.00	—
B	***POST-1920 ISSUES***					
D	BW	25	Boxing Lessons (1935)		£4.00	£100.00
—	C	25	Bridge Problems (folders) (85 × 50mm) (1924)		£22.00	—
A1	U	25	Castles§ (1939)		£1.20	£30.00
A1	U	25	Cathedrals§ (May, 1939)		£1.40	£35.00
—	C	25	Dickens' Character Series (75 × 58mm) (1939)		80p	£20.00
—	C	25	The Game of Poker§ (75 × 58mm) (1936)		30p	£7.50
—	C	50	General Knowledge§ (70 × 42mm) (1925)		£3.50	—
—	BW	32	Golf Strokes (70 × 45mm) (1923)		£12.00	—
A1	C	60	'Happy Families' (1937)		£1.25	£75.00
—	C	50	Household Hints§ (advertisement fronts) (70 × 45mm) (1925)		£1.30	£65.00
C	BW	30	Lawn Tennis Strokes (1924):			
			A Numbers 1 to 25		£5.00	—
			B Numbers 26 to 30		£15.00	—
—	U	50	Modern Dancing (folders) (74 × 43mm) (1926)		£13.00	—
A2	C	25	Pigeons (c1926)		£7.00	£175.00
A2	C	25	Song Birds (c1926)		£6.00	£150.00
A1	C	25	Sports and Pastimes (1925)	Ha.551	£4.00	£100.00
—	C	25	Toy Models (The Country Fair) (73 × 66mm) (c1930)	Ha.552	36p	£9.00
A	C	25	The World's Police (c1935)		£4.00	£100.00

§Joint Cope and Richard Lloyd issues.

E. CORONEL, London

PRE-1919 ISSUE

A	C	25	*Types of British and Colonial Troops (1900)	H.76	£60.00	—

DAVID CORRE & CO., London

PRE-1919 ISSUE

—	C	1	Advertisement Card — The New Alliance (70 × 42mm) (c1915)		—	£275.00
D	C	40	*Naval and Military Phrases (1900)	H.14	£65.00	—

JOHN COTTON LTD., Edinburgh

POST-1920 ISSUES

—	C	50	*Bridge Hands (folders) (82 × 66mm) (1934)		£8.00	—
A1	U	50	*Golf Strokes — A/B (1936)		£8.00	—
A1	U	50	*Golf Strokes— C/D (1937)		£9.00	—
A1	U	50	*Golf Strokes— E/F (1938)		£13.00	—
A1	U	50	*Golf Strokes — G/H (1939)		—	—
A1	U	50	*Golf Strokes — I/J (1939)		—	—

A. & J. COUDENS LTD, London

POST-1920 ISSUES

A1	P	60	British Beauty Spots (1923):	Ha.553		
			A Printed back, numbered		£1.10	£65.00
			B Printed back, unnumbered		£2.00	—
			*C Back rubber stamped 'Cymox Cigarettes ...'		£4.00	—
			*D *Plain back*		£4.00	—

A. & J. COUDENS LTD, London *(continued)*

Size	*Print-ing*	*Number in set*		*Handbook reference*	*Price per card*	*Complete set*
A	P	60	Holiday Resorts in East Anglia (1924)		£1.00	£60.00
A2	BW	25	Sports Alphabet (1924)	Ha.551	£6.00	£150.00

THE CRAIGMILLAR CREAMERY CO. LTD, Midlothian

PRE-1919 ISSUE

H	C	1	*Views of Craigmillar (c1901)		—	£250.00

W.R. DANIEL & CO., London

PRE-1919 ISSUES

A2	C	30	*Colonial Troops (c1902):	H.40		
			A Black back		£75.00	—
			B Brown back		£75.00	—
A2	C	25	*National Flags and Flowers — Girls (c1901)	H.123	£110.00	—

W.T. DAVIES & SONS, Chester

A PRE-1919 ISSUES

A	C	? 37	*Actresses — 'DAVAN' (c1902)	H.124	£70.00	—
A	C	25	Army Life (1915)	H.78	£10.00	—
A	BW	12	*Beauties (1903)	H.125	£35.00	—
A	C	50	Flags and Funnels of Leading Steamship Lines (1913)	H.67	£9.00	—
A	BW	? 12	Newport Football Club (c1904)	H.126	£125.00	—
A	BW	5	Royal Welsh Fusiliers (c1904)	H.127	£160.00	—

B POST-1920 ISSUES

A2	U	42	Aristocrats of the Turf (1924):	Ha.554		
			1 Nos 1-30 — 'A Series of 30'		£4.00	—
			2 Nos 31-42 — 'A Series of 42'		£14.00	—
A2	U	36	Aristocrats of the Turf, Second Series (1924)		£4.00	—
A	C	25	Boxing (1924)	H.311	£4.00	£100.00

S. H. DAWES, Luton

PRE-1919 ISSUE

D	C	30	*Army Pictures, Cartoons, etc (c1916)	H.12	£75.00	—

J.W. DEWHURST, Morecambe

PRE-1919 ISSUE

D	C	30	*Army Pictures, Cartoons, etc (c1916)	H.12	£75.00	—

R.I. DEXTER & CO., Hucknall

PRE-1919 ISSUE

D2	U	30	*Borough Arms (1900)	H.128	90p	£27.00

A. DIMITRIOU, London

POST-1920 ISSUE

—	C	? 3	Advertisement Cards (100 × 65mm) (c1930)		£100.00	—

GEORGE DOBIE & SON LTD, Paisley

A POST-1920 ISSUES

—	C	? 22	Bridge Problems (folders) (circular 64mm diam.) (c1933)		£22.00	—

GEORGE DOBIE & SON LTD, Paisley *(continued)*

Size	*Printing*	*Number in set*		*Handbook reference*	*Price per card*	*Complete set*
A	C	25	Weapons of All Ages (1924)		£6.00	£150.00
B	***POST-1940 ISSUES***					
—	C	32	Four-Square Book (Nd 1-32) (75 × 50mm) (1963)		£1.25	—
—	C	32	Four-Square Book (Nd 33-64) (75 × 50mm) (1963)		£1.25	£40.00
—	C	32	Four-Square Book (Nd 65-96) (75 × 50mm) (1963)		80p	£25.00

DOBSON & CO. LTD

PRE-1919 ISSUE

A	C	8	The European War Series (c1917)	H.129	£38.00	—

THE DOMINION TOBACCO CO. (1929) LTD, London

POST-1920 ISSUES

A	U	25	Old Ships (1934)		£1.40	£35.00
A	U	25	Old Ships (Second Series) (1935)		70p	£17.50
A	U	25	Old Ships (Third Series) (1936)		70p	£17.50
A	U	25	Old Ships (Fourth Series) (1936)		£1.00	£25.00

JOSEPH W. DOYLE LTD, Manchester

POST-1920 ISSUES

—	P	18	*Beauties, Nd X.1-X.18 (89 × 70mm) (c1925)		£12.00	—
D	P	12	Dirt Track Riders Nd. CC.A.1-CC.A.12 (c1925)		£45.00	—
D	P	12	Views Nd. CC.B.1-CC.B.12 (c1925)		£26.00	—
D	P	12	Views Nd CC.C.1-CC.C.12 (c1925)		£26.00	—
D	P	12	*Beauties Nd. CC.D.1-CC.D.12 (c1925)		£26.00	—
D	P	12	*Beauties Nd CC.E.1-CC.E.12 (c1925)		£26.00	—

MAJOR DRAPKIN & CO., London

A	***PRE-1919 ISSUES***					
D	BW	12	**Actresses 'FRAN'* (c1910)	H.175	£6.00	—
—	BW	? 1	*Army Insignia (83 × 46mm) (c1915)	H.130	£130.00	—
—	—	? 111	'Bandmaster' Conundrums (58 × 29mm) (c1910)	H.131	£8.00	—
A2	BW	? 29	Boer War Celebrities 'JASAS' — 'Sweet Alva Cigarettes' (c1901)	H133	£100.00	—
A1	P		*Celebrities of the Great War (1916):	H.135		
		36	A *Printed back*		70p	£25.00
		34	B *Plain back*		70p	£24.00
—	BW	96	Cinematograph Actors (42 × 70mm) (1913)	H.134	£9.00	—
A	C	25	How to Keep Fit — Sandow Exercises (c1912):	H.136		
			A 'Drapkin's Cigarettes'		£12.00	£300.00
			A1 'Drapkin's Cigarettes' short cards, cut officially		£12.00	—
			B 'Crayol Cigarettes'		£12.00	£300.00
D	U	48	Photogravure Masterpieces (1915)	H.137	£9.00	—
—	C	25	*Soldiers and Their Uniforms, cutouts (1914):	H.138	—	£75.00
			A 'Drapkin's Cigarettes'		From 90p	—
			B 'Crayol Cigarettes'		From 90p	—
D	BW		**Views of the World* (c1912):	H.176		
		12	A Caption in two lines		£4.50	£55.00
		8	B Caption in one line		£30.00	—
D	BW	8	**Warships* (c1912)	H.463	£9.00	—

MAJOR DRAPKIN & CO., London *(continued)*

Size	*Print-ing*	*Number in set*		*Handbook reference*	*Price per card*	*Complete set*
B	***POST-1920 ISSUES***					
C	C	8	*Advertisement Cards (c1925):	Ha.555		
			1 Packings (4)		£6.50	£26.00
			2 Smokers (4)		£6.00	£24.00
	BW	50	Around Britain (1929) (export):			
C			A Small size		£1.20	£60.00
B1			B Large size		£2.25	—
	C	50	Around the Mediterranean (1926) (export):	Ha.610		
C			A Small size		£1.30	£65.00
B1			B Large size		£2.00	—
A2	P	40	Australian and English Test Cricketers (1928)		£1.70	£70.00
A1	U	25	British Beauties (1930) (export)		£2.40	£60.00
	C	15	Dogs and Their Treatment (1924):			
A			A Small size		£5.00	£75.00
B2			B Large size		£6.00	£90.00
A	C	40	The Game of Sporting Snap (1928)		£3.00	£120.00
			Instruction Booklet		—	£10.00
	C	50	Girls of Many Lands (1929):			
D			A Small size		£2.50	—
—			B Medium size (76 × 52mm)		32p	£16.00
A2	BW	54	Life at Whipsnade Zoo (1934)	Ha.556	50p	£27.00
D2	C	50	'Limericks' (1929):	Ha.557		
			A White card		90p	£45.00
			B Cream card		90p	£45.00
A2	P	36	National Types of Beauty (1928)	Ha.558	60p	£22.00
	C	25	Optical Illusions (1926):			
A			A Small size. Home issue, name panel (23 × 7mm)		£2.40	£60.00
A			B Small size. Export issue, name panel (26 × 10mm)		£2.40	£60.00
B2			C Large 'size. Home issue		£3.00	£75.00
	C	25	Palmistry:			
A			A Small size (1927)		£2.60	£65.00
B			B Large size (1926)		£2.60	£65.00
	C	25	Puzzle Pictures (1926):			
A			A Small size		£2.80	£70.00
B			B Large size		£3.40	£85.00
A2	P	36	Sporting Celebrities in Action (1930) (export)		—	£200.00
			35 different (No. 18 withdrawn)		£3.00	£100.00
C	***SILKS***					
—	C	40	Regimental Colours and Badges of the Indian Army (70 × 50mm) (paper-backed) (c1915):	Ha.502-5		
			A The Buffs' back		£3.50	—
			B No brand back		£27.00	—
D	***MISCELLANEOUS***					
A	C	1	'Grey's' Smoking Mixture Advertisement Card (plain back) (c1935)		—	£5.00

DRAPKIN & MILLHOFF, London

PRE-1919 ISSUES

A	U		*Beauties 'KEWAI' (c1898):	Ha.139-1		
		? 1	A 'Eldona Cigars' back		£100.00	—
		? 1	B 'Explorer Cigars' back		£100.00	—
A	BW	25	*Boer War Celebrities — 'PAM' (c1901)	H.140	£27.00	—
C	C	30	*Colonial Troops (c1902)	H.40	£45.00	—
—	BW	? 7	*'Pick-me-up' Paper Inserts (112 × 44mm) (c1900)	H.141	£90.00	—
—	U	? 1	**Portraits* (48 × 36mm) (c1900)	H.461	£90.00	—
A2	U	? 3	*Pretty Girl Series — 'BAGG' (c1900)	H.45	£125.00	—

J. DUNCAN & CO. LTD, Glasgow

Size	*Printing*	*Number in set*		*Handbook reference*	*Price per card*	*Complete set*
A	***PRE-1919 ISSUES***					
D1	C	48	*Flags, Arms and Types of Nations (c1910):	H.115		
			A Back in Blue		£27.00	—
			B Back in Green		£50.00	—
A	C	20	Inventors and Their Inventions (c1915)		£50.00	—
A	C	30	Scottish Clans, Arms of Chiefs and Tartans (c1910):	H.142		
			A Back in black		£80.00	—
			B Back in green		£17.00	—
—	C		Scottish Gems: (58 × 84mm):	H.143		
—	C	72	1st series (c1912)		£12.00	—
—	C	50	2nd series (c1913)		£12.00	—
—	C	50	3rd series (c1914)		£12.00	—
D	C	25	*Types of British Soldiers (c1910)	H.144	£45.00	—
B	***POST-1920 ISSUES***					
D1	C	50	'Evolution of the Steamship' (c1925)	Ha.559	—	£65.00
			47/50 ditto		65p	£30.00
			'Olimpia II'		—	£23.00
			'Castalia' and 'Athenia'		£6.00	—
H1	BW	50	Scottish Gems (known as '4th Series') (c1925)	Ha.143D	50p	£25.00

G. DUNCOMBE, Buxton

PRE-1919 ISSUE

D	C	30	*Army Pictures, Cartoons, Etc (c1916)	H.12	£75.00	—

ALFRED DUNHILL LTD., London

POST-1940 ISSUE

—	U	25	Dunhill Kingsize Ransom (75 × 45mm) (1985)		£1.40	—

EDWARD VII CIGARETTES

PRE 1919 ISSUE

A2	C	40	*Home and Colonial Regiments (c1900)	H.69	£200.00	—

EDWARDS, RINGER & CO., Bristol

PRE 1919 ISSUE

—	BW	50	How to Count Cribbage Hands (79 × 62mm) (c1908)		£75.00	—

EDWARDS, RINGER & BIGG, Bristol

A	***PRE-1919 ISSUES***					
A	U	25	Abbeys and Castles — Photogravure series (c1912):			
			A Type-set back		£8.00	£200.00
			B 'Statue of Liberty' back		£8.00	£200.00
			C 'Stag Design' back		£8.00	£200.00
A	U	25	Alpine Views — Photogravure series (c1912):			
			A 'Statue of Liberty' back		£8.00	£200.00
			B 'Stag Design' back		£8.00	£200.00
A	C	12	*Beauties — 'CERF' (1905)	H.57	£50.00	—
A	U	25	*Beauties — 'FECKSA', 1900 Calendar back	H.58	£32.00	—
A	C	50	*Birds and Eggs (1906)	H.60	£11.00	£550.00
A	BW	? 1	Boer War and Boxer Rebellion Sketches (c1901)		£100.00	—
A	BW	25	*Boer War Celebrities — 'STEW' 1901 Calendar back	H.105	£40.00	—
A	C	1	Calendar for 1899		£250.00	—
A	C	1	Calendar (1905), Exmore Hunt Stag design back		£250.00	—
A	C	1	Calendar (1910)		£250.00	—

EDWARDS, RINGER & BIGG, Bristol *(continued)*

Size	*Print-ing*	*Number in set*		*Handbook reference*	*Price per card*	*Complete set*
A	U	25	Coast and Country — Photogravure series (1911):			
			A 'Statue of Liberty' back		£8.00	£200.00
			B 'Stag Design' back		£8.00	£200.00
A	C	23	*Dogs series (1908):	H.64		
			A 'Exmoor Hunt' back		£8.00	—
			B 'Klondyke' back		£4.00	£90.00
A	C	3	Easter Manoeuvres of Our Volunteers (1897)	H.146	£275.00	—
A	C	25	Flags of All Nations, 1st series (1906)	H.37	£7.00	£175.00
A	C	12	Flags of All Nations, 2nd series (1907)	H.37	£11.00	£135.00
A	C	37	*Flags of All Nations (1907):	H.37		
			A Globe and Grouped Flags back		£6.00	—
			B 'Exmoor Hunt' back:			
			i 4½d per oz		£7.00	—
			ii Altered to 5d by hand		£7.00	—
			iii 5d label added		£9.00	—
			C 'Stag' design back		£6.00	£225.00
			D Upright titled back		£7.00	—
A	C	50	Life on Board a Man of War (1905)	H.38	£8.50	—
—	C	1	'Miners Bound for Klondyke' (41 × 81mm) (1897)		—	£400.00
A	C	10	Portraits of His Majesty the King in Uniforms of the British and Foreign Nations (1902)	H.147	£35.00	£350.00
A	C	50	A Tour Round the World (Mar. 1909)	H.75	£8.00	£400.00
A	C	56	War Map of the Western Front (1916)		£9.00	—
A	U	54	War Map of the Western Front, etc Series No. 2 (1917):			
			A 'Exmoor Hunt' back		£9.00	—
			B 'New York Mixture' back		£9.00	—
B	***POST-1920 ISSUES***					
A	C	25	British Trees and Their Uses (1933)		£2.40	£60.00
A	C	50	Celebrated Bridges (1924)	H.346	£2.20	£110.00
	U		Cinema Stars (1923):			
A2		50	A Small size		£1.20	£60.00
—		25	B Medium size (67 × 57mm)		£1.60	£40.00
A	C	25	Garden Life (1934)	H.449	£3.00	£75.00
A	C	25	How to Tell Fortunes (1929)		£3.60	£90.00
A	C	50	Mining (1925)	H.450	£2.20	£110.00
A	C	25	Musical Instruments (1924)	Ha.547	£3.20	£80.00
A	C	25	Optical Illusions (1936)	Ha.560	£2.20	£55.00
A	C	25	Our Pets (1926)	Ha.561	£2.20	£55.00
A	C	25	Our Pets, 2nd series (1926)	Ha.561	£2.20	£55.00
A	C	25	Past and Present (1928)		£3.20	£80.00
A	C	25	Prehistoric Animals (1924)		£4.00	£100.00
A	C	25	Sports and Games in Many Lands (1935)		£3.20	£80.00

S. EISISKI, Rhyl

PRE-1919 ISSUES

D	U	? 4	*Actresses 'ANGOOD' (c1900)	H.187	£125.00	—
A	U	? 6	*Actresses — 'COPEIS' (c1900)	H.108	£125.00	—
A	U	? 22	*Beauties — 'FENA' (c1900)	H.148	£125.00	—
A	U	? 1	*Beauties — 'KEWA I', back inscribed 'Eisiski's New Gold Virginia Cigarettes' (c1900)	Ha.139-1	£125.00	—
A	U	? 1	*Beauties — 'KEWA II', back inscribed 'Eisiski's Rhyl Best Bird's Eye Cigarettes' (c1900)	Ha.139-2	£125.00	—
A	U	? 3	*Beauties — 'KEWA II' Rubber-stamped back (c1900)	H.139	£125.00	—

ELDONS LTD

Size	Printing	Number in set		Handbook reference	Price per card	Complete set
			PRE-1919 ISSUE			
A1	C	30	*Colonial Troops — 'Leon de Cuba' Cigars (c1900)	H.40	£95.00	—

R. J. ELLIOTT & CO. LTD., Huddersfield

			PRE 1919 ISSUE			
A2	C	1	Advertisement Card — Bulldog (c1910)		—	£150.00

EMPIRE TOBACCO CO., London

			PRE-1919 ISSUE			
D	C	? 6	Franco-British Exhibition (c1907)	Ha.471	£150.00	—

THE EXPRESS TOBACCO CO. LTD, London

			POST-1920 ISSUE			
—	U	50	'How It is Made'(Motor Cars) (76 × 51mm) (1931)		£2.50	—

L. & J. FABIAN, London

			POST-1920 ISSUE			
D1	P	24	The Elite Series (Beauties) (most numbers preceded by letters 'LLF') (c1935)		£34.00	—

FAIRWEATHER & SONS, Dundee

			PRE-1919 ISSUE			
A	C	50	Historic Buildings of Scotland (c1914)		£40.00	—

W. & F. FAULKNER, London

12 page reference book available — £3.25

A	***PRE-1919 ISSUES***					
C	C	26	*Actresses — 'FROGA A' (c1900)	H.20	£40.00	—
D2	C	12	*'Ation Series (1901)		£20.00	—
C	C	? 24	*Beauties (c1898)	H.150	£60.00	—
A	U	49	*Beauties — 'FECKSA' (1901)	H.58	£17.00	—
A	BW	16	*British Royal Family (1901)	H.28	£32.00	—
D2	C	12	*Coster Series (1900)	H.151	£20.00	—
A	BW	20	Cricketers Series (1901)	H.29	£225.00	—
D2	C	12	Cricket Terms (1899)	H.152	£60.00	—
D2	C	12	Football Terms, 1st Series (1900)	H.153	£20.00	—
D2	C	12	Football Terms, 2nd Series (1900)	H.154	£20.00	—
D2	C	12	*Golf Terms (1901)	H.155	£75.00	—
D2	C	12	Grenadier Guards (1899)	H.156	£20.00	—
A2	C	40	*Kings and Queens (1902)	H.157	£20.00	—
D2	C	12	Kipling Series (1900)	H.158	£20.00	—
D2	C	12	The Language of Flowers (1900):	H.159		
			A 'Grenadier' Cigarettes		£30.00	—
			B 'Nosegay' Cigarettes		£30.00	—
D2	C	12	*Military Terms, 1st series (1899)	H.50	£20.00	—
D2	C	12	*Military Terms, 2nd series (1899)	H.160	£22.00	—
D2	C	12	*Nautical Terms, 1st series (1900)	H.161	£18.00	—
D2	C	12	*Nautical Terms, 2nd series (1900):	H.162		
			A 'Grenadier' Cigarettes		£18.00	—
			B 'Union Jack Cigarettes'		£20.00	—

W. & F. FAULKNER, London *(continued)*

Size	*Printing*	*Number in set*		*Handbook reference*	*Price per card*	*Complete set*
D2	C		'Our Colonial Troops' (1900):			
			A Grenadier Cigarettes:			
		30	i With copyright Nos 1-30		£22.00	—
		90	ii Without copyright Nos 1-90		£12.00	—
		60	B Union Jack Cigarettes Nos 31-90		£14.00	—
A	C	20	Our Gallant Grenadiers, 1-20:	H.163		
			A Without ITC Clause (1901):			
			i Thick card		£16.00	£320.00
			ii Thin card		£16.00	£320.00
			B With ITC Clause, thin card (1902)		£25.00	£500.00
A	C	20	Our Gallant Grenadiers, 21-40 (1903)		£20.00	£400.00
D2	C	12	*Policemen of the World (1899)	H.164	£28.00	—
D2	C	12	*Police Terms (1899)	H165	£20.00	—
D2	C	12	*Puzzle series (1897):	H.166		
			A 'Grenadier Cigarettes		£125.00	—
			B 'Nosegay Cigarettes		£50.00	—
A	BW	25	*South African War Scenes (1901)	H.167	£12.00	£300.00
D2	C	12	Sporting Terms (1900)	H.168	£25.00	—
D2	C	12	Street Cries (1902)	H.169	£20.00	—
B	***POST-1920 ISSUES***					
A	C	25	Angling (1929)		£6.00	—
A	C	50	Celebrated Bridges (1925)	H.346	£2.20	£110.00
A	C	25	Old Sporting Prints (1930)	Ha.563	£3.00	£75.00
A	C	25	Optical Illusions (1935)	Ha.560	£2.40	£60.00
A	C	25	Our Pets (1926)	Ha.561	£3.00	£75.00
A	C	25	Our Pets, 2nd series (1926)	Ha.561	£2.60	£65.00
A	C	25	Prominent Racehorses of the Present Day (1923)		£2.80	£70.00
A	C	25	Prominent Racehorses of the Present Day, 2nd series (1924)		£4.60	£130.00

FIELD FAVOURITES CIGARETTES

PRE-1919 ISSUE

D	P	? 1	*Footballers (c1895)		£300.00	—

FINLAY & CO. LTD, Newcastle-on-Tyne and London

PRE-1919 ISSUES

D1	BW	? 8	Our Girls (c1910)	H.170	£125.00	—
A	U	30	World's Aircraft (c1912)		£60.00	—

FLYNN, Dublin

PRE-1919 ISSUE

A	C	26	*Beauties — 'HOL' (c1900)	H.192	£200.00	—

C. D. FOTHERGILL, St Helens

PRE-1919 ISSUE

—	C	? 1	*'Play Up' Sporting Shields (c1895)		£125.00	—

FRAENKEL BROS, London

PRE-1919 ISSUES

A2	C	? 2	*Beauties — 'Don Jorg (c1898)	H.493-1	£180.00	—
A	U	? 22	*Beauties — 'FENA' (c1898)	H.148	£90.00	—

FRAENKEL BROS, London *(continued)*

Size	Printing	Number in set		Handbook reference	Price per card	Complete set
A	C	25	*Beauties — 'GRACC' (c1898)	H.59	£120.00	—
A	U	24	*Beauties — 'HUMPS' (c1900)	H.222	£100.00	—
A	U	26	*Music Hall Artistes (c1900):	H.171		
			A Pink card		£90.00	—
			B White card		£90.00	—
A2	C	25	*Types of British and Colonial Troops (c1900)	H.76	£65.00	—

FRANKLYN, DAVEY & CO., Bristol

A	***PRE-1919 ISSUES***					
A	C	12	*Beauties — 'CERF' (1905)	H.57	£50.00	—
D2	C	50	*Birds (c1895)		£45.00	—
A2	BW	? 8	*Boer War Generals — 'FLAC' (1901)	H.47	£85.00	—
A	C	25	Ceremonial and Court Dress (Oct. 1915)	H.145	£8.00	—
A	C	50	*Football Club Colours (1909)	H.68	£10.00	£500.00
A	C	50	Naval Dress and Badges (1916)	H.172	£9.00	—
A	C	25	*Star Girls (c1898)	Ha.30	£135.00	—
A	C	10	Types of Smokers (c1898)		£50.00	£500.00
A	C	50	Wild Animals of the World (c1902)	H.77	£9.00	£450.00
B	***POST-1920 ISSUES***					
A	C	25	Boxing (1924)	H.311	£3.00	£75.00
A	C	50	Children of All Nations (1934)		70p	£35.00
A	C	50	Historic Events (1924)	H.464	£2.40	£120.00
A	U	25	Hunting (1925)		£1.00	£25.00
A	U	50	Modern Dance Steps (1929)		£3.60	£180.00
A	U	50	Modern Dance Steps, 2nd series (1931)		70p	£35.00
A	C	50	Overseas Dominions (Australia) (1923)	H.451	£4.00	£200.00
C	***MISCELLANEOUS***					
—	C	? 1	Comic Dog Folder (opens to 183 × 65mm) (1898)	Ha.490	—	£250.00

A.H. FRANKS & SONS, London

PRE-1919 ISSUES

D1	BW	56	*Beauties — 'Beauties Cigarettes' (c1900)	H.173	£60.00	—
D	C	? 24	*Nautical Expressions (c1900)	H.174	£70.00	—
A1	C	25	*Types of British and Colonial Troops (c1900)	H.76	£55.00	—

J.J. FREEMAN, London

PRE-1919 ISSUES

D	BW	12	*Actresses — 'FRAN' (c1912)	H.175	£35.00	—
D	BW	12	*Views of the World (c1910)	H.176	£35.00	—

J. R. FREEMAN, London

A POST-1920 ISSUE						
—	U	12	*'Manikin' Cards (77 × 49mm) (c1920)	Ha.481	£70.00	—
B POST-1940 ISSUE						
C1	U	33	Football Challenge (1969)		£4.00	—

C. FRYER & SONS LTD, London

A	***PRE-1919 ISSUES***					
A2	C	? 25	*Boer War and General Interest: (c1900)	H.13		
			A Brown leaf design back		£100.00	—
			B Green leaf design back		£100.00	—
			C Green daisy design back		£100.00	—

C. FRYER & SONS LTD, London *(continued)*

Size	Printing	Number in set		Handbook reference	Price per card	Complete set
D	C	40	*Naval and Military Phrases (c1905)	H.14	£45.00	—
A2	BW	? 10	*'Vita Berlin' series (c1902)	H.177	£130.00	—
B	***POST-1920 ISSUE***					
—	—	50	Clan Sketches (101 × 74mm) (paper folders with wording only) — 'Pibroch Virginia' (c1930)	Ha.628	£9.00	—

FRYER & COULTMAN, London

PRE-1919 ISSUE

—	C	12	*French Phrases, 1893 Calendar back (96 × 64 mm)	H.178	£200.00	—

J. GABRIEL, London

PRE-1919 ISSUES

A	BW	10	*Actresses — 'HAGG A' (1900)	H.24	£65.00	—
A2	C	25	*Beauties — 'GRACC' (c1898)	H.59	£120.00	—
A	BW	20	Cricketers series (1901)	H.29	£325.00	—
A	C	40	*Home and Colonial Regiments (c1902):	H.69		
			20 Caption in blue		£80.00	—
			20 Caption in brown		£80.00	—
A	U	? 52	*Pretty Girl series — 'BAGG' (c1898)	H.45	£70.00	—
A2	C	25	*Types of British and Colonial Troops (c1900)	H.76	£65.00	—

GALA CIGARETTES

PRE-1919 ISSUE

D1	U	? 1	Stamp Card c1910	Ha.589-2	—	£120.00

GALLAHER LTD, Belfast and London

40 page reference book available — £3.25

A	***PRE-1919 ISSUES***					
D	P	110	*Actors and Actresses (c1900)	H.179	£4.50	—
D	C	25	The Allies Flags: (1914):			
			A Toned card		£5.00	—
			B White card		£5.00	—
D	C	100	Association Football Club Colours (1910):			
			A Grey border		£5.00	—
			B Brown border		£5.00	—
A	C	52	*Beauties (c1900):	H.180		
			A Without inset		£12.00	—
			B With Playing Card inset		£12.00	—
D	C	50	*Birds and Eggs (c1905)	H.60		
			A 'Gallaher Ltd' Label		£35.00	—
			B 'Manufactured by Gallaher' Label		£7.50	—
D	C	100	Birds' Nests and Eggs series (1919):			
			A White card		£1.30	£130.00
			B Toned card		£1.30	—
D	C		Boy Scout series Grey-green back (1911):			
		100	A 'Belfast and London'		£1.60	£160.00
		86	B 'London and Belfast'		£1.80	—
D	U	50	British Naval series (1914)		£4.50	£225.00
D	P	100	English and Scotch Views (c1910)		£3.20	£320.00
D	C	100	Fables and Their Morals, (1912):			
			A Numbered Outside Set Title Panel		£1.50	£150.00
			B & C Later printings, see Post-1920 issues			
D	C	100	The Great War series (1915)		£2.30	£230.00

GALLAHER LTD, Belfast and London *(continued)*

Size	*Print-ing*	*Number in set*		*Handbook reference*	*Price per card*	*Complete set*
D	C	100	The Great War series — Second Series (1916)		£2.30	£230.00
D	C		The Great War, Victoria Cross Heroes (1915-16):			
		25	1st series 1-25		£4.00	£100.00
		25	2nd series 26-50		£4.00	£100.00
		25	3rd series 51-75		£4.00	£100.00
		25	4th series 76-100		£4.00	£100.00
		25	5th series 101-125		£4.00	£100.00
		25	6th series 126-150		£4.00	£100.00
		25	7th series 151-175		£4.00	£100.00
		25	8th series 176-200		£4.00	£100.00
D	C	100	How to do it (1916)		£3.00	£300.00
D			Irish View Scenery (c1910):	H.181		
	BW	400	1-400, matt:			
			A Numbered on back		£2.00	—
			B Unnumbered, plain back		£3.00	—
	P	400	1-400, glossy — see H.181			
			A Black photo		90p	£360.00
			B Brown photo		£2.50	—
			C As A, but series title and No. omitted		£2.00	—
			D Numbered 1-200 plain back		£3.00	—
	P	600	1-600, glossy — see H.181			
			A Nos 1 to 500		90p	£450.00
			B Nos 501 to 600		£4.00	—
D	C	100	'Kute Kiddies' series (1916)		£3.50	£350.00
D	P	50	Latest Actresses (1910):			
			A Black photo		£12.00	—
			B Chocolate photo		£17.00	—
A	C	50	*Regimental Colours and Standards (Nd 151-200) (1899)		£6.00	£300.00
A	C	50	Royalty series (1902)		£6.00	£300.00
A	C	111	The South African series (Nd 101-211) (1901):			
			A White back		£5.00	—
			B Cream back		£5.00	—
D	C	100	'Sports' series (1912)		£5.00	£500.00
D	U	? 87	*Stage and Variety Celebrities (collotype) (c1898):	H.182		
			A 'Gallager' back		£65.00	—
			B 'Gallaher' back		£65.00	—
			C As B but larger lettering, etc		£65.00	—
D	C	100	Tricks and Puzzles series, green back (1913)		£3.75	£375.00
A	C	50	*Types of the British Army — unnumbered (1897):	H.183		
			A 'Battle Honours' back		£8.00	—
			B 'The Three Pipes ...' — green back		£8.00	—
A	C	50	*Types of the British Army — Nd 1-50 (1898):			
			A 'The Three Pipes ...' — brown back		£8.00	—
			B 'Now in Three ...' — brown back		£8.00	—
A	C	50	*Types of British and Colonial Regiments — Nd 51-100 (1900):			
			A 'The Three Pipes ...' — brown back		£8.00	—
			B 'Now in Three ...' — brown back		£8.00	—
D	C	100	Useful Hints series (1915)		£2.80	£280.00
D	U	25	Views in North of Ireland (1912)		£42.00	—
D	C	50	Votaries of the Weed (1916)		£5.00	£250.00
D	C	100	'Why is it?' series (1915):			
			A Green back		£3.00	£300.00
			B Brown back		£3.00	£300.00
D	C	100	Woodland Trees series (1912)		£4.00	£400.00

GALLAHER LTD, Belfast and London *(continued)*

Size	*Print-ing*	*Number in set*		*Handbook reference*	*Price per card*	*Complete set*
			POST-1920 ISSUES			
	C	48	Aeroplanes (1939)		80p	£40.00
A2	C	25	Aesop's Fables (1931):	Ha.518		
			A Inscribed 'A Series of 25'		£1.20	£30.00
			B Inscribed 'A Series of 50'		£1.20	£30.00
	C	100	Animals and Birds of Commercial Value (1921)		70p	£70.00
	C	48	Army Badges (1939)		70p	£35.00
–	U	24	Art Treasures of the World (76 × 56mm) (1930)		44p	£11.00
–	P	48	Beautiful Scotland (77 × 52mm) (1939)	Ha.564-1	80p	£40.00
	C	100	Boy Scout Series brown back (1922)		£1.50	£150.00
	C	48	British Birds (1937)		30p	£15.00
	C	100	British Birds by Rankin (1923):	Ha.537		
			A 'By Rankin'		£10.00	—
			B 'By George Rankin'		£1.00	£100.00
	C	75	British Champions of 1923 (1924)		£1.35	£100.00
	C	48	Butterflies and Moths (1938)		28p	£14.00
	C	25	Champion Animals & Birds of 1923 (1924)		£1.40	£35.00
	C	48	Champions (1934):			
			A Front without letterpress		50p	£25.00
			B Front with captions, subjects re-drawn		50p	£25.00
	C	48	Champions, 2nd Series (1935)		40p	£20.00
	C	48	Champions of Screen & Stage (1934):			
			A Red back		60p	£30.00
			B Blue back, 'Gallaher's Cigarettes' at base		90p	£45.00
			C Blue back, 'Gallaher Ltd' at base		90p	£45.00
	U	100	Cinema Stars (1926)		£1.40	£140.00
–	P	48	Coastwise (77 × 52mm) (1938)	Ha.564-2	70p	£35.00
	C	24	Dogs (1934):			
			A Captions in script letters:			
			1 Small size		£1.70	£40.00
			2 Large size		£1.70	£40.00
			B Captions in block letters:			
			1 Small size		£1.00	£24.00
			2 Large size		£1.00	£24.00
	C	48	Dogs (1936)		45p	£22.00
	C	48	Dogs Second Series (1938)		40p	£20.00
	C	100	Fables and Their Morals:			
			A First printing, pre-1919 issues			
			B & C Numbered in set title panel			
			B Thin numerals (1922)			
			1 White card		75p	£75.00
			2 Yellow card		75p	£75.00
			C Thick numerals (1922)		75p	£75.00
	U	100	Famous Cricketers (1926)		£2.50	£250.00
	C	48	Famous Film Scenes (1935)		60p	£30.00
	U	100	Famous Footballers, green back (1925)		£1.40	£140.00
	C	50	Famous Footballers, brown back (1926)		£1.70	£85.00
	C	48	Famous Jockeys (1936)		£1.00	£50.00
	C	48	Film Episodes (1936)		60p	£30.00
	C	48	Film Partners (1935)		70p	£35.00
–	P	48	Flying (77 × 52mm) (1938)	Ha.564-3	£1.00	—
	C	100	Footballers, red back (1928):			
			1 Nos. 1-50 — Action pictures		£1.60	£80.00
			2 Nos. 51-100 — Portraits		£1.80	£90.00
	C	50	Footballers in Action (1928)		£1.70	£85.00
	C	48	Garden Flowers (1938)		20p	£10.00

GALLAHER LTD, Belfast and London *(continued)*

Size	*Print-ing*	*Number in set*		*Handbook reference*	*Price per card*	*Complete set*
D		100	Interesting Views:			
	P		A Uncoloured, glossy (1923)		£1.60	£160.00
	CP		B Hand-coloured, matt (1925)		£2.25	£225.00
B2	P	48	Island Sporting Celebrities (Channel Islands) (1938)		£1.20	£60.00
D	C	50	Lawn Tennis Celebrities (1928)		£3.00	—
A	C	24	Motor Cars (1934)		£4.00	£100.00
D	C	48	My Favourite Part (1939)		60p	£30.00
D	C	48	The Navy (1937):			
			A 'Park Drive ...' at base of back		60p	£30.00
			B 'Issued by ...' at base of back		80p	£40.00
—	P	48	Our Countryside (72 × 52mm) (1938)	Ha.564-4	90p	—
D	C	100	Plants of Commercial Value (1923)		80p	£80.00
D	C	48	Portraits of Famous Stars (1935)		£1.00	£50.00
D	C	48	Racing Scenes (1938)		60p	£30.00
D	C	100	The Reason Why (1924)		75p	£75.00
D	C	100	Robinson Crusoe (1928)		£1.50	£150.00
B2	P	48	Scenes from the Empire (1939) (export)	Ha.565	30p	£15.00
—	P	24	Shots from the Films (77 × 52mm) (1936)	Ha.566	£2.50	£60.00
D	C	48	Shots from Famous Films (1935)		60p	£30.00
D	C	48	Signed Portraits of Famous Stars (1935)		£1.80	—
D	C	48	Sporting Personalities (1936)		40p	£20.00
D	C	48	Stars of Screen & Stage (1935):			
			A Back in green		60p	£30.00
			B Back in brown		£1.50	£75.00
D	C	48	Trains of the World (1937)		80p	£40.00
D	C	100	Tricks & Puzzles Series, black back (1933):			
			Nos. 1-50		80p	£40.00
			Nos. 51-100		80p	£40.00
D	C	48	Wild Animals (1937)		28p	£14.00
D	C	48	Wild Flowers (1939)		30p	£15.00
D	C	100	The 'Zoo' Aquarium (1924)		£1.20	£120.00
D	C	50	'Zoo' Tropical Birds, 1st Series (1928)		£1.30	£65.00
D	C	50	'Zoo' Tropical Birds, 2nd Series (1929)		£1.30	£65.00
C	***SILKS***					
—	C	24	Flags — Set 1 (68 × 48mm) (paper-backed) (1916)	Ha.501-1	£7.50	—

SAMUEL GAWITH, Kendal

POST-1920 ISSUE

—	BW	25	The English Lakeland (90 × 70mm) (1926)		£18.00	—

F. GENNARI LTD, London

PRE-1919 ISSUE

A	U	50	War Portraits (1916)	H.86	£65.00	—

LOUIS GERARD LTD, London

POST-1920 ISSUES

D1	U	50	Modern Armaments (1938):	Ha.567		
			A Numbered		80p	£40.00
			B Unnumbered		£1.00	£50.00

LOUIS GERARD LTD, London *(continued)*

Size	*Print-ing*	*Number in set*		*Handbook reference*	*Price per card*	*Complete set*
D1	U	24	Screen Favourites (1937):	Ha.568		
			A Inscribed 'Louis Gerard & Company'		£3.00	—
			B Inscribed 'Louis Gerard Limited'		£3.00	—
D1	C	48	Screen Favourites and Dancers (1937)	Ha.569	£2.20	£110.00

W.G. GLASS & CO. LTD, Bristol

PRE-1919 ISSUES

A	BW	20	*Actresses — 'BLARM' (c1900)	H.23	£65.00	—
A2	BW	10	*Actresses — 'HAGG A' (c1900)	H.24	£65.00	—
A	U	25	*Beauties — 'FECKSA (c1901)'	H.58	£80.00	—
D1	BW	20	*Boer War Cartoons ('Roseland Cigarettes') (c1901)	H.42	£80.00	—
A	BW	25	*Boer War Celebrities — 'STEW' (c1901)	H.105	£70.00	—
A	BW	16	*British Royal Family (1901)	H.28	£65.00	—
A2	BW	20	Cricketers Series (1901)	H.29	£300.00	—
D	C	40	*Naval and Military Phrases (c1902)	H.14	£85.00	—
A	BW	19	*Russo-Japanese Series (1904)	H.184	£55.00	—

R. P. GLOAG & CO, London

(Cards bear advertisements for 'Citamora' and/or 'The Challenge Flat Brilliantes' without maker's name)

PRE-1919 ISSUES

A2	U	? 8	*Actresses — 'ANGLO' (c1896)	H.185	£180.00	—
D			*Beauties — Selection from 'Plums' (c1898):	H.186		
	BW		A 'The Challenge Flat' front:			
		? 41	(a) front in black and white		£85.00	—
	U	? 3	(b) front in brown printed back		£130.00	—
	U	? 3	(c) front in brown, plain back		£130.00	—
	BW	? 10	B 'Citamora' front in black and white		£130.00	—
A	C	40	*Home and Colonial Regiments (c1900):	H.69		
			20 Caption in blue		£45.00	—
			20 Caption in brown		£45.00	—
D	C	30	*Proverbs (c1901)	H.15	£80.00	—
A2	C	25	*Types of British and Colonial Troops (c1900)	H.76	£55.00	—

GLOBE CIGARETTE CO.

PRE-1919 ISSUE

D	BW	25	*Actresses — French (c1900)	H.1	£160.00	—

GOLDS LTD, Birmingham

PRE-1919 ISSUES

A2	BW	1	Advertisement Card (Chantecler) (c1905)		£275.00	—
	C	18	Motor Cycle Series (c1914):	Ha.469		
			A Back in blue, numbered		£50.00	—
			B Back in grey, numbered		£60.00	—
			C Back in grey, unnumbered		£60.00	—
—	BW	? 14	*Prints from Noted Pictures (68 × 81mm) (c1908)	Ha.216	£110.00	—

T. P. & R. GOODBODY, Dublin and London

PRE-1919 ISSUES

—	U	? 20	*Actresses — 'ANGOOD' (36 × 60mm) (c1898)	H.187	£140.00	—
A2	U	? 4	*Beauties — 'KEWA' (c1898)	Ha.139	£125.00	—

T. P. & R. GOODBODY, Dublin and London *(continued)*

Size	Printing	Number in set		Handbook reference	Price per card	Complete set
D	BW		*Boer War Celebrities — 'CAG' (1901)	H.79		
		25	See H.79 — Fig. 79-B		£30.00	—
		16	See H.79 — Fig. 79-C		£35.00	—
		16	See H.79 — Fig. 79-D		£35.00	—
A2	C		Colonial Forces (c1900):	H.188		
		? 40	A Brown back		£70.00	—
		? 40	B Black back		£70.00	—
—	U	? 49	*Dogs (1910) (36 × 60mm)	H.189	£65.00	—
C	C	26	Eminent Actresses — 'FROGA A' (c1900)	H.20	£40.00	—
C	C	20	Irish Scenery (Five Printings) (c1905)	H.190	£38.00	—
A2	U		*Pretty Girl Series — 'BAGG' (c1898):	H.45		
		? 3	A Red stamped back		£100.00	—
		? 4	B Violet stamped back		£100.00	—
A	C	25	Types of Soldiers (c1914)	H.144	£50.00	—
D	U	20	*War Pictures (c1915)	H.122	£24.00	—
C	C	12	'With the Flag to Pretoria' (c1901)	H.191	£90.00	—
B	***POST-1920 ISSUES***					
D	C	50	Questions & Answers in Natural History (1924)		£2.60	£120.00
A	C	25	Sports & Pastimes — Series 1 (1925)	H.225	£6.00	£150.00

GORDON'S, Glasgow

PRE-1919 ISSUE

A2	BW	? 4	Billiards — By George D. Gordon (c1910)		£170.00	—

GRAVESON, Mexboro'

PRE-1919 ISSUES

A2	C	30	*Army Pictures, Cartoons, Etc (c1916)	H.12	£75.00	—
A	U	50	War Portraits (1916)	H.86	£65.00	—

FRED GRAY, Birmingham

PRE-1919 ISSUE

A	C	25	*Types of British Soldiers (c1914)	H.144	£90.00	—

GRIFFITHS BROS., Manchester

POST-1920 ISSUE

—	P	18	*Beauties (89 × 70mm) (c1925)		£70.00	—

W. J. HARRIS, London

PRE-1919 ISSUES

A2	C	26	*Beauties 'HOL' (c1900)	H.192	£30.00	—
C	C	30	*Colonial Troops (c1900)	H.40	£80.00	—
A1	C	25	*Star Girls (c1899)	H.30	£180.00	—

JAS. H. HARRISON, Birmingham

PRE-1919 ISSUE

C	C	18	Motor Cycle Series (c1914)	Ha.469	£65.00	—

HARVEY & DAVEY, Newcastle-on-Tyne

PRE-1919 ISSUES

D1	C	50	*Birds and Eggs (c1905)	H.60	£4.00	£200.00

HARVEY & DAVEY, Newcastle-on-Tyne *(continued)*

Size	Print-ing	Number in set		Handbook reference	Price per card	Complete set
A1	C	? 11	*Chinese and South African Series (c1901)	H.193	£110.00	—
C	C	30	*Colonial Troops (c1900)	H.40	£65.00	—
A1	C	25	*Types of British and Colonial Troops (c1901)	H.76	£75.00	—

W. & H. HEATON, Birkby

PRE-1919 ISSUE

—	BW	? 6	Birkby Views (70 × 39mm) (c1912)	H.226	£150.00	—

HENLY & WATKINS LTD, London

POST-1920 ISSUES

A1	C	25	Ancient Egyptian Gods — 'Matossian's Cigarettes' (1924)	Ha.570		
			*A Plain back		£5.00	£125.00
			B Back in blue		£6.00	£150.00

HIGNETT BROS. & CO., Liverpool

A PRE-1919 ISSUES

C	C	26	*Actresses — 'FROGA A' (c1900)	H.20	£50.00	—
A2	U	25	*Actresses — Photogravure (c1900)	H.194	£22.00	—
D1	BW	28	*Actresses — 'PILPI I' (c1901)	H.195	£20.00	—
D1	P	50	*Actresses — 'PILPI II' (c1901)	H.196	£12.00	—
A	U	1	Advertisement Card. Smoking mixture (c1890)		—	£325.00
—	C	60	Animal Pictures ... (38 × 70mm) (c1900)	H.197	£27.00	—
D	U	50	*Beauties — gravure (c1898):	H.198		
			A 'Cavalier' back		£65.00	—
			B 'Golden Butterfly' back		£65.00	—
C	C	? 2	*Beauties — 'CHOAB' (c1900)	H.21	£110.00	—
A1	C	? 19	Cabinet, 1900	H.199	£70.00	—
A	C	25	Cathedrals and Churches (1909)		£4.40	£110.00
A	C	25	Company Drill (1915)		£4.40	£110.00
A	C	25	Greetings of the World (1907 — re-issued 1922)		£3.00	£75.00
A	C	50	Interesting Buildings (1905)	H.70	£5.00	£250.00
—	C	40	*Medals (34 × 72mm) (1901):	H.200		
			A 'Butterfly Cigarettes'		£22.00	—
			B Officially cut for use in other brands		£22.00	—
A	BW	25	Military Portraits (1914)	H.201	£5.00	£125.00
A	C	25	Modern Statesmen (1906):			
			A 'Butterfly' back		£5.00	£125.00
			B 'Pioneer' back		£5.00	£125.00
A	C	20	*Music Hall Artistes (c1900)	H.202	£50.00	—
—	C	1	Oracle Butterfly (shaped) (c1898)		—	£125.00
A	C	25	Panama Canal (1914)		£6.00	£150.00
A2	C	12	*Pretty Girl Series — 'RASH' (c1900)	H.8	£50.00	—
—	BW	25	*V.C. Heroes (35 × 72mm) (1901)	H.203	£45.00	—
A	C	20	*Yachts (c1902):	H.204		
			A Gold on black back		£60.00	—
			B Black on white back		£60.00	—

B POST-1920 ISSUES

A	C	50	Actors — Natural and Character Studies (1938)	Ha.571-1	£1.50	£75.00
A	C	50	A.F.C. Nicknames (1933)	Ha.571-2	£4.00	—
A	C	50	Air-Raid Precautions (1939)	Ha.544	80p	£40.00
A	C	50	Arms and Armour (1924)	H.273	£2.80	£140.00

HIGNETT BROS. & CO., Liverpool *(continued)*

Size	*Printing*	*Number in set*		*Handbook reference*	*Price per card*	*Complete set*
A	C	50	British Birds and Their Eggs (1938)	Ha.571-3	£2.20	—
A	U	50	Broadcasting (1935)	Ha.571-4	£2.00	—
A	U	50	Celebrated Old Inns (1925)		£2.80	£140.00
A	C	50	Champions of 1936 (1937)	Ha.571-5	£2.40	£120.00
A	C	25	Common Objects of the Sea-Shore (1924)		£2.20	£55.00
A	C	50	Coronation Procession (sectional) (1937)	Ha.571-6	£2.00	—
A	C	50	Dogs (1936)	Ha.571-7	£1.80	£90.00
A	C	50	Football Caricatures (1935)	Ha.571-8	£2.50	£125.00
A	C	50	Football Club Captains (1935)	Ha.571-9	£2.50	£125.00
A	U	25	Historical London (1926)		£2.40	£60.00
A	C	50	How to Swim (1935)	Ha.571-10	80p	£40.00
A	C	25	International Caps and Badges (1924)		£3.20	£80.00
A	C	25	Life in Pond & Stream (1925)		£2.40	£60.00
A	C	50	Modern Railways (1936)	Ha.571-11	£2.30	£115.00
A	C	50	Ocean Greyhounds (1938)	Ha.571-12	£1.40	£70.00
A	U	25	*The Prince of Wales' Empire Tour (1924)		£2.40	£60.00
A	U	50	Prominent Cricketers of 1938 (1938)	Ha.571-13	£2.60	£130.00
A	C	50	Prominent Racehorses of 1933 (1934)	Ha.571-14	£2.40	£120.00
A	C	50	Sea Adventure (1939)	Ha.571-15	40p	£20.00
A	C	25	Ships Flags & Cap Badges (1926)		£2.80	£70.00
A	C	25	Ships Flags and Cap Badges, 2nd Series (1927)		£3.60	£90.00
A	C	50	Shots from the Films (1936)	Ha.571-16	£2.50	£125.00
A	C	50	Trick Billiards (1934)	Ha.571-17	£3.00	—
A	U	25	Turnpikes (1927)		£2.40	£60.00
A	C	50	Zoo Studies (1937)	Ha.571-18	90p	£45.00

R. & J. HILL LTD, London

28 page reference book available — £3.25

A PRE-1919 ISSUES

A	C	26	*Actresses — 'FROGA A' (c1900)	H.20	£50.00	—
D	BW	30	*Actresses, Continental (c1905):	H.205		
			A 'The Seven Wonders' back		£16.00	—
			B 'Black and White Whisky' back		£25.00	—
			C Plain back		£16.00	—
D	BW		*Actresses — 'HAGG B' (c1900):	H.24		
		? 16	A 'Smoke Hill's Stockrider ...'		£35.00	—
		? 10	B 'Issued with Hill's High Class'		£35.00	—
—	BW	25	*Actresses (Belle of New York Series) (1899):	H206		
			A White back (41 × 75mm)		£22.00	—
			B Toned back, thick card (39 × 74mm)		£22.00	—
D1	U	20	*Actresses, chocolate tinted (1917):	H.207		
			A 'Hill's Tobaccos' etc back		£16.00	—
			B 'Issued with Hill's ...' back		£20.00	—
			C Plain back		£16.00	—
C	C	20	*Animal Series (1909):			
			A 'R. & J. Hill Ltd.' back		£24.00	—
			B 'Crowfoot Cigarettes' back		£23.00	—
			C 'The Cigarettes with which ...' back		£30.00	—
			D Space at back		£20.00	—
			E Plain Back		£25.00	—
A	BW	? 14	*Battleships (c1908):	H.208		
			A 'For the Pipe Smoke Oceanic ...' back		£130.00	—
			B Plain back		£50.00	—
A	C	25	*Battleships and Crests (1901)		£16.00	£400.00
D2	C	12	*Boer War Generals ('Campaigners') (c1901)	H.209	£32.00	£385.00

Size	*Printing*	*Number in set*		*Handbook reference*	*Price per card*	*Complete set*
A1	C	20	Breeds of Dogs (1914):	H.211		
			A 'Archer's M.F.H.' back		£17.00	—
			B 'Hill's Badminton' back		£17.00	—
			C 'Hill's Verbena Mixture' back		£17.00	—
			D 'Spinet Tobacco' back		£17.00	—
D1	BW	? 48	*British Navy Series (c1902)	H.210	£25.00	—
A	BW	? 1	*Celebrated Pictures (c1905)		£150.00	—
C	C		*Colonial Troops (c1900):	H.40		
		30	A i 'Hill's Leading Lines ...' back		£22.00	—
		30	A ii 'Perfection vide Dress ...' back		£22.00	—
		50	B 1-50. 'Sweet American' back		£22.00	—
D1	U	28	Famous Cricketers Series (1912):			
			A Red back, blue picture		£60.00	—
			B Deep blue back, brown picture		£60.00	—
			C Blue back, black picture		£60.00	—
D1	BW	20	Famous Footballers Series (1912)		£16.00	£320.00
—	U	25	Famous Pictures: (41 × 70mm) (c1912):	H.468		
			A 'Prize Coupon' back		£4.00	£100.00
			B Without 'Prize Coupon' back		£4.00	£100.00
C	C	30	*Flags and Flags with Soldiers (c1902)	H41	£22.00	—
—	C	24	*Flags, Arms and Types of Nations, 'Black & White' Whisky advert back (41 × 68mm) (c1910)	H.115	£10.00	£240.00
D	BW	20	Football Captain Series. Nd. 41-60 (1906):			
			A Small title		£25.00	—
			B Larger title, back re-drawn		£30.00	—
—		10	Fragments from France (38 × 67mm) (1916):	H.212		
	C		A Coloured, caption in script		£20.00	£200.00
	U		B Sepia-brown on buff, caption in block		£22.00	£220.00
	U		C As B, but black and white		£65.00	—
—	C	10	Fragments from France, different subjects, caption in block (38 × 67mm) (1916)	H.212	£20.00	£200.00
A1	U	25	Hill's War Series (c1916)	H.35	£11.00	£275.00
C2	C	20	Inventors and Their Inventions Series, Nd. 1-20, (1907):	H.213		
			A Black back, white card		£4.50	£90.00
			B Black back, toned card (shorter)		£6.00	—
C2	C	20	Inventors and Their Inventions Series, Nd. 21-40, (1907)		£7.00	£140.00
—		15	*Japanese Series (40 × 66mm) (1904):	H.214		
	C		A 'Hills' on red tablet		£60.00	—
	BW		B 'Hills' on black tablet		£42.00	—
—	C	20	Lighthouse Series — without frame lines to picture (42 × 68mm) (c1903)		£35.00	—
—	C	30	Lighthouse Series — with frame line. Nos. 1-20 re-touched and 10 cards added (c1903)		£35.00	—
D	C	20	National Flag Series (1914)	Ha.473	£7.00	£140.00
			Plain back		£7.00	—
—	BW	24	*Naval Series Unnumbered (42 × 64mm) (1901)	H.215	£45.00	—
D1	BW	30	Naval Series Nd. 21-50 (1902):	H.215		
			A Numbered 21-40		£12.00	—
			B Numbered 41-50		£50.00	—
C	C	20	Prince of Wales Series (1911)	H.22	£12.00	£240.00
—	U	? 14	*Prints from Noted Pictures (68 × 81mm) (c1908)	H.216	£100.00	—
—	BW	20	Rhymes — black and white sketches (c1905)	H.217	£24.00	—
A1		30	*Statuary — Set 1 (c1900):	Ha.218-1		
	U		A Brown front		£75.00	—
	BW		B Black and white front, matt		£30.00	—
	BW		C Black and white front, varnished		£11.00	—

Size	*Print-ing*	*Number in set*		*Handbook reference*	*Price per card*	*Complete set*
A	BW	30	*Statuary — Set 2 (c1900):	Ha.218-2		
			A Front in black and white		£8.00	£240.00
			B Front greenish-black		£8.00	—
C1	BW		*Statuary — Set 3 (c1900):	Ha.218-3		
		? 21	A Name panel white lettering on black background		£20.00	—
		? 4	B Name panel black lettering on grey background		£50.00	—
		? 23	C Name panel black lettering on white background		£50.00	—
D	C	20	*Types of the British Army (1914):			
			A 'Badminton' back		£27.00	—
			B 'Verbena' back		£27.00	—
A	U	25	World's Masterpieces — 'Second Series' (c1915)		£2.00	£50.00
B	***POST-1920 ISSUES***					
C	U	30	The All Blacks (1924)		£4.50	£135.00
A	BW	25	Aviation Series (1934):			
			A 'Issued by R. & J. Hill ...'		£2.40	£60.00
			B 'Issued with "Gold Flake Honeydew" ...'		£2.80	£70.00
	U	50	Caricatures of Famous Cricketers (1926):			
C			A Small size		£2.60	£130.00
B1			B Large size		£1.60	£80.00
D1	C	50	Celebrities of Sport (1939):			
			A 'Issued by R. & J. Hill ...'		£1.80	£90.00
			B 'Issued with "Gold Flake Honeydew" ...'		£3.00	—
A2	C	35	Cinema Celebrities (1936):	Ha.572		
			A Inscribed 'These Cigarettes are guaranteed'		85p	£30.00
			B Inscribed 'The Spinet House'		£1.00	£35.00
D1	BW	40	Crystal Palace Souvenir:			
			A Front matt (1936)		£1.25	£50.00
			B Front varnished (1937)		£1.25	£50.00
D1	C	48	Decorations and Medals (1940):			
			A 'Issued by R. & J. Hill ...'		£1.50	£75.00
			B 'Issued with Gold Flake Cigarettes'		£3.00	—
	P		Famous Cinema Celebrities (1931):	Ha.573		
		? 48	Set 1:			
—			A Medium size (74 × 56mm) inscribed 'Series A'		£4.00	—
A			B1 Small size, inscribed 'Spinet Cigarettes'		£4.00	—
A			B2 Small size, without 'Spinet Cigarettes'		£4.00	—
		50	Set 2:			
—			C Small size (66 × 41mm) inscribed 'Series C':			
			1 'Devon Cigarettes' at base of back		£7.00	—
			2 'Toucan Cigarettes' at base of back		£6.00	—
			3 Space at base of back blank		£4.00	—
			D Medium size (74 × 56mm) inscribed 'Series D':			
			1 'Kadi Cigarettes' at base of back		£4.00	—
			2 Space at base of back blank		£4.00	—
C	U	40	Famous Cricketers (1923)		£4.50	£180.00
	U	50	Famous Cricketers, including the S. Africa Test Team — 'Sunripe Cigarettes' (1924):			
C			A Small size		£3.50	£175.00
B1			B Large size		£4.00	£200.00
—	C	30	Famous Engravings — Series XI (80 × 61mm) (c1920)		£4.50	—
A2	BW	40	Famous Film Stars (1938):			
			A Text in English		£1.00	£40.00
			B *Text in Arabic, caption in English (see also Modern Beauties)*		£1.00	£40.00
C	U	50	Famous Footballers (1923)		£2.50	£125.00

R. & J. HILL LTD, London *(continued)*

Size	*Print-ing*	*Number in set*		*Handbook reference*	*Price per card*	*Complete set*
D	C	50	Famous Footballers (1939):	Ha.574		
			A Shoreditch address		£1.70	£85.00
			B 'Proprietors of Hy. Archer ...'		£1.70	£85.00
D	C	25	Famous Footballers, Nd. 51-75 (1939)		£2.20	£55.00
D	C	50	Famous Ships:			
			A Front matt (1939)		90p	£45.00
			B Front varnished (1940)		80p	£40.00
D	C	48	Film Stars and Celebrity Dancers (1935)		£1.40	£70.00
	C		Historic Places from Dickens' Classics (1926):			
D		50	A Small size		60p	£30.00
B1			B Large size:			
			1 Nos. 2-26, small numerals		70p	£17.50
			2 Nos. 1-50, large numerals		60p	£30.00
	U	50	Holiday Resorts (1925):			
C			A Small size:			
			1 Back in grey		90p	£45.00
			2 Back in brown		£1.30	—
B1			B Large size:			
			1 Back in grey		80p	£40.00
			2 Back in brown		£1.30	—
A	BW	20	**Inventors and Their Inventions (plain back)* (1934)	H.213	£1.25	£25.00
			Magical Puzzles — see 'Puzzle Series'			
A2	BW		Modern Beauties (1939):			
		50	A Titled 'Modern Beauties'. Text in English		£1.00	£50.00
		40	B *Titled 'Famous Film Stars' (selection). Text in Arabic, no captions*		£2.00	—
	C	30	Music Hall Celebrities — Past and Present (1930):			
D1			A Small size		£1.85	£55.00
B1			B Large size		£1.85	£55.00
D	C	30	Nature Pictures — 'The Spotlight Tobaccos' (c1930)		£1.10	£33.00
C2	C	30	Nautical Songs (1937)		80p	£24.00
	U	30	'Our Empire' (1929):			
D1			A Small size		33p	£10.00
B1			B Large size		40p	£12.00
—	BW		Popular Footballers — Season 1934-5 (68 × 49mm):			
		30	'Series A' — Nd. 1-30		£2.20	£65.00
		20	'Series B' — Nd. 31-50		£2.50	£50.00
	U		Public Schools and Colleges (1923):	Ha.575		
		50	A 'A Series of 50':			
C			1 Small size		70p	£35.00
B1			2 Large size		70p	£35.00
		75	B 'A Series of 75':			
C			1 Small size		90p	£70.00
B1			2 Large size		90p	£70.00
A1	C	50	Puzzle Series:			
			A Titled 'Puzzle Series' (1937)		£1.00	£50.00
			B Titled 'Magical Puzzles' (1938)		£1.50	£75.00
	U	50	The Railway Centenary — 'A Series of 50' (1925):			
C			A Small size		£1.30	£65.00
B1			B Large size:			
			1 Back in brown		£1.30	£65.00
			2 Back in grey		£3.00	—
	U	25	The Railway Centenary — '2nd Series — 51 to 75' (1925):			
C			A Small size		£1.60	£40.00
B1			B Large size		£1.60	£40.00

R. & J. HILL LTD, London *(continued)*

Size	*Print-ing*	*Number in set*		*Handbook reference*	*Price per card*	*Complete set*
C2	P	42	Real Photographs — Set 1 (Bathing Beauties) (c1930):	Ha.576-1		
			A 'London Idol Cigarettes' at base of back:			
			1 Front black and white, glossy		£2.50	—
			2 Front brown, matt		£2.50	—
			B Space at base of back blank:			
			1 Front black and white, glossy		£2.50	—
			2 Front brown, matt		£2.50	—
C2	P	42	Real Photographs — Set 2 (Beauties) (c1930)	Ha.576-2	£3.00	—
			The River Thames — see 'Views of the River Thames'			
D1	P	50	Scenes from the Films (1932):			
			A Front black and white		£2.50	—
			B Front sepia		£2.50	—
A2	BW	40	Scenes from the Films (1938)		75p	£30.00
D1		35	Scientific Inventions and Discoveries (1929):	Ha.213		
	C		A Small size, 'The Spinet House ...' back		£1.00	£35.00
	BW		B Small size, 'The Spotlight Tobaccos ...' back		£1.00	£35.00
B1	C		C Large size		£1.00	£35.00
Dl	P	50	Sports (1934):			
			A Titled 'Sports', numbered front and back		£4.00	—
			B Titled 'Sports Series', numbered front only		£10.00	—
			*C Untitled, numbered front only		£10.00	—
D1	C	100	*Transfers (c1935)	Ha.596-2	£5.00	—
B2	CP		Views of Interest:			
		48	'A First Series ...' Nd. 1-48 (1938):			
			A 'The Spinet House ...' back		25p	£12.50
			B 'Sunripe & Spinet Ovals ...' back		25p	£12.50
		48	'Second Series ...' Nd. 49-96 (1938)		25p	£12.50
		48	'Third Series ...' Nd. 97-144 (1939)		25p	£12.50
		48	'Fourth Series ...' Nd. 145-192 (1939)		40p	£20.00
		48	'Fifth Series ...' Nd. 193-240 (1939)		40p	£20.00
B2	CP		Views of Interest — British Empire Series ...:			
		48	'1st Issue — Canada — Nos. 1-48' (1940)		30p	£15.00
		48	'2nd Issue — India — Nos. 49-96' (1940)		£2.50	£120.00
	U	50	Views of London (1925):	Ha.577		
C			A Small size		80p	£40.00
B1			B Large size		90p	£45.00
	C	50	Views of the River Thames (1924):			
D			A Small size:			
			Nos. 1-25		£1.60	£40.00
			Nos. 26-50		£1.40	£35.00
B1			B Large size:			
			1 Back in green (thin card)		£1.30	£65.00
			2 Back in green and black (thick card)		£1.30	£65.00
	U	50	Who's Who in British Films (Nov. 1927):			
A2			A Small size		£1.60	£80.00
B2			B Large size		£1.60	£80.00
C	C	84	Wireless Telephony (1923)		£1.20	£100.00
B1	U	20	Wireless Telephony — Broadcasting Series (1923)		£2.25	£45.00
	U	50	Zoological Series (1924):	Ha.578		
C			A Small size:			
			1 Back in light brown		80p	£40.00
			2 Back in grey		90p	£45.00
B1			B Large size:			
			1 Back in light brown		90p	£45.00
			2 Back in dark brown		90p	£45.00

R. & J. HILL LTD, London *(continued)*

Size	*Print-ing*	*Number in set*		*Handbook reference*	*Price per card*	*Complete set*
C POST-1940 ISSUE						
A	U	50	Famous Dog Breeds 1954 (Admiral Cigarettes Slides)		£7.00	—
D CANVASES. Unbacked canvases. The material is a linen fabric, glazed to give the appearance of canvas. Specimens are found rubber stamped in red on back 'The Pipe Tobacco de Luxe Spinet Mixture'.						
—	C	30	'Britain's Stately Homes' (78 × 61mm) (c1915)		£3.50	—
—	C		*Canvas Masterpieces — Series 1 (73 × 61mm) (c1915):			
			A 'Badminton Tobacco Factories ...' back:			
		40	1 'H.T. & Co., Ltd., Leeds' at right base		£1.30	—
		20	2 Cardigan Press, Leeds' at right base (Nos. 21-40)		£1.30	—
		10	3 Without printers' credit (Nos. 21-30)		£1.30	—
		3	4 As 3, but size 73 × 53mm (Nos. 23-25)		£1.30	—
		40	B 'The Spinet House ...' back		£2.00	£80.00
—	C	40	*Canvas Masterpieces — Series 2, Nd. 41-80 (73 × 61mm) (c1915)		£2.00	£80.00
—	C	10	*Canvas Masterpieces — Series 2, Nd. 1-10 (c1915):			
			Nos. 1 to 5		£2.00	£10.00
			Nos. 6 to 10		£3.00	£15.00
—	C	5	Chinese Pottery and Porcelain — Series 1 (132 × 108mm) (c1915)		—	£20.00
			4 Different (minus No. 5)		60p	£2.50
—	C	11	Chinese Pottery and Porcelain — Series 2 (107 × 62mm) (c1915)		£5.00	—
—	C	23	*Great War Leaders — Series 10 (73 × 60mm) (1919)		£5.00	—

L. HIRST & SON, Leeds

PRE-1919 ISSUE						
—	C	? 5	*Soldiers and their Uniforms (cutouts) (c1915)	H.138	£125.00	—

J. W. HOBSON, Huddersfield

PRE-1919 ISSUE						
C2	C	18	Motor Cycle Series (c1914)	Ha.469	£75.00	—

J. & T. HODGE, Glasgow

PRE-1919 ISSUES						
—	C	? 4	*British Naval Crests (70 × 38mm) (c1896)	H.219	£200.00	—
A	BW	16	British Royal Family (c1901)		£130.00	—
—	U		*Scottish Views (c1898):	Ha.220		
		? 11	A Thick card (74 × 39mm)		£100.00	—
		? 10	B Thin card (80 × 45mm)		£100.00	—

HOOK OF HOLLAND CIGARETTES

PRE-1919 ISSUE						
A	U	? 3	*Footballers (c1905)		£180.00	—

HUDDEN & CO. LTD, Bristol

A PRE-1919 ISSUES						
C	C	26	*Actresses — 'FROGA A' (c1900)	H.20	£55.00	—
C	C	25	*Beauties — 'CHOAB' (c1900)	H.21	£50.00	—
A2	U	? 20	*Beauties — 'Crown Seal Cigarettes' (c1898)	H.221	£110.00	—
A	U	? 24	*Beauties — 'HUMPS' (c1898):	H.222		
			A Blue scroll back		£60.00	—
			B Orange scroll back		£55.00	—
			C Typeset back in brown		£200.00	—

HUDDEN & CO. LTD, Bristol *(continued)*

Size	Printing	Number in set		Handbook reference	Price per card	Complete set
D1	C	? 12	Comic Phrases (c1900)	H.223	£100.00	—
A	C	25	*Flags of All Nations (c1905)	H.37	£16.00	£400.00
—	C	48	*Flowers and Designs (55 × 34mm) (c1900):	H.224		
			A 'Hudden Cigarettes' back		£85.00	—
			B 'Hudden's — Dandy Dot' back		£120.00	—
A	C	18	*Pretty Girl Series — 'RASH' (c1900)	H.8	£70.00	—
A	C	25	Soldiers of the Century, Nd. 26-50 (1901)		£40.00	—
A	C	25	*Star Girls (c1900)	H.30	£80.00	—
A	C	25	Types of Smokers (c1903)		£40.00	—
B	***POST-1920 ISSUES.*** All export					
D	U	25	Famous Boxers (1927)	Ha.579	£30.00	—
C	U	50	Public Schools and Colleges (c1925)	Ha.575	£2.00	£100.00
A	C	25	Sports and Pastimes Series 1 (c1925)	H.225	£55.00	—

HUDSON

PRE-1919 ISSUE

C	C	25	*Beauties — selections from 'BOCCA' (c1900)	H.39	£200.00	—

HUNTER, Airdrie

PRE-1919 ISSUE

A	BW	? 11	*Footballers (c1910)	H.227	£250.00	—

J. T. ILLINGWORTH & SONS, Kendal

A	***PRE-1919 ISSUE***					
A	BW	? 12	Views from the English Lakes (c1895)	H.228	£140.00	—
B	***POST-1920 ISSUES***					
—	P	48	Beautiful Scotland (77 × 52mm) (1939)	Ha.564-1	£1.50	—
C1	C	25	*Cavalry (1924)		£5.00	£125.00
—	P	48	Coastwise (77 × 52mm) (1938)	Ha.564-2	£1.00	£50.00
A	C	25	'Comicartoons' of sport (1927)		£5.00	£125.00
—	P	48	Flying (77 × 52mm) (1938)	Ha.564-3	£1.25	£60.00
A	C	25	*Motor Car Bonnets (1925)		£7.00	£175.00
A	C	25	*Old Hostels (1926)		£6.00	£150.00
—	P	48	Our Countryside (77 × 52mm) (1938)	Ha.564-4	£1.50	£75.00
—	P	24	Shots from the Films (1937)	Ha.566	£3.50	—

THE IMPERIAL TOBACCO CO. (of Great Britain & Ireland) Ltd, Bristol

PRE-1919 ISSUES

A	C	50	British Birds (c1910)	H.229	£4.50	—
C	C	1	Folder — Coronation of His Majesty King Edward VII (1902)		—	£90.00

INTERNATIONAL TOBACCO CO. LTD, London

POST-1920 ISSUES

A	***HOME ISSUES***					
—	C	28	Domino cards (69 × 35mm) (1938)		22p	£6.00
	U		Famous Buildings and Monuments of Britain (1934) (bronze metal plaques in cellophane envelopes):	Ha.580		
		50	'Series A':			
A1			1 Nos. 1-30, small size		80p	£24.00
B2			2 Nos. 31-50, large size		90p	£18.00
		50	'Series B':			
A1			1 Nos. 51-80, small size		£1.40	£42.00
B2			2 Nos. 81-100, large size		£1.40	£28.00

NTERNATIONAL TOBACCO CO. LTD, London *(continued)*

ze	*Print-ing*	*Number in set*		*Handbook reference*	*Price per card*	*Complete set*
	C	50	International Code of Signals (1934)		60p	£30.00
	C	48	Screen Lovers — 'Summit' (unissued) (c1940)		£2.80	—
			***EXPORT ISSUES**. Inscribed 'International Tobacco (Overseas), Ltd.'*			
2	C	100	Film Favourites (c1937):	Ha.581		
			A Back in grey		£1.80	—
			B Back in black		£1.80	—
-	C	100	'Gentlemen! The King!' — (60 small, 40 large) (1937):	Ha.582		
			A Back in blue		40p	£40.00
			B Back in black		20p	£20.00

'he same plaques were also used for an export issue, with envelopes inscribed 'International Tobacco verseas), Ltd.'

L.S. TOBACCO CO., London

RE-1919 ISSUES

			('Star of the World' Cigarettes)			
	BW	20	*Boer War Cartoons (1901)	H.42	£80.00	—
?	BW	? 29	*Boer War Celebrities — 'JASAS' (c1901)	H.133	£100.00	—
2	C	30	*Colonial Troops (c1901)	H.40	£65.00	—

ETER JACKSON, London

)ST-1920 ISSUES

HOME ISSUES

P		Beautiful Scotland (1939):	Ha.564-1		
	28	A Small size		£1.25	£35.00
	48	B Medium size, 77 × 52mm		£1.00	£50.00
P		Coastwise (1938):	Ha.564-2		
	28	A Small size		£1.25	£35.00
	48	B Medium size, 77 × 52mm		£1.25	£60.00
P	27	Famous Films (1934)		£3.00	£80.00
P	28	Famous Film Stars (1935)		£3.00	£85.00
P	28	Film Scenes (1936)		£3.00	£85.00
P	28	Film Scenes (1936)		£4.50	£125.00
P		Flying (1938):	Ha.564-3		
	28	A Small size		£3.00	—
	48	B Medium size (77 × 52mm)		£3.00	—
P	28	Life in the Navy (1937)		£1.50	£42.00
P	28	Life in the Navy (1937)		£2.00	£55.00
P		Our Countryside (1938):	Ha.564-4		
	28	A Small size		£1.00	£28.00
	48	B Medium size (77 × 52mm)		£1.25	£60.00
P		Shots from the Films (1937):	Ha.566		
	28	A Small size		£2.50	£70.00
	24	B Medium size (77 × 52mm)		£3.00	£75.00
P	28	Stars in Famous Films (1935)		£3.00	£85.00

***EXPORT ISSUES**. Inscribed 'Peter Jackson (Overseas), Ltd.'*

C	100	'Gentlemen! The King!' (60 small, 40 large) (1937):	Ha.582		
		A Overprinted on International black back		£1.00	£100.00
		B Overprinted on International blue back		£1.00	—
		C Reprinted with Jackson's name at base:			
		i Back in black		80p	£80.00
		ii Back in blue		£1.50	—

PETER JACKSON, London *(continued)*

Size	Printing	Number in set		Handbook reference	Price per card	Complete set
—	C	150	The Pageant of Kingship — 90 small, 60 large (1937):			
			A Inscribed 'Issued by Peter Jackson'		50p	£75.00
			B Inscribed 'Issued by Peter Jackson (Overseas, Ltd.':			
			1 Printed on board		50p	£75.00
			2 Printed on paper		33p	£50.00
—	C	250	Speed — Through the Ages (170 small, 80 large) (1937)	Ha.583	30p	£75.00

JACOBI BROS. & CO. LTD, London

PRE-1919 ISSUE

Size	Printing	Number in set		Handbook reference	Price per card	Complete set
A	BW	? 29	*Boer War Celebrities — 'JASAS' (c1901):	H.133		
			A Black and white front		£110.00	—
			B As A, but mauve tinted		£110.00	—

JAMES & CO. (Birmingham) LTD

PRE-1919 ISSUE

Size	Printing	Number in set		Handbook reference	Price per card	Complete set
—	C	20	Arms of Countries (c1915):			
			A Size 70 × 40mm		£110.00	—
			B Size 70 × 49mm		£110.00	—

JAMES'S (GOLD LEAF NAVY CUT)

PRE-1919 ISSUE

Size	Printing	Number in set		Handbook reference	Price per card	Complete set
A	U	? 11	Pretty Girl Series — 'BAGG' (c1898)		£160.00	—

J.B. JOHNSON & CO., London

PRE-1919 ISSUE

Size	Printing	Number in set		Handbook reference	Price per card	Complete set
A	C	25	*National Flags and Flowers — Girls (c1900)	H.123	£130.00	—

JOHNSTON'S CIGARETTES

PRE-1919 ISSUE

Size	Printing	Number in set		Handbook reference	Price per card	Complete set
A	U	? 1	*British Views (c1910)		£150.00	—

JONES BROS., Tottenham

PRE-1919 ISSUES

Size	Printing	Number in set		Handbook reference	Price per card	Complete set
A	BW	18	*Spurs Footballers (1912):	H.230		
			A 12 small titles		From £8.00	—
			B 5 large titles		From £8.00	—
			C 1 Team Group of 34		£350.00	—

A.I. JONES & CO. Ltd, London

PRE-1919 ISSUE

Size	Printing	Number in set		Handbook reference	Price per card	Complete set
—	C	1	*Advertisement Card — Alexia Mixture (80 × 46mm) (c1900)		£350.00	—
D	C	12	Nautical Terms (c1905)	H.231	£40.00	—

A.S. JONES, Grantham

PRE-1919 ISSUE

Size	Printing	Number in set		Handbook reference	Price per card	Complete set
D	C	30	Army Pictures, Cartoons, etc (c1916)	H.12	£75.00	—

ALEX. JONES & CO., London

Size	Printing	Number in set		Handbook reference	Price per card	Complete set
PRE-1919 ISSUES						
D2	U	? 9	*Actresses — 'ANGOOD' (c1898)	Ha.187	£130.00	—
A	BW	1	Portrait of Queen Victoria 1897		—	£130.00

T. E. JONES & CO., Aberavon

PRE-1919 ISSUES						
D	C	13	*Conundrums (c1900)	H.232	£130.00	—
—	C	48	*Flags of All Nations (35 × 60mm) (c1899)	H.233	£80.00	—
—	BW	? 41	*Footballers (34 × 63mm) (1899)		£110.00	—
D	C	? 12	Well-known Proverbs (c1900)	H.235	£140.00	—

C.H. JORDEN LTD, London

PRE-1919 ISSUE						
—	P	? 12	*Celebrities of the Great War (c1915) (35 × 64mm)	H.236	£70.00	—

J. & E. KENNEDY, Dublin

PRE-1919 ISSUE						
A	U	25	*Beauties — 'FECKSA' (c1900)	H.58	£45.00	—

RICHARD KENNEDY, Dundee

PRE-1919 ISSUE						
—	C	? 24	*Naval & Military Cartoons (130 × 90mm) (c1905)		£125.00	—
A	U	50	War Portraits (1916)	H.86	£65.00	—

KINNEAR LTD, Liverpool

PRE-1919 ISSUES						
A	C	? 13	*Actresses (c1898)	H.237	£110.00	—
D1	BW	? 15	*Australian Cricketers (1897)	H.238	£225.00	—
A	C	? 12	*Cricketers (c1895)	H.269	£350.00	—
A2	C	25	*Footballers and Club Colours (c1898)	H.239	£100.00	—
—	U	2	The Four Generations (Royal Family) (65 × 70mm) (1897)		£275.00	—
—	BW	1	'A Gentleman in Kharki' (44 × 64mm) (1900)		—	£65.00
A	C		*Jockeys (1896):	H.240		
		12	— see H.240—A		£40.00	—
		1	— see H.240—B		£80.00	—
		1	— see H.240—C		£80.00	—
		3	— see H.240—D		£80.00	—
		25	— see H.240—E		£80.00	—
A	C	? 2	*Prominent Personages (c1902)	Ha.479	£220.00	—
D1	U	13	*Royalty (1897)	H.241	£40.00	—
—	U	? 24	Views (49 × 35mm) (c1899)		£225.00	—

B. KRIEGSFELD & CO., Manchester

PRE-1919 ISSUES						
—	C	1	*Advertisement Card— Apple Blossom (c1900)		£350.00	—
A2	U	? 45	*Beauties — 'KEWA' (c1900):	H.139		
			A Matt surface		£80.00	—
			B Glossy surface		£130.00	—
A	C	? 9	Celebrities (c1900)	H.242	£130.00	—
A	C	50	*Flags of All Nations (c1900)	H.233	£60.00	—
A	C	50	*Phrases and Advertisements (c1900)	H.243	£80.00	—

A. KUIT LTD, Manchester

Size	Printing	Number in set		Handbook reference	Price per card	Complete set
			PRE-1919 ISSUES			
—	C	? 12	*Arms of Cambridge Colleges* (17 × 25mm) (c1914)	H.458	£80.00	—
—	C	? 12	*Arms of Companies* (30 × 33mm) (c1914)	H.459	£80.00	—
—	C	30	British Beauties — oval card (36 × 60mm) (c1914)	H.244	£50.00	—
—	P	? 14	*'Crosmedo' Bijoucards (55 × 37mm) (c1915)	H.245	£110.00	—
A	U	25	Principal Streets of British Cities and Towns (1916)		£100.00	—
A	CP	50	Types of Beauty (c1914)	H.246	£100.00	—

LAMBERT & BUTLER, London

32 page reference book available — £3.25

Size	Printing	Number in set		Handbook reference	Price per card	Complete set
			A PRE-1919 ISSUES			
A1	BW	20	*Actresses — 'BLARM' (c1900)	H.23	£23.00	£460.00
—	C	10	*Actresses and Their Autographs (c1898):	H.247		
			A Wide card (70 × 38mm): 'Tobacco' back		£140.00	—
			B Narrow card (70 × 34mm): 'Cigarettes' back		£120.00	—
A2	BW	50	*Admirals (1900):	H.248		
			A 'Flaked Gold Leaf Honeydew' back		£16.00	—
			B 'May Blossom' back		£16.00	—
			C 'Prize Medal Bird's Eye' back		£16.00	—
			D 'Viking' back		£20.00	—
C	C	1	*Advertisement Card — Spanish Dancer (1898)	H.249	—	£350.00
A	C	40	Arms of Kings and Queens of England (1906)		£4.00	£160.00
A	C	25	Aviation(1915)		£3.20	£80.00
A2	C	26	*Beauties — 'HOL' (c1900):	H.192		
			A 'Flaked Gold Leaf Honey Dew' back		£32.00	—
			B 'Log Cabin' back		£32.00	—
			C 'May Blossom' back		£32.00	—
			D 'Viking Navy Cut' back		£32.00	—
A	C	50	Birds and Eggs (1906)	H.60	£3.20	£160.00
C	BW	25	*Boer War and Boxer Rebellion — Sketches (1904)	H.46	£26.00	—
C	B	10	*Boer War Generals — 'FLAC' (1901)	H.47	£32.00	—
C	U	20	*Boer War Generals 'CLAM' (1900):	H.61		
			I 10. No frame lines to back:			
			A Brown back		£28.00	—
			B Black back		£28.00	—
			II 10. With frame lines to back:			
			A Brown back		£28.00	—
			B Black back		£28.00	—
C	U	1	*Boer War Series — 'The King of Scouts' (Col. R.S.S. Baden-Powell) (1901)		—	£350.00
—	C	50	*Conundrums (38 × 57mm) (1901):	H.250		
			A Blue back — thick card		£18.00	—
			B Green back		£13.00	—
A2	C	12	Coronation Robes (1902)	H.251	£18.00	£220.00
A	C	20	International Yachts (1902)		£50.00	—
A	C	25	Japanese Series (1904):			
			A Thick toned card		£7.00	£175.00
			B Thin white card		£7.00	£175.00
—	C	4	*Jockeys, no frame lines (35 × 70mm) (c1903)	H.252	£40.00	£160.00
—	C	10	*Jockeys with frame lines (35 × 70mm) (c1903)	H.252	£40.00	£400.00
A	C	1	*Mayblossom Calendar, 1900		—	£400.00
A	C	25	Motors (1908):			
			A Green back		£25.00	—
			B Plain back		£25.00	—

Size	*Printing*	*Number in set*		*Handbook reference*	*Price per card*	*Complete set*
A	BW	25	Naval Portraits (1914)	H.253	£3.60	£90.00
A	BW	50	Naval Portraits, incl. above 25 (1915)	H.253	£3.60	£180.00
A	C	50	The Thames from Lechlade to London:			
			A Small numerals (1907)		£5.00	£250.00
			B Large numerals (1908)		£5.00	£250.00
			C Plain back		£5.00	—
—	C	4	*Types of the British Army & Navy (35 × 70mm) (c1897):	H.254		
			A 'Specialities' back in brown		£65.00	—
			B 'Specialities' back in black		£65.00	—
			C 'Viking' back in black		£65.00	—
A	C	25	*Waverley series (1904)	H.255	£10.00	£250.00
A	C	25	Winter Sports (1914)		£3.40	£85.00
A	C	25	Wireless Telegraphy (1909)		£4.60	£115.00
A	C	25	World's Locomotives, Nd. 1-25 (1912)		£4.00	£100.00
A	C	50	World's Locomotives Nd. 1-50 (1912)		£4.60	£230.00
A	C	25	World's Locomotives, Nd. 1A-25A (c1913)		£4.60	£115.00
	POST-1920 ISSUES					
A	C	50	Aeroplane Markings (1937)		£1.50	£75.00
A	C	25	British Trees and Their Uses (1927)		£1.80	£45.00
A	C	25	Common Fallacies (1928)		£2.00	£50.00
A	C	25	Dance Band Leaders (1936)		£4.00	£100.00
A	C	50	Empire Air Routes (1936)		£1.60	£80.00
A	BW	25	Famous British Airmen and Airwomen (1935)		£1.40	£35.00
A	U	25	Fauna of Rhodesia (1929)		90p	£22.50
A	C	50	Find Your Way:			
			A Address 'Box No. 152, London' (1932)		£1.40	£70.00
			B Address 'Box No. 152, Drury Lane, London' (1932)		£1.40	£70.00
			C Overprinted in red (1933)		£1.40	£70.00
A	BW	1	D Joker Card (1932)		—	£11.00
A	C	50	Footballers 1930-1 (1931)		£3.20	—
A	C	25	Garden Life (1930)	H.449	90p	£22.50
A	C	25	Hints and Tips for Motorists (1929)		£3.60	£90.00
A	U	25	A History of Aviation:			
			A Front in green (1932)		£2.00	£50.00
			B Front in brown (1933)		£2.40	£60.00
A	C	50	Horsemanship (1938)		£2.20	£110.00
A	C	25	How Motor Cars Work (1931)		£2.20	£55.00
A	C	50	Interesting Customs and Traditions of the Navy, Army and Air Force (1939)		£1.00	£50.00
A	C	25	Interesting Musical Instruments (1929)		£2.60	£65.00
A	C	50	Interesting Sidelights on the Work of the GPO (1939)		£1.00	£50.00
A	C	50	Keep Fit (1937)		80p	£40.00
A	C	25	London Characters (1934):			
			A With Album Clause		£2.00	£50.00
			B Without Album Clause		£20.00	—
A	C	25	Motor Car Radiators (1928)		£6.00	£150.00
	C	25	Motor Cars — 'A Series of 25', green back (1922)		£2.40	£60.00
A	C	25	Motor Cars — '2nd Series of 25' (1923)		£2.40	£60.00
	C	50	Motor Cars — '3rd Series of 50' (1926)		£3.60	£180.00
A	C	25	Motor Cars — 'A Series of 25', grey back (1934)		£3.40	£85.00
	C	50	Motor Cycles (1923)		£3.50	£175.00
A	C	50	Motor Index Marks (1926)		£2.50	£125.00
	C	25	Pirates and Highwaymen (1926)	Ha.584	£1.20	£30.00
	U	25	Rhodesian Series (1928)		£1.00	£25.00

LAMBERT & BUTLER, London *(continued)*

Size	*Print-ing*	*Number in set*		*Handbook reference*	*Price per card*	*Complete set*
A	U	25	Third Rhodesian Series (1930)		60p	£15.0
A	C	25	Wonders of Nature (1924)		60p	£15.0

LAMBKIN BROS., Cork

POST-1920 ISSUES

A	C	36	*Country Scenes — Small size (1924) (6 sets of 6):			
			Series 1 — Yachting		£5.00	–
			Series 2 — Country		£5.00	–
			Series 3 — Far East		£5.00	–
			Series 4 — Sailing		£5.00	–
			Series 5 — Country		£5.00	–
			Series 6 — Country		£5.00	–
C	C	36	*Country Scenes — Large size (1924) (6 sets of 6):			
			Series 7 — Yachting		£5.00	–
			Series 8 — Country		£5.00	–
			Series 9 — Far East		£5.00	–
			Series 10 — Sailing		£5.00	–
			Series 11 — Country		£5.00	–
			Series 12 — Windmill Scenes		£5.00	–
—	C	? 9	**Irish Views, anonymous. inscribed 'Eagle, Cork'* (68 × 67mm) (c1925)	Ha.585	£40.00	–
—	C	? 5	*'Lily of Killarney' Views (73 × 68mm) (c1925)	Ha.586	£70.00	–

LANCS & YORKS TOBACCO MANUFACTURING CO. LTD, Burnley (L. & Y. Tob. Mfg. Co.)

PRE-1919 ISSUE

C	C	26	*Actresses — 'FROGA A' (c1900)	H.20	£180.00	–

C. & J. LAW, Hertford

PRE-1919 ISSUES

A	C	25	*Types of British Soldiers (c1914)	H.144	£22.00	–
A	U	50	War Portraits (1916)	H.86	£65.00	–

R.J. LEA LTD, Manchester

A PRE-1919 ISSUES

A	C	1	*Advertisement Card — Swashbuckler (c1913)		£250.00	–
A1	C	50	Chairman Miniatures 1-50 (1912):			
			A No border		£2.80	£140.0
			B Gilt border		£2.80	£140.0
A1	C	50	Chairman and Vice Chair Miniatures, 51-100 (1912)		£2.80	£140.0
A1	BW	25	Chairman War Portraits (marked 'War Series' on front) (1915)		£5.00	£125.0
A	C	70	Cigarette Transfers (Locomotives) (1916)		£6.00	–
A	BW	25	Civilians of Countries Fighting with the Allies (1914)		£10.00	£250.0
A1	C	50	Flowers to Grow (The Best Perennials) (1913)		£4.00	£200.0
A1	C	50	Modern Miniatures (1913)		—	£355.0
			46 different, less 1, 8, 12, 32		£1.30	£60.0
A1	C	12	More Lea's Smokers (1906):	H.256		
			A Green borders		£80.00	–
			B Red borders		£80.00	–
A1	C	50	Old English Pottery and Porcelain, 1-50 (1912)		£2.00	£100.0
A1	C	50	Old Pottery and Porcelain, 51-100 (1912):			
			A 'Chairman Cigarettes'		£1.60	£80.0
			B 'Recorder Cigarettes'		£5.00	–

R.J. LEA LTD, Manchester *(continued)*

Size	*Print-ing*	*Number in set*		*Handbook reference*	*Price per card*	*Complete set*
A1	C	50	Old Pottery and Porcelain, 101-150 (1912):			
			A 'Chairman Cigarettes'		£1.60	£80.00
			B 'Recorder Cigarettes'		£5.00	—
A1	C	50	Old Pottery and Porcelain, 151-200 (1913)		£1.60	£80.00
A1	C	50	Old Pottery and Porcelain, 201-250 (1913)		£1.60	£80.00
A	BW	25	War Pictures (1915)		£4.40	£110.00
B POST-1920 ISSUES						
		48	Coronation Souvenir (1937):			
A2	P		A Small size, glossy:			
			1 Lea's name		50p	£25.00
			2 'Successors to ...'		40p	£20.00
A2	BW		B Small size, matt:			
			1 Lea's name		60p	£30.00
			2 Successors to		45p	£22.50
—	P		C Medium size (77 × 51mm)		60p	£30.00
A2	C	50	Dogs (1923):			
			1 Nos. 1-25 — A White card		£3.60	—
			B Cream card		£3.60	—
			2 Nos. 26-50		£5.40	—
A2	C	25	English Birds (1922):			
			A Glossy front		£2.60	£65.00
			B Matt front		£4.00	£100.00
A2	C	25	The Evolution of the Royal Navy (1925)		£1.80	£45.00
A2	P	54	Famous Film Stars (1939)		£1.30	£70.00
	CP	48	Famous Racehorses of 1926 (1927):			
A2			A Small size		£2.00	£100.00
			B Medium size (75 × 50mm)		£2.50	£125.00
		48	Famous Views (1936):			
A2	P		A Small size — 1 Glossy		25p	£12.50
	BW		2 Matt		60p	£30.00
—	P		B Medium size (76 × 51mm)		50p	£25.00
A2	P	36	Film Stars — 'A First Series ...' (1934)		£2.25	£80.00
A2	P	36	Film Stars — 'A Second Series ...' (1934)		£2.00	£70.00
A2	C	25	Fish (1926)		£1.60	£40.00
A2		48	Girls from the Shows (1935):			
	P		A Glossy front		£2.00	£100.00
	BW		B Matt front		£2.20	£110.00
A2		54	Radio Stars (1935):			
	P		A Glossy front		£1.80	£95.00
	BW		B Matt front		£1.80	£95.00
A2	C	50	Roses (1924)		£1.40	£70.00
A2	C	50	Ships of the World (1925)		£1.80	£90.00
		48	Wonders of the World (1938):			
A2	P		A Small size — 1 Glossy		50p	£25.00
	BW		2 Matt		60p	£30.00
	P		B Medium size (76 × 50mm)		60p	£30.00
SILKS. All paper-backed.						
—	C		*Butterflies and Moths III (c1925):	Ha.505-7		
		12	1 Small size (70 × 44mm)		£4.00	£50.00
		12	2 Large size (70 × 88mm)		£4.00	£50.00
		6	3 Extra-large size (143 × 70mm)		£4.50	£27.00
—	C	54	*Old Pottery — Set 1 (68 × 38mm) (c1915)	Ha.505-14	90p	£50.00
—	C	72	*Old Pottery — Set 2 (61 × 37mm) (c1915)	Ha.505-14	90p	£65.00
—	C	50	Regimental Crests and Badges — Series I (48mm sq.) (c1920)	Ha.502-4	£1.20	£60.00

R.J. LEA LTD, Manchester *(continued)*

Size	Printing	Number in set		Handbook reference	Price per card	Complete set
—	C	50	Regimental Crests and Badges — Series II (48 mm sq.) (c1920)	Ha.502-4	£1.80	£90.00
D	***MISCELLANEOUS***					
—	C	24	Old English Pottery and Porcelain (Post Card Size) (Inscribed Chairman Cigarette Series or other firms' names) (c1910)	Ha.257	£6.00	—

ALFRED L. LEAVER, London

Size	Printing	Number in set		Handbook reference	Price per card	Complete set
POST-1920 ISSUE						
—	U	12	Manikin Cards (70 × 51mm) (c1925)	Ha481	£70.00	—

J. LEES, Northampton

Size	Printing	Number in set		Handbook reference	Price per card	Complete set
PRE-1919 ISSUE						
A	C	? 21	Northampton Town Football Club (No. 301-321) (c1912)		£80.00	—

A. LEWIS & CO. (WESTMINSTER) LTD, London

Size	Printing	Number in set		Handbook reference	Price per card	Complete set
A	***PRE-1919 ISSUE***					
A	U	50	War Portraits (1916)	H.86	£65.00	—
B	***POST-1920 ISSUE***					
A2	C	52	Horoscopes (1938)	Ha.587	80p	£42.00

H. C. LLOYD & SON, Exeter

Size	Printing	Number in set		Handbook reference	Price per card	Complete set
PRE-1919 ISSUES						
A	U	28	Academy Gems (c1900):	H.258		
			A Red-brown tint		£50.00	—
			B Purple tint		£50.00	—
			C Green tint		£50.00	—
D	BW	? 26	*Actresses and Boer War Celebrities (c1900)	H.260	£40.00	—
—	BW		*Devon Footballers and Boer War Celebrities (c1901):	H.259		
		? 42	Set 1 — Without framelines (70 × 41mm)		£45.00	—
		? 6	Set 2 — With framelines (70 × 45mm)		£100.00	—
A1	C	25	*Star Girls — 'Tipsy Loo Cigarettes' (c1898)	H.30	£200.00	—
—	BW	36	War Pictures (73 × 69mm) (c1914)		£120.00	—

RICHARD LLOYD & SONS, London

Size	Printing	Number in set		Handbook reference	Price per card	Complete set
A	***PRE-1919 ISSUES***					
—	BW	25	*Boer War Celebrities (35 × 61mm) (1899)	H.261	£32.00	—
—	U	? 21	*General Interest — Actresses, Celebrities and Yachts (62 × 39mm) (c1900)	H.262	£85.00	—
A1	C	96	*National Types, Costumes and Flags (c1900)	H.263	£30.00	—
A	C	10	*Scenes from San Toy* (c1905)	H.462	£9.00	£90.00
B	***POST-1920 ISSUES.*** Most cards inscribed 'Branch of Cope Bros. & Co., Ltd.' See also under 'Cope Bros					
A	C	25	Atlantic Records (1936)		£2.80	£70.00
A2	P	27	Cinema Stars, glossy — 'A Series of 27', Nd. 1-27 (c1934)		£5.50	—
A2	P	27	Cinema Stars, glossy — 'A Series of 27', Nd. 28-54 (c1934)		£1.50	£40.00
A2	P	27	Cinema Stars, glossy — 'Third Series of 27', Nd. 55-81 (1935)		£5.50	—
A2	U	25	Cinema Stars, matt — 'A Series of 25' (c1937)		£1.60	£40.00
A	BW	25	*Famous Cricketers (Puzzle Series) (1930)		£5.00	£125.00

RICHARD LLOYD & SONS, London *(continued)*

Size	*Print-ing*	*Number in set*		*Handbook reference*	*Price per card*	*Complete set*
D	C		Old Inns:			
		25	A1 Titled 'Old English Inns' (1923)		£1.40	£35.00
		25	A2 Titled 'Old Inns — Series 2' (1924)		£2.60	£65.00
		50	B Titled 'Old Inns' (1925)		£1.20	£60.00
A	BW	25	Tricks and Puzzles (1935)		80p	£20.00
A2	U	25	Types of Horses (1926):			
			A Back in light brown		£3.20	£80.00
			B Back in dark brown		£3.20	£80.00
A2	U	25	'Zoo' Series (1926)	Ha.588	90p	£22.50

LUSBY LTD, London

PRE-1919 ISSUE

D	C	25	Scenes from Circus Life (c1900)	H.264	£110.00	—

HUGH McCALL, Edinburgh, Glasgow and Aberdeen

POST-1920 ISSUE

C	C	? 1	*RAF Advertisement Card (c1924)	Ha.594	£130.00	—

D. & J. MACDONALD, Glasgow

PRE-1919 ISSUES

A	C	? 10	*Actresses — 'MUTA' (c1891)	H.265	£110.00	—
A	BW	25	*Cricketers (c1902)	H.266	£325.00	—
—	BW	? 22	*Cricket and Football Teams (71 × 69mm) (c1902)	Ha.267	£225.00	—
—	C	? 1	County Cricket Team (71 × 69mm) (1900)		£750.00	—

MACKENZIE & CO., Glasgow

PRE-1919 ISSUES

—	P	50	*Actors and Actresses (32 × 58mm) (c1902)	H.268	£17.00	—
—	U	50	Victorian Art Pictures — Photogravure (32 × 58mm) (c1908)		£18.00	—
A	BW	50	The Zoo (c1910)		£22.00	—

WM. M'KINNELL, Edinburgh

PRE-1919 ISSUE

A	C	20	European War Series (1915)	H.129	£75.00	—
A	U	50	War Portraits (1916)	H.86	£65.00	—

MACNAUGHTON, JENKINS & CO. LTD, Dublin

POST-1920 ISSUES

—	C	50	Castles of Ireland (1924):			
			A Size 76 × 45mm		£2.80	£140.00
			B Size 74 × 44mm		£3.20	—
D	C	50	Various Uses of Rubber (1924)		£2.20	£110.00

A. McTAVISH, Elgin

PRE-1919 ISSUE

D	C	30	*Army Pictures, Cartoons etc (c1916)	H12	£75.00	—

McWATTIE & SONS, Arbroath

PRE-1919 ISSUE

D	C	30	*Army Pictures, Cartoons etc (c1916)	H.12	£75.00	—

THE MANXLAND TOBACCO CO., Isle of Man

Size	Printing	Number in set		Handbook reference	Price per card	Complete set
PRE-1919 ISSUES						
D	BW	? 5	*Views in the Isle of Man (c1900)	Ha.491	£200.00	—

MARCOVITCH & CO., London

A POST-1920 ISSUE						
A2	P	18	**Beauties (anonymous with plain backs, numbered left base of front)* (1932)	Ha.627	£1.00	£18.00
B POST-1940 ISSUE						
—	U	7	The Story in Red and White (75 × 66mm) (1955)		£1.80	£12.50

MARCUS & CO., Manchester

PRE-1919 ISSUES						
A	C	? 12	*Cricketers, 'Marcus Handicap Cigarettes' (1895)	H.269	£350.00	—
A	C	25	*Footballers and Club Colours (1896)	H.239	£100.00	—

T.W. MARKHAM, Bridgwater

PRE-1919 ISSUE						
—	BW	? 18	Somerset Views and scenes (68 × 42mm) (c1906)		£100.00	—

MARSUMA LTD, Congleton

PRE-1919 ISSUE						
A	BW	50	*Famous Golfers and Their Strokes (c1914)		£38.00	—

C. MARTIN, Moseley

PRE-1919 ISSUE						
D	C	30	*Army Pictures, Cartoons etc. (c1916)	H12	£75.00	—

MARTINS LTD, London

PRE-1919 ISSUES						
A	C	1	''Arf a Mo', Kaiser!' (c1915)		—	£55.00
—	U	? 14	Carlyle Series — folding card (c1918)	H.270	£90.00	—
D	U	25	*VC Heroes (c1916)		£22.00	£550.00

R. MASON & CO., London

PRE-1919 ISSUES						
C	C	30	*Colonial Troops (c1902)	H.40	£50.00	—
D2	C	40	*Naval and Military Phrases (c1904)	H.14	£45.00	—

JUSTUS VAN MAURIK

POST-1920 ISSUE						
—	C	12	*Dutch Scenes (108 × 70mm) (c1920)	Ha.622	£100.00	—

MAY QUEEN CIGARETTES

POST-1940 ISSUE						
—	C	12	Interesting Pictures (68 × 48mm) (c1960)		£1.00	—

MENTORS LTD, London

PRE-1919 ISSUE						
—	C	32	Views of Ireland (42 × 67mm) (c1912)	H.271	£9.00	—

J. MILLHOFF & CO. LTD, London

Size	Printing	Number in set		Handbook reference	Price per card	Complete set
A	***PRE-1919 ISSUE***					
			Theatre Advertisement Cards (c1905):			
—	BW	? 9	A Medium size (83 × 56mm)		£90.00	—
—	BW	? 2	B Large size (108 × 83mm)		£100.00	—
00B	***POST-1920 ISSUES***					
	CP		Antique Pottery (1927):			
A2		54	A Small size		80p	£43.00
—		56	B Medium size (74 × 50mm)		80p	£45.00
	C		Art Treasures:			
D		30	A Small size (1927)		90p	£27.00
B		50	B Large size (1926)		60p	£30.00
B	C	25	Art Treasures — '2nd Series of 50', Nd. 51-75 (1928)		90p	£22.50
B	C	25	England, Historic and Picturesque — 'Series of 25' (1928)		90p	£22.50
B	C	25	England, Historic and Picturesque — 'Second Series ...' (1928)		90p	£22.50
A2	P	27	Famous Golfers (1928)		£12.00	—
	P	27	Famous 'Test' Cricketers (1928):			
A2			A Small size		£4.50	—
			B Medium size (76 × 51mm)		£4.50	—
—	C	25	Gallery Pictures (76 × 51mm) (1928)		£1.20	£30.00
A2	C	50	'Geographia' Map Series (sectional) (1931)		£1.60	£80.00
	CP		The Homeland Series (1933):	Ha.539		
A2		54	A Small size		28p	£15.00
—		56	B Medium size (76 × 51mm)		30p	£17.00
A2	P	36	In the Public Eye (1930)		£1.10	£40.00
D	C	25	Men of Genius (1924)		£4.00	£100.00
B	C	25	Picturesque Old England (1931)		£1.00	£25.00
A2	P		Real Photographs:	Ha.538		
		27	'A Series of 27' —			
			A Matt front (c1931)		75p	£20.00
			B Glossy front (c1931)		40p	£11.00
		27	'2nd Series of 27' (c1931)		75p	£20.00
		27	'3rd Series of 27' (c1932)		40p	£11.00
		27	'4th Series of 27' (c1932)		75p	£20.00
		27	'5th Series of 27' (c1933)		£1.00	£27.00
		27	'6th Series of 27' (c1933)		£1.00	£27.00
C	C	25	Reproductions of Celebrated Oil Paintings (1928)	Ha.542	£1.20	£30.00
B	C	25	Roses (1927)		£2.40	£60.00
A2	C	50	Things to Make — 'De Reszke Cigarettes' (1935)		60p	£30.00
A2	C	50	What the Stars Say — 'De Reszke Cigarettes' (1934)		50p	£25.00
A2	P	36	Zoological Studies (1929)		25p	£9.00
C	***MISCELLANEOUS***					
—	U		'RILETTE' Miniature Pictures (60 × 45mm) (c1925):			
		20	A Inscribed Series of 20		£3.50	—
		25	B Inscribed Series of 25		£3.50	—
		30	C Inscribed Series of 30		£3.50	—
		42	D Inscribed Series of 42		£3.50	—
		43	E Inscribed Series of 43		£3.50	—
		56	F Inscribed Series of 56		£3.50	—
		74	G Inscribed Series of 74		£3.50	—

MIRANDA LTD, London

POST-1920 ISSUES

A	C	20	Dogs (c1925)	H.211	£6.00	£120.00

MIRANDA LTD, London *(continued)*

Size	*Printing*	*Number in set*		*Handbook reference*	*Price per card*	*Complete set*
A	C	25	Sports and Pastimes — Series I (c1925)	H.225	£5.00	£125.00

STEPHEN MITCHELL & SON, Glasgow

A	***PRE-1919 ISSUES***					
C	C	51	*Actors and Actresses — Selection from 'FROGA B and C' (c1900)	H.20	£18.00	—
C	U	25	*Actors and Actresses — 'FROGA C' (c1900)	H.20	£18.00	—
C	U	50	*Actors and Actresses — 'FROGA D' (c1900)	H.20	£18.00	—
C	U	26	*Actresses — 'FROGA B' (c1900)	H.20	£18.00	—
A	U	1	Advertisement Card 'Maid of Honour' (c1900)		—	£350.00
A	C	50	Arms and Armour (1916)	H.273	£3.60	£180.00
A	C	25	Army Ribbons and Buttons (1916)		£4.00	£100.00
C	BW	25	*Boxer Rebellion — Sketches (c1904)	H.46	£22.00	—
D1	BW	25	British Warships, 1-25 (1915)		£6.00	£150.00
D1	BW	25	British Warships, Second series 26-50 (1915)		£6.00	£150.00
A	C	50	Interesting Buildings (1905)	H.70	£5.50	£275.00
A	C	25	Medals (1916)	H.71	£4.60	£115.00
A	C	25	Money (1913)		£4.60	£115.00
A	C	25	*Regimental Crests, Nicknames and Collar Badges (1900)	H.274	£11.00	£275.00
A	C	25	Scottish Clan Series No. 1 (1903)	H.33	£12.00	£300.00
A	C	25	Seals (1911)		£4.60	£115.00
A	C	25	Sports (1907)	H.275	£12.00	£300.00
A	C	25	Statues and Monuments (1914)		£4.60	£115.00
B	***POST-1920 ISSUES***					
A	C	50	Air Raid Precautions (1938)	Ha.544	90p	£45.00
A	C	25	Angling (1928)		£4.40	£110.00
A	C	50	Clan Tartans — 'A Series of 50' (1927)		£1.80	£90.00
A	C	25	Clan Tartans — '2nd Series, 25' (1927)		90p	£22.50
A	C	25	Empire Exhibition, Scotland, 1938 (1938)		80p	£20.00
A2	C	25	Famous Crosses (1923)		70p	£17.50
A	C	50	Famous Scots (1933)		80p	£40.00
A	U	50	First Aid (1938)		£1.00	£50.00
A	U	50	A Gallery of 1934 (1935)		£2.00	£100.00
A	U	50	A Gallery of 1935 (1936)		£1.90	£95.00
A	C	50	Humorous Drawings (1924)	Ha.590	£2.20	£110.00
A	C	40	London Ceremonials (1928)		£1.25	£50.00
A	C	30	A Model Army (cut-outs) (1932)		£1.20	£36.00
A	C	25	Old Sporting Prints (1930)	Ha.563	£1.40	£35.00
A	U	50	Our Empire (1937)	Ha.522	50p	£25.00
A	C	70	River and Coastal Steamers (1925)		£2.40	—
A	C		A Road Map of Scotland (1933):			
		50	A Small numerals		£2.00	£100.00
		50	B Large numerals in circles		£2.00	£100.00
		50	C Overprinted in red		£2.50	£125.00
		1	D Substitute card (Blue)		—	£15.00
A	C	50	Scotland's Story (1929)		£1.80	£90.00
A	U	50	Scottish Footballers (1934)		£1.80	£90.00
A	U	50	Scottish Football Snaps (1935)		£1.80	£90.00
A	C	25	Stars of Screen and History (1939)		£1.80	£45.00
—	C	25	Village Models Series (1925):	Ha.591		
A			A Small size		£2.20	£55.00
			B Medium size (68 × 62mm)		£4.00	£100.00
—	C	25	Village Models Series — 'Second' (1925):			
A			A Small size		£2.20	£55.00
			B Medium size (68 × 62mm)		£4.00	£100.00

STEPHEN MITCHELL & SON, Glasgow *(continued)*

Size	*Printing*	*Number in set*		*Handbook reference*	*Price per card*	*Complete set*
A	U	50	Wonderful Century (1937)		60p	£30.00
A	U	50	The World of Tomorrow (1936)		£1.00	£50.00

MOORGATE TOBACCO CO., London

POST-1940 ISSUE

—	BW	30	The New Elizabethan Age (20 small, 10 large) (1953):			
			A Matt front		£2.50	—
			B Varnished front		£1.80	£55.00

B. MORRIS & SONS LTD, London

A PRE-1919 ISSUES

—	BW	30	*Actresses (41 × 68mm) (1898)	H.276	£2.00	£60.00
C	U		*Actresses — 'FROGA A (c1900):	H.20		
		? 24	A 'Borneo Queen' back		£27.00	—
		? 15	B 'Gold Seals' back		£27.00	—
		? 9	C 'Morris's Cigarettes' back		£27.00	—
		? 7	D 'Tommy Atkins' back		£75.00	—
—	C	? 4	*Actresses — selection from 'FROGA B' — 'Morris's High Class Cigarettes' on front (76 × 66mm) (c1900)	H.20	£250.00	—
A1	P	1	*Advertisement Card (Soldier and Girl) (c1900)		£350.00	—
A	U	21	*Beauties — 'MOM' (c1900):	H.277		
			A 'Borneo Queen' back		£27.00	—
			B 'Gold Seals' back		£27.00	—
			C 'Morris's Cigarettes' back		£27.00	—
			D 'Tommy Atkins' back		£75.00	—
A	C		*Beauties — 'CHOAB' (c1900):	H.21		
		? 17	A 'Gold Flake Honeydew' back		£40.00	—
		? 29	B 'Golden Virginia' back		£40.00	—
		? 19	C 'Levant Favourites' back		£40.00	—
		? 21	D 'Reina Regenta' back		£40.00	—
A	U	? 47	*Beauties — Collotype (c1897)	H.278	£120.00	—
A	C	20	Boer War, 1900 (VC Heroes)	H.279	£35.00	—
A	BW	25	*Boer War Celebrities — 'PAM' (c1901)	H.140	£24.00	—
A	C	30	*General Interest — six cards each entitled (c1910):	H.280		
			i Agriculture in the Orient		£6.50	£40.00
			ii Architectural Monuments		£6.50	£40.00
			iii The Ice Breaker		£6.50	£40.00
			iv Schools in Foreign Countries		£6.50	£40.00
			v Strange Vessels		£6.50	£40.00
D	BW	20	London Views (c1905):	H.34		
			A 'American Gold' back		£30.00	—
			B 'Morris's Gold Flake' back		£30.00	—
			C 'Smoke Borneo Queen' back		£30.00	—
			D 'Smoke Reina Regenta' back		£30.00	—
A	C	25	Marvels of the Universe Series (c1912)	H.281	£4.00	£100.00
D	C	50	National and Colonial Arms (1917)		£6.00	£300.00
C	U	25	War Celebrities (1915)		£5.00	£125.00
D	C	25	War Pictures (1916)	H.51	£7.00	£175.00

B POST-1920 ISSUES

A1	C	50	Animals at the Zoo (1924):	Ha.520		
			A Back in blue		70p	£35.00
			B Back in grey		80p	£40.00
A1	C	35	At the London Zoo Aquarium (1928)		50p	£17.50

B. MORRIS & SONS LTD, London *(continued)*

Size	Printing	Number in set		Handbook reference	Price per card	Complete set
A1	BW	25	Australian Cricketers (1925)		£3.00	£75.00
A2	C	25	Captain Blood (1937)		£1.00	£25.00
D	U	50	Film Star Series (1923)		£2.80	—
D	U	25	Golf Strokes Series (1923)		£5.00	£125.00
A1	—	12	Horoscopes (wording only) (1936):			
			A White card		£1.00	—
			B Cream card		50p	£6.00
A2	C	25	How Films are Made (1934):			
			A White card		£1.20	£30.00
			B Cream Card		£1.40	£35.00
A1	BW	50	How to Sketch (1929)		£1.00	£50.00
A1	C	25	Measurement of Time (1924)		£1.20	£30.00
D	U	25	Motor Series (Motor parts) (1922)		£4.00	£100.00
A1	C	25	The Queen's Dolls' House (1925)		£2.80	£70.00
D	U	25	Racing Greyhounds — 'Issued by Forecasta' (1939)		£1.40	£35.00
A1	BW	24	Shadowgraphs (1925)		£2.00	£50.00
A1	C	13	Treasure Island (1924)		£1.20	£16.00
A1	C	50	Victory Signs (1928)		50p	£25.00
A	C	25	Wax Art Series (1931)		50p	£12.50
A	C	25	Whipsnade Zoo (1932)		50p	£12.50
D	C	25	Wireless Series (1923)		£3.60	£90.00
C SILKS						
—	C	? 24	Battleship Crests (70 × 50mm) (paper backed) (c1915)	Ha.504-3	£28.00	—
—	C		English Flowers (78 × 56mm) (paper backed) (c1915):	Ha.505-4		
		25	A Series of 25		£3.60	£90.00
		50	B Series of 50		£4.20	—
—	C	25	English and Foreign Birds (78 × 56mm) (paper backed) (c1915)	Ha.505-1	£4.00	£100.00
—	C	25	**Regimental Colours IV* (75 × 55m) (unbacked and anonymous (c1915))	Ha.502-9	£2.60	£65.00

PHILIP MORRIS & CO. LTD, London

POST-1920 ISSUES

Size	Printing	Number in set		Handbook reference	Price per card	Complete set
	U	50	British Views (1924):			
C			A Small size		£2.70	—
—			B Large size (79 × 67mm)		£2.70	—

P. MOUAT & CO., Newcastle-on-Tyne

PRE-1919 ISSUE

Size	Printing	Number in set		Handbook reference	Price per card	Complete set
C	C	30	*Colonial Troops (c1902)	H.40	£110.00	—

MOUSTAFA LTD, London

POST-1920 ISSUES

Size	Printing	Number in set		Handbook reference	Price per card	Complete set
D2	CP	50	Camera Studies (1923):			
			A Front with number and caption, back in black		£2.70	—
			* B *Front without letterpress, plain back*		£2.70	—
D2	C	25	*Cinema Stars — Set 8* (1924)	Ha.515-8	£4.00	—
A2	C	40	Leo Chambers Dogs Heads (1924)		£2.50	£100.00
D2	C	25	*Pictures of World Interest* (1923)		£2.60	—
A2	P	25	Real Photos (Views) (1925)		40p	£10.00

MUNRO, Glasgow

PRE-1919 ISSUE

Size	Printing	Number in set		Handbook reference	Price per card	Complete set
C	C	? 1	Colonial Troops (c1900)		£130.00	—

B. MURATTI SONS & CO. LTD, Manchester and London

Size	*Printing*	*Number in set*		*Handbook reference*	*Price per card*	*Complete set*
A	***PRE-1919 ISSUES***					
—	U	? 24	*Actresses, cabinet size, collotype (106 × 69mm) (c1898)	H.282	£125.00	—
C	C	26	*Actresses — 'FROGA A' (c1900):	H.20		
			A 'To the Cigarette Connoisseur' back		£22.00	—
			B 'Muratti's Zinnia Cigarettes' back		£25.00	—
—	C		*Actresses and Beauties — Green Corinthian column framework — 'Neb-Ka' vertical backs (117 × 67mm) (c1900):			
		? 15	Actresses — selection from 'FROGA C'	H.20	£140.00	—
		? 3	Beauties — selection from 'MOM'	H.277	£140.00	—
—	C		*Actresses and Beauties — brown and yellow ornamental framework (117 × 67mm) (c1900):			
			I 'Neb-Ka' horizontal backs:			
		? 17	i Actresses — selection from 'FROGA A'	H.20	£140.00	—
		? 20	ii Beauties — selection from 'CHOAB'	H.21	£140.00	—
		? 6	II Rubber stamped back. Beauties — selection from 'CHOAB'	H.21	£140.00	—
		? 24	III Plain back — Beauties — selection from 'CHOAB'	H.21	£140.00	—
—	C		*Advertisement Cards, Globe design back (88 × 66mm) (c1900):	H.283		
		? 10	i Brown borders to front		£275.00	—
		? 19	ii White borders to front		£275.00	—
C	C	50	*Beauties — 'CHOAB' (Zinnia back) (c1900):	H.21		
			A Black printing on back		£40.00	—
			B Olive green printing on back		£45.00	—
—	C	? 54	*Beautiful Women, Globe design back (54 × 75mm) (c1900)	H.284	£90.00	—
—	BW	20	*Boer War Generals — 'CLAM' (35 × 61mm) (c1901)	H.61	£32.00	—
—	C	15	*Caricatures (42 × 62mm) (c1903):	H.285		
			A 'Sole Manufacturers of ...' brown back		£25.00	—
			B 'Muratti's Zinnia Cigarettes' brown back		£25.00	—
			C 'Muratti's Zinnia Cigarettes' black back		£25.00	—
			D 'Muratti's Vassos Cigarettes' (not seen)		—	—
			E As D, but 'Vassos' blocked out, brown back		£45.00	—
—	C	35	Crowned Heads (53 × 83mm) (c1912)		£13.00	—
C	C	52	*Japanese Series, Playing Card inset (c1904)		£13.00	—
			Plain back		£12.00	—
—	P		Midget Post Card Series (1902):	H.286		
		? 99	A Matt Front (90 × 70mm)		£11.00	—
		? 5	B Matt Front (80 × 65mm)		£11.00	—
			C Glossy front (85 × 65mm few 75-80 × 65mm):			
		? 136	i With serial numbers		£11.00	—
		? 76	ii Without serial numbers		£11.00	—
—	P	? 99	'Queens' Post Card Series (90 × 70mm) (c1902):	H.287		
			A Front in black/sepia		£15.00	—
			B Front in reddish brown		£15.00	—
A1	BW	19	*Russo-Japanese Series (1904)	H.184	£11.00	£210.00
A1	C	25	*Star Girls (c1898)	H.30	£140.00	—
A	U	? 51	*Views of Jersey (c1912):	H.288		
			A Plain back		£13.00	—
			B 'Opera House, Jersey' back		£16.00	—
A	U	25	*War Series — 'MURATTI I', white card (1916)	H.289	£20.00	—
A	U	50	*War Series — 'MURATTI II', toned card (1917) Nos. 1-25 (and alternative cards)	H.290	£12.00	—

B. MURATTI SONS & CO. LTD, Manchester and London *(continued)*

Size	Printing	Number in set		Handbook reference	Price per card	Complete set
B	***POST-1920 ISSUES***					
A2	P	24	Australian Race Horses (export) (c1930)		80p	£20.00
C	***SILKS.*** For summary of paper-backed issues, see Ha.497.					
—	C		*Flags — Set 3 (70 × 52mm) (paper backed) (c1915):	Ha.501-3		
		25	1st Series — Series C, Nd. 20-44		£3.50	—
		24	2nd Series:			
			Series A, Nd. 26-49		£3.50	—
			Series E, Nd. 48-72, paper backing in grey (No. 52 unissued)		£3.50	—
			Series E, Nd. 48-72, paper backing in green (No. 52 unissued)		£3.50	—
—	C		*Flags — Set 8 (paper backed) (c1915):	Ha.501-8		
		3	Series A, Nd. 1-3 (89 × 115mm)		£8.50	—
		1	Series B, Nd. 19 (70 × 76mm)		—	£10.00
		18	Series C, Nd. 1-18 (89 × 115mm)		£8.50	—
		3	Series D, Nd. 45-47 (89 × 115mm)		£8.50	—
		6	Series F, Nd. 73-78 (89 × 115mm)		£7.50	—
—	C	18	*Great War Leaders — Series P (89 × 115mm) (paper backed) (c1916)	Ha.504	£11.00	—
—	C		*Regimental Badges I (paper backed) (c1915):	Ha.502-1		
		25	Series A, Nd. 1-25 (70 × 52mm)		£4.50	—
		48	Series B, Nd. 1-48 (76 × 70mm)		£5.50	—
		15	Series B, Nd. 4-18 (76 × 70mm)		£5.50	—
		16	Series G, Nd. 79-94 (76 × 70mm)		£8.00	—
—	C	25	*Regimental Colours I — Series CB (76 × 70mm) (paper backed) (c1915)	Ha.502-6	£8.50	—
—	C	72	*Regimental Colours V — Series RB (70 × 52 mm) (paper backed) (c1915)	Ha.502-10	£5.50	—
D	***CANVASES.*** Unbacked canvases. The material is not strictly canvas, but a linen fabric glazed to give the appearance of canvas.					
—	C	40	Canvas Masterpieces — Series M (71 × 60mm) (c1915):			
			A Shaded back design, globe 12mm diam		£5.50	—
			B Unshaded back design, globe 6mm diam		£2.00	£80.00
—	C	16	Canvas Masterpieces — Series P (114 × 90mm) (c1915)		£12.00	—

MURRAY, SONS & CO. LTD, Belfast

Size	Printing	Number in set		Handbook reference	Price per card	Complete set
A	***PRE-1919 ISSUES***					
A	BW	20	*Actresses — 'BLARM' (c1900):	H.23		
			A 'Pineapple Cigarettes' back		£90.00	—
			B 'Special Crown Cigarettes' back		£100.00	—
C	C	15	Chess and Draughts Problems — Series F (1912)	H.291	£55.00	—
A	BW	54	*Cricketers and Footballers — Series H (c1912):	H.292		
			20 Cricketers. A Thick card		£65.00	—
			B Thin card		£65.00	—
			C Brown Printing		£120.00	—
			34 Footballers. A Thick card		£25.00	—
			B Thin card		£25.00	—
—	C	20	Football Flags (shaped) (60 × 32mm) (c1905):			
			A Maple Cigarettes		£55.00	—
			B Murray's Cigarettes		£55.00	—
C	C	25	*Football Rules (c1911):			
			1-12 Rugby Football		£25.00	—
			13-25 Association Football		£25.00	—
A	BW	104	*Footballers — Series J (c1910)	H.293	£25.00	—

Size	*Printing*	*Number in set*		*Handbook reference*	*Price per card*	*Complete set*
C	U	25	*Irish Scenery Nd. 101-125 (1905):			
			A 'Hall Mark Cigarettes'		£22.00	—
			B 'Pine Apple Cigarettes'		£22.00	—
			C 'Special Crown Cigarettes'		£22.00	—
			D 'Straight Cut Cigarettes'		£22.00	—
			E 'Yachtsman Cigarettes'		£22.00	—
C	BW	25	Polo Pictures — E Series (1911)	H.294	£22.00	—
—	U	50	Prominent Politicians — B Series (41 × 70mm) (1909):	H.295		
			A Without '... in two strengths' in centre of back		£18.00	—
			B With '... in two strengths' in centre of back		£2.50	£125.00
C	U	25	Reproduction of Famous Works of Art — D Series (1910)	H.296	£18.00	£450.00
C	U	25	Reproductions of High Class Works of Art — C Series (1910)	H.297	£20.00	£500.00
A1	C	35	*War Series — Series K (1915)	H.298	£22.00	—
C2	U	25	*War Series — Series L, Nd. 100-124 (c1916):			
			A Sepia		£3.00	£75.00
			B Grey-brown		£3.00	—
			C Purple-brown		£3.00	—
B POST-1920 ISSUES						
D1	P	22	Bathing Beauties (1929)		£5.00	—
A1	BW	40	Bathing Belles (1939)	Ha.592	25p	£10.00
D1	P	22	Cinema Scenes (1929)		£5.00	—
A1	BW	25	Crossword Puzzles (c1925)		£55.00	—
D1	P	26	Dancers (1929)		£5.00	—
D	P		Dancing Girls (1929):			
		25	A 'Belfast-Ireland' at base		£3.00	£75.00
		25	B 'London & Belfast' at base		£2.60	£65.00
		26	C Inscribed 'Series of 26'		£3.00	—
A	C	20	Holidays by the LMS (1927)	Ha.593	£9.00	—
A1	C	20	Inventors Series (1924)	H.213	£4.00	£80.00
—	C	50	Puzzle Series (1925):			
A1			A With coupon attached at top		£16.00	—
			B Without coupon		£5.00	—
D2	C	50	Stage and Film Stars — 'Erinmore Cigarettes' (c1926)		£2.50	£125.00
A1	BW	25	Steam Ships (1939)		£1.00	£25.00
A1	C	50	The Story of Ships (1940)		35p	£17.50
A2	C	25	Types of Aeroplanes (1929)		£1.20	£30.00
C	C	20	Types of Dogs (1924):	Ha.211		
			A Normal back		£5.00	—
			B Normal back, with firm's name rubber-stamped in red		£5.00	—
C SILKS						
—	C	? 16	*Flags, small (70 × 42mm) — 'Polo Mild Cigarettes' (plain paper backing) (c1915)	Ha.498-1	£20.00	—
—	C	? 3	*Flags and Arms, large (102 × 71mm) — 'Polo Mild Cigarettes' (plain paper backing) (c1915)	Ha.498-2	£65.00	—
—	C	? 31	*Orders of Chivalry II, 'Series M' (70 × 42mm) (paper backed, Nd. 35-65) (c1915)	Ha.504-15	£16.00	—
—	C	? 25	*Regimental Badges (70 × 42mm) — 'Polo Mild Cigarettes' (plain paper backing) (c1915)	Ha.498-3	£16.00	—

H.J. NATHAN, London

PRE-1919 ISSUE

D	C	40	Comical Military and Naval Pictures (c1905)	H.14	£55.00	—

JAMES NELSON, London

Size	Printing	Number in set		Handbook reference	Price per card	Complete set
PRE-1919 ISSUE						
A	P	? 22	*Beauties — 'FENA' (c1899)	H.148	£160.00	—

THE NEW MOSLEM CIGARETTE CO., London

PRE-1919 ISSUE						
D	C	30	*Proverbs (c1902)	H.15	£70.00	—

E.J. NEWBEGIN, Sunderland

PRE-1919 ISSUES						
—	P	50	*Actors and Actresses (39 × 60mm) (c1902)	H.299	£45.00	—
A	BW	10	*Actresses — 'HAGG A' (c1900)	Ha.24	£130.00	—
D	C	? 4	Advertisement Cards (c1900)		£375.00	—
A	BW	20	Cricketers Series (1901)	H.29	£300.00	—
A	BW	19	*Russo-Japanese Series (1904)		£110.00	—
D	C	? 12	Well-Known Proverbs (c1905)	H.235	£100.00	—
D	C	25	Well-Known Songs (c1905)	H.300	£100.00	—

W.H. NEWMAN, Birmingham

PRE-1919 ISSUES						
C	C	18	Motor Cycle Series (c1914)	Ha.469	£70.00	—

THOS. NICHOLLS & CO., Chester

PRE-1919 ISSUE						
A	C	50	Orders of Chivalry (1916)	H.301	£5.00	£250.00

THE NILMA TOBACCO COY., London

PRE-1919 ISSUES						
A	C	40	*Home and Colonial Regiments (c1903):	H.69		
			20 Caption in blue		£70.00	—
			20 Caption in brown		£70.00	—
D	C	30	*Proverbs (c1903)	H.15	£70.00	—

M.E. NOTARAS LTD, London

POST-1920 ISSUES						
A2	P	36	National Types of Beauty (c1925)	Ha.558	75p	£27.00
—	U	24	*Views of China (68 × 43mm) (1925)		60p	£15.00

OGDENS LTD, Liverpool

244 page reference book available — £12.50

A PRE-1919 ISSUES

Home Issues *(excluding 'Guinea Gold' and 'Tabs', but including some early issued abroad).*

C	C	? 25	*Actresses — coloured, 'Ogden's Cigarettes contain no glycerine' back (c1895):	H.302		
			A Titled in black		£85.00	—
			B Titled in brown		£85.00	—
D2	U	? 1	*Actresses — green, green borders (c1900)	H.303	£200.00	—
D1	U	50	*Actresses — green photogravure (c1900)	H.304	£8.50	—
D	P	? 583	*Actresses — 'Ogden's Cigarettes' at foot (c1900)	H.305	£2.30	—
D	P		*Actresses and Beauties — collotype (c1895):	H.306		
		? 76	i named:			
			A *Plain back*		£70.00	—
			B 'Midnight Flake' back		£45.00	—

Size	*Print-ing*	*Number in set*		*Handbook reference*	*Price per card*	*Complete set*
		? 21	ii unnamed:			
			A *Plain back*		£70.00	—
			B 'Midnight Flake' back:			
			(blue)		£45.00	—
			(red)		£70.00	—
D	P		*Actresses and Beauties — collotype, 'Ogden's Cigarettes' back (1895):	H.306		
		? 41	i named		£45.00	—
		? 36	ii unnamed		£45.00	—
A	P	? 204	*Actresses and Beauties — woodbury-type (c1894)	H.307	£35.00	—
—	C	192	Army Crests and Mottoes (39 × 59mm) (c1902)		£4.00	—
A	C	28	*Beauties — 'BOCCA' (c1900)	H.39	£23.00	—
—	C	50	*Beauties — 'CHOAB' (c1900):	H.21		
			1-25 (size 65 × 36mm)		£26.00	—
			26-50 (size 67 × 37mm)		£26.00	—
A	C	26	*Beauties — 'HOL' (c1900):	H.192		
			A 'Guinea Gold' red rubber stamp back		£110.00	—
			B Blue Castle Design back		£17.00	£440.00
A2	C	52	*Beauties — 'Playing Card' series (c1900):	H.308		
			A 52 with playing card inset		£26.00	—
			B 26 without playing card inset		£32.00	—
A2	C	52	*Beauties and Military — PC inset (c1898)		£26.00	—
—	P	50	Beauty Series, numbered, 'St. Julien Tobacco' (36 × 54mm) (c1900)		£2.50	£125.00
D	P	? 65	Beauty Series, unnumbered, issued Australia (c1900)	H.309	£65.00	—
A	C	50	Birds' Eggs (1904):			
			A White back		£1.90	£95.00
			B Toned back		£1.80	£90.00
D	P	? 141	*Boer War and General Interest — 'Ogden's Cigarettes' at foot (c1900)	H.310	£2.60	—
H2	P	? 52	*Boer War and General Interest — 'Ogden's Cigarettes' at foot (c1900)		£30.00	—
—	P	? 3	*Boer War & General Interest (Liners) 'Ogdens Cigarettes' at foot (72 × 55mm) (c1900)	H.310	£130.00	—
A	C	50	Boxers (1915)		£6.00	£300.00
A	C	25	Boxing (1914)	H.311	£5.00	£125.00
—	C	? 6	*Boxing Girls (165 × 94mm) (c1895)	Ha.482	£350.00	—
A	C	50	Boy Scouts (1911):	H.62		
			A Blue back		£2.50	£125.00
			B Green back		£3.60	£180.00
A	C	50	Boy Scouts, 2nd series (1912):	H.62		
			A Blue back		£2.50	£125.00
			B Green back		£3.60	£180.00
A	C	50	Boy Scouts, 3rd series (1912):	H.62		
			A Blue back		£2.50	£125.00
			B Green back		£3.60	£180.00
A	C	50	Boy Scouts, 4th series, green back (1913)		£2.60	£130.00
A	C	25	Boy Scouts, 5th series, green back (1914)		£2.80	£70.00
A	C	50	British Birds:	H.229		
			A White back (1905)		£1.90	£95.00
			B Toned back (1906)		£1.80	£90.00
A	C	50	British Birds, Second Series (1908)		£2.00	£100.00
A	C	50	British Costumes from 100 BC to 1904 (1905)	H.312	£6.00	£300.00
A	C	50	Club Badges (1914)		£5.00	£250.00
—	C	? 24	*Comic Pictures (1890-95) (size varies)	H.313	£275.00	—
A2	C	12	*Cricket and Football Terms — Women, '(c1896)	H.314	£325.00	—

OGDENS LTD, Liverpool *(continued)*

Size	*Printing*	*Number in set*		*Handbook reference*	*Price per card*	*Complete set*
A	U	? 50	*Cricketers and Sportsmen (c1898)	H.315	£65.00	—
A	U	28	*Dominoes — Actresses — 'FROGA A' back (c1900):	H.20		
			A Mitred corners (7 backs)		£24.00	—
			B Unmitred corners (7 backs)		£24.00	—
A	U	28	*Dominoes — Beauties — 'MOM' back (c1900)	H.277	£24.00	—
A2	BW	55	*Dominoes — black back (1909)		£1.40	£75.00
A	C	50	Famous Footballers (1908)		£3.50	£175.00
A	C	50	Flags and Funnels of Leading Steamship Lines (1906)	H.67	£4.00	£200.00
—	C	43	*Football Club Badges (shaped for buttonhole) (c1910)	H.316	£6.00	—
A	C	51	Football Club Colours (1906):	H.68		
			Nos. 1-50		£3.20	£160.00
			No. 51		—	£5.00
A	C	50	Fowls, Pigeons and Dogs (1904)	H.64	£2.80	£140.00
—	C	1	*History of the Union Jack (threefold card) (51 × 37mm closed) (1901)		—	£200.00
A	BW	50	Infantry Training (1915)	H.317	£2.40	£120.00
K2	C	52	*Miniature Playing Cards — Actresses and Beauties back (c1900):	H.319		
			I Unnamed, no numeral (76 backs known)		£4.00	—
			II Unnamed, 'numeral 40' (26 backs known)		£4.00	—
			III Named, 'numeral 46' (26 backs known)	H.20	£4.00	—
			IV Named, no numeral (26 backs known)	H.20	£4.00	—
K2	C	52	*Miniature Playing Cards, blue Tabs 'Shield and Flower' design back (1909)		£3.00	—
K2	C	52	*Miniature Playing Cards, yellow 'Coolie Plug' design back:			
			A Yellow back (1904)		£3.00	—
			B Yellow back with white border (1904)		£3.00	—
A	BW	50	Modern War Weapons (1915):	H.320		
			A Original numbering		£2.80	£140.00
			B Numbering re-arranged		£10.00	—
A	C	50	Orders of Chivalry (1907)		£3.00	£150.00
A	C	25	Owners, Racing Colours and Jockeys (1914)		£4.00	£100.00
A	C	50	Owners, Racing Colours and Jockeys (1906)		£3.00	£150.00
A	C	25	Poultry (1915):			
			A 'Ogden's Cigarettes' on front		£4.00	£100.00
			B Without 'Ogden's Cigarettes' on front		£4.00	£100.00
A	C	25	Poultry, 2nd series, as 'B' above (1916)		£4.40	£110.00
A	C	25	Pugilists and Wrestlers, Nd. 1-25 (1908)		£4.00	£100.00
A	C	25	Pugilists and Wrestlers, Nd.26-50:			
			A White back (1909)		£4.00	£100.00
			B Toned back (1908)		£4.00	£100.00
A	C	25	Pugilists and Wrestlers, 2nd series, Nd. 51-75 (1909)		£4.00	£100.00
A	C	50	Racehorses (1907)		£3.00	£150.00
A	C	25	Records of the World (1908)		£2.80	£70.00
A	C	50	Royal Mail (1909)	H.82	£4.20	£210.00
A	C	50	Sectional Cycling Map (1910)	H.74	£3.20	£160.00
A	C	50	*Shakespeare Series (c1903):	H.321		
			A Unnumbered		£13.00	£650.00
			B Numbered		£13.00	£650.00
A	C		Soldiers of the King (1909):			
		50	A Grey printing on front		£4.50	£225.00
		25	B Brown printing on front		£6.00	—
D	C	25	*Swiss Views, Nd. 1-25 (c1905)		£4.00	£100.00
D	C	25	*Swiss Views, Nd. 26-50 (c1905)		£5.00	£125.00

Size	*Print-ing*	*Number in set*		*Handbook reference*	*Price per card*	*Complete set*
D	C	48	Victoria Cross Heroes (1901)	H.322	£12.00	£600.00
B	'Guinea Gold' Series (The S and X numbers represent the reference numbers quoted in the Ogden's Reference Book).					
D	P	1148	1-1148 Series (c1900):			
			Nos. 1-200		40p	£80.00
			Nos. 201-500		£1.00	—
			Nos. 501-900, excl. 523 and 765		90p	—
			Nos. 901-1000, excl. 940, 943, 947 and 1000		£1.50	—
			Nos. 1001-1148, excl. 1003, 1006-8, 1024, 1030, 1033, 1034, 1037, 1040, 1042, 1048, 1066, 1081, 1082, 1088		£1.50	—
			Scarce Nos: 523, 940, 943, 947, 1000, 1003, 1007, 1008, 1024, 1030, 1033, 1034, 1037, 1040, 1042, 1048, 1066, 1088		£40.00	—
			Very scarce Nos. 765, 1006, 1081, 1082		—	—
D	CP	?	Selected numbers from 1-1148 Series (c1900)		£4.00	—
D	P		400 New Series I (c1902)		80p	£320.00
D	P		400 New Series B (c1902)		£1.00	£400.00
D	P		300 New Series C (c1902)		80p	£240.00
D	P	? 318	Set 73S Base B Actresses (c1900)		£2.50	—
			Set 75S Base D (c1900):			
D	P	? 320	List DA — White Panel Group		£1.00	—
D	P	? 58	List DB — The Denumbered Group		£2.20	—
D	P	? 62	List DC — The Political Group		£1.00	—
D	P	? 186	List DD — Boer War etc		70p	—
D	P	? 46	List DE — Pantomime and Theatre Group		£3.80	—
D	P	? 374	List DF — Actors and Actresses		£1.20	—
D	P	? 40	Set 76S Base E Actors and Actresses (c1900)		£3.00	—
D	P	? 58	Set 77S Base F Boer War etc (c1901)		90p	—
			Set 78S Base I (c1900):			
			List IA — The small Machette Group:			
D	P	83	I Actors and Actresses		£1.00	—
D	P	14	II London Street Scenes		£2.75	—
D	P	32	III Turner Pictures		£1.50	—
D	P	11	IV Cricketers		£12.00	—
D	P	18	V Golf		£20.00	—
D	P	10	VI Views and Scenes Abroad		£1.60	—
D	P	30	VII Miscellaneous		£1.30	—
D	P	639	List IB — The Large Machette Group		£1.00	—
D	P	5	List IC — The White Panel Group		£5.00	—
D	P	30	Set 79S Base J Actresses (c1900)		£3.50	—
D	P	239	Set 80S Base K Actors and Actresses (c1900)		£2.30	—
D	P	215	Set 81S Base L Actors and Actresses (c1900)		£2.20	—
			Set 82S Base M (c1901):			
D	P	3	List Ma Royalty		£3.00	£9.00
D	P	77	List Mb Cricketers		£20.00	—
D	P	50	List Mc Cyclists		£5.50	—
D	P	150	List Md Footballers		£9.00	—
D	P	50	List Me Pantomime and Theatre Group		£6.00	—
D	P	33	List Mf Footballers and Cyclists		£9.00	—
D	P	27	List Mg Boer War and Miscellaneous		90p	—
D	P	? 2948	List Mh Actors and Actresses		90p	—
Ba	Guinea Gold Series, Large and Medium					
	P	71	Set 73X Actresses Base B (c1900)		£14.00	—
	P	1	Set 74X Actress Base C (c1900)		—	£40.00

Size	*Printing*	*Number in set*		*Handbook reference*	*Price per card*	*Complete set*
	P	571	Set 75X Actors, Actresses, Boer War Etc Base D (c1901)		From £2.00	—
	P	21	Set 78X Actresses Base I (c1900)		£40.00	—
	P	403	Set 82X Actors, Actresses, Boer War Etc Base M (c1901)		£1.50	—

C 'TABS' SERIES

(Numbers in parentheses following word 'item' represent the reference numbers quoted in Ogden's Reference Book. The listing includes both home and overseas 'Tabs' issues.)

Size	*Printing*	*Number in set*		*Handbook reference*	*Price per card*	*Complete set*
D	BW	200	*Actresses (item 7) (c1900)		£2.50	—
D	BW	200	*Actresses and Foreign Views (item 14) (c1900)		£2.00	—
D	BW	? 331	*Composite Tabs Series, with 'Labour Clause' (item 63) (1901):			
			1 General de Wet		—	£4.00
			1 General Interest		—	£5.00
			17 Heroes of the Ring		£6.00	—
			1 HM the Queen		—	£5.00
			2 HRH the Prince of Wales		£4.00	£8.00
			14 Imperial Interest		£1.00	£14.00
			106 Imperial or International Interest		80p	—
			3 International Interest		£2.00	£6.00
			14 International Interest or a Prominent British Officer		80p	£11.00
			22 Leading Athletes		£2.20	—
			15 Leading Favourites of the Turf		£3.50	—
			54 Leading Generals at the War		£1.00	£54.00
			2 Members of Parliament		£3.50	£7.00
			11 Notable Coursing Dogs		£6.00	—
			12 Our Leading Cricketers		£13.00	—
			17 Our Leading Footballers		£5.00	—
			37 Prominent British Officers		90p	£35.00
			1 The Yacht 'Columbia'		—	£6.00
			1 The Yacht 'Shamrock'		—	£6.00
D	BW	? 65	*Composite Tabs Series, without 'Labour Clause' (item 64) (c1900):			
			36 General Interest		£24.00	—
			29 Leading Artists of the Day		£22.00	—
D	BW	? 114	*Composite Tabs Series, Sydney issue (item 65) (c1900):			
			15 English Cricketer Series		£45.00	—
			1 Christian de Wet		£10.00	—
			1 Corporal G. E. Nurse, VC		£9.00	—
			1 Imperial Interest		£10.00	—
			27 Imperial or International Interest		£8.00	—
			6 International Interest		£8.00	—
			1 Lady Sarah Wilson		£9.00	—
			40 Leading Generals at the War		£8.00	—
			13 Prominent British Officers		£8.00	—
D	BW	150	General Interest, Series 'A' (1901)		60p	£90.00
D	BW	200	General Interest, Series 'B' (1902)		60p	£120.00
D	BW	470	General Interest, Series 'C' (1902):			
			C.1-200		60p	£120.00
			C.201-300		£2.20	—
			C.301-350		80p	£40.00
			No Letter, Nd 1-120		90p	£110.00
D	BW	200	General Interest, Series 'D' (1902)		60p	£120.00
D	BW	120	General Interest, Series 'E' (1902)		90p	£110.00

Size	*Print-ing*	*Number in set*		*Handbook reference*	*Price per card*	*Complete set*
D	BW	420	General Interest, Series 'F' (1902):			
			F.1-200		90p	—
			F.201-320		90p	—
			F.321-420		£2.50	—
D	BW	? 500	General Interest, Sydney issue (c1902):			
			Nd 1-100 on front		£2.75	—
			Nd 101-400 on back		£2.75	—
			Unnumbered, mostly similar numbered cards 101-200 (item 99-a)		£5.00	—
D	BW	196	*General Interest, unnumbered, similar style C.201-300 (item 95) (1902):			
			75 Stage Artists		80p	—
			42 Celebrities		80p	—
			56 Footballers		£2.50	—
			23 Miscellaneous		80p	—
D	BW	100	*General Interest, unnumbered, similar style C.301-350 (item 96) (1902):			
			28 Actresses		90p	—
			40 Castles		£1.00	—
			12 Dogs		£1.25	—
			20 Miscellaneous		90p	—
D	BW	300	*General Interest, unnumbered, similar style F.321-420 (item 97) (1903):			
			A 100 with full stop after caption		£1.20	£120.00
			B Without full stop after caption:			
			79 I Stage Artistes		90p	£70.00
			21 II Cricketers		£10.00	—
			25 III Football		£4.00	—
			15 IV Golf		£15.00	—
			10 V Cyclists		£5.00	—
			9 VI Fire Brigades		£5.00	—
			5 VII Aldershot Gymnasium		£3.00	£15.00
			36 VIII Miscellaneous		80p	—
D	BW	? 110	*General Interest, 'oblong' back (item 98) (c1900)		£14.00	—
D	BW	? 75	*Leading Artistes of the Day, numbered 126-200, plain backs (item 109) (see H.1) (c1900)		£11.00	—
D	BW	? 71	Leading Artistes of the Day with 'Labour Clause' (item 110) (c1900):			
			A Type-set back		£1.00	—
			B Plain back		£20.00	—
D	BW	? 25	Leading Artistes of the Day, without 'Labour Clause' (item 111-1) (c1900):			
			A With caption, type-set back		£13.00	—
			B With caption, plain back		£13.00	—
			C Without caption, type-set back		£13.00	—
D	BW	? 86	Leading Artistes of the Day, without 'Labour Clause' (item 111-2) (c1900):			
			A Type-set back		£11.00	—
			B Plain back		£11.00	—
D	BW	25	Leading Generals at the War, with descriptive text (item 112) (c1900):			
			A 'Ogden's Cigarettes' back		£2.00	—
			B 'Ogden's Tab Cigarettes' back		£1.40	£35.00
D	BW		Leading Generals at the War, without descriptive text (item 113) (c1900):			
		? 47	A 'Ogden's Tab Cigarettes' back (47 known)		£1.00	—

Size	*Print-ing*	*Number in set*		*Handbook reference*	*Price per card*	*Complete set*
		? 25	B 'Ogden's Lucky Star' back (25 known)		£4.50	—
D	BW	50	*Stage Artistes and Celebrities (item 157) (c1900)		£2.20	£110.00
D	***POST-1920 ISSUES***					
A	C	25	ABC of Sport (1927)		£2.60	£65.00
A	C	50	Actors — Natural and Character Studies (1938)	Ha.571-1	£1.00	£50.00
A	C	50	AFC Nicknames (1933)	Ha.571-2	£3.50	£175.00
A	C	50	Air-Raid Precautions (1938)	Ha.544	70p	£35.00
A	C	50	Applied Electricity (1928)		£1.10	£55.00
A	U	36	Australian Test Cricketers, 1928-29		£3.00	£110.00
A	C	50	Billiards, by Tom Newman (1928)		£1.50	£75.00
A	C	50	Bird's Eggs (cut-outs) (1923)		90p	£45.00
A	C	50	The Blue Riband of the Atlantic (1929)		£2.50	£125.00
A	C	50	Boy Scouts (1929)		£1.50	£75.00
A	C	50	British Birds (Cut-Outs) (1923)		90p	£45.00
A	C	50	British Birds and Their Eggs (1939)	Ha.571-3	£2.20	£110.00
A	U	50	Broadcasting (1935)	Ha.571-4	£1.20	£60.00
A	C	50	By the Roadside (1932)		£1.00	£50.00
A	C	44	Captains of Association Football Clubs and Colours (1926)		£2.50	£110.00
A	U	50	Cathedrals and Abbeys (1936):			
			A Cream card		90p	£45.00
			B White card		90p	£45.00
A	C	50	Champions of 1936 (1937)	Ha.571-5	£1.60	£80.00
A	C	50	Children of All Nations (cut-outs) (1923)		90p	£45.00
A	C	50	Colour in Nature (1932)		90p	£45.00
A	C	50	Construction of Railway Trains (1930)		£2.20	£110.00
A	C	50	Coronation Procession (sectional) (1937)	Ha.571-6	£1.40	£70.00
A	U	50	Cricket, 1926		£2.40	£120.00
A	C	25	Derby Entrants, 1926		£2.40	£60.00
A	C	50	Derby Entrants, 1928		£1.80	£90.00
A	U	50	Derby Entrants, 1929		£2.20	£110.00
A	C	50	Dogs (1936)	Ha.571-7	£1.80	£90.00
A	C	25	Famous Dirt-Track Riders (1929)		£3.60	£90.00
A	U	50	Famous Rugby Players (1926-27)		£2.00	£100.00
A	C	50	Football Caricatures (1935)	Ha.571-8	£2.20	£110.00
A	C	50	Football Club Captains (1935)	Ha.571-9	£1.60	£80.00
A	C	50	Foreign Birds (1924)		80p	£40.00
A	U	25	Greyhound Racing — '1st Series ...' (1927)		£3.40	£85.00
A	U	25	Greyhound Racing — '2nd Series ...' (1928)		£3.40	£85.00
A	C	50	How to Swim (1935)	Ha.571-10	80p	£40.00
A	C	50	Jockeys, and Owners' Colours (1927)		£2.40	£120.00
A	C	50	Jockeys, 1930		£2.40	£120.00
A	C	50	Leaders of Men (1924)		£1.80	£90.00
A	C	25	Marvels of Motion (1928)		£1.80	£45.00
A	C	50	Modern British Pottery (1925)		90p	£45.00
A	C	50	Modern Railways (1936)	Ha.571-11	£2.00	£100.00
A	C	25	Modes of Conveyance (1927)		£2.40	£60.00
A	C	50	Motor Races (1931)		£2.40	£120.00
A	C	50	Ocean Greyhounds (1938)	Ha.571-12	£1.00	£50.00
A	C	25	Optical Illusions (1923)	Ha.560	£2.40	£60.00
A	C	25	Picturesque People of the Empire (1927)		£1.40	£35.00
A	U	50	Picturesque Villages (1936)		£1.00	£50.00
A	C	25	Poultry Alphabet (1924)		£3.00	£75.00
A	C	25	Poultry Rearing and Management — '1st Series ...' (1922)		£2.40	£60.00

OGDENS LTD, Liverpool *(continued)*

Size	Print-ing	Number in set		Handbook reference	Price per card	Complete set
A	C	25	Poultry Rearing and Management — '2nd Series ...' (1923)		£2.40	£60.00
A	U	50	Prominent Cricketers of 1938 (1938)	Ha.571-13	£1.60	£80.00
A	C	50	Prominent Racehorses of 1933 (1934)	Ha.571-14	£1.60	£80.00
A	U	50	Pugilists in Action (1928)		£3.20	£160.00
A	C	50	Racing Pigeons (1931)		£3.00	£150.00
A	C	50	Sea Adventure (1939)	Ha.571-15	25p	£12.50
A	C	50	Shots from the Films (1936)	Ha.571-16	£1.60	£80.00
A	U	25	Sights of London (1923)		£1.40	£35.00
A	C	50	Smugglers and Smuggling (1932)		£1.70	£85.00
A	U	50	Steeplechase Celebrities (1931)		£1.80	£90.00
A	C	50	Steeplechase Trainers, and Owners' Colours (1927)		£1.80	£90.00
A	C	50	The Story of Sand (1934)		80p	£40.00
A	C	50	Swimming, Diving and Life-Saving (1931)	Ha.523	£1.00	£50.00
A	C	25	Trainers, and Owners' Colours — '1st Series ...' (1925)		£2.00	£50.00
A	C	25	Trainers, and Owners' Colours — '2nd Series ...' (1926)		£2.20	£55.00
A	C	50	Trick Billiards (1934)	Ha.571-17	£1.30	£65.00
A	C	50	Turf personalities (1929)		£2.20	£110.00
A	C	25	Whaling (1927)		£2.40	£60.00
A	C	50	Yachts and Motor Boats (1930)		£1.80	£90.00
A	C	50	Zoo Studies (1937)	Ha.571-18	50p	£25.00

THE ORLANDO CIGARETTE & CIGAR CO., London

PRE-1919 ISSUE

A	C	40	*Home & Colonial Regiments (c1901)	H.69		
			20 Caption in blue		£200.00	—
			20 Caption in brown		£200.00	—

OSBORNE TOBACCO CO. LTD, Portsmouth & London

POST-1940 ISSUES

A	U	50	Modern Aircraft (1953):			
			A Dark Blue back		35p	£17.50
			B Light Blue back		40p	£20.00
			C Brown back		50p	£25.00

W.T. OSBORNE & CO., London

PRE-1919 ISSUE

D	C	40	*Naval and Military Phrases (c1904)	H.14	£40.00	—

J.A. PATTREIOUEX, Manchester

A 1920s PHOTOGRAPHIC SERIES. Listed in order of letters and/or numbers quoted on cards. References after word 'back' refer to the nine backs illustrated in Handbook Part II under Ha.595.

H2	P	50	*Animals and Scenes — Unnumbered ('Junior Member'). Back 4 (c1925)	Ha.595-1	£1.20	—
H2	P	50	Animals and Scenes, Nd 1-50. Back 1 (c1925)		£1.20	—
H2	P	50	*Scenes, Nd 201-250 ('Junior Member'). Back 4 (c1925)		£1.20	—
C	P	96	Animals and Scenes, Nd 250-345 (c1925):			
			A Back in style [illegible] in (i) grey		£1.00	—
			(ii) brown		£1.00	—
			* B 'Junior Member' back 9		£1.00	—

J.A. PATTREIOUEX, Manchester *(continued)*

Size	*Print-ing*	*Number in set*		*Handbook reference*	*Price per card*	*Complete set*
C	P	96	Animals and Scenes, Nd 346-441 (c1925):			
			A Back 2		£1.00	—
			B Back style 1 and back 3		£1.00	—
			* C 'Junior Member' back 9		£1.00	—
H	P	50	*Animal Studies, Nd A42-A91 ('Junior Member'). Back 4 (c1925)		£1.00	—
H	P	50	*Animal Studies, Nd A92-A141 ('Junior Member'). Back 4 (c1925)		£1.00	—
H	P	50	*Animal Studies, Nd A151-A200 ('Junior Member'). Back 4 (c1925)		£1.00	—
C	P		*Natives and Scenes (c1925):			
		36	A 'Series 1/36 B' on front, Nd 1-36 ('Junior Member'). Back 9		£1.30	—
		96	B 'Series 1/96 B' on front, Nd 1-96. Back 6		£1.00	—
C	P	96	*Foreign Scenes, Nd 1/96C-96/96C. Back 6 (c1925)		£1.00	—
C	P	96	Cricketers, Nd C1-C96, 'Casket Cigarettes' on front (c1925):			
			A Back 5		£40.00	—
			* B Plain back		£40.00	—
C	P	96	*Animals — 'Series Nos CA1 to 96'. Back 7 (c1925)		£1.00	—
C	P	96	*Natives and Scenes (c1925):			
			A 'C.B.1 to 96' on front. Back 7:			
			1 Nd 1-96		£1.00	—
			2 Nd C.B.1-C.B.96		£1.00	—
			B 'J.S. 1 to 96' on front. 'Junior Member'. Back 9		£1.00	—
C	P	96	*Animals and Scenes — 'CC1 to 96' on front. Back 7 (c1925)		£1.00	—
H2	P	50	*British Scenes — 'Series C.M.1-50.A' on front. Back style 7 (c1925)		£1.20	—
H2	P	50	*Foreign Scenes (c1925):			
			A 'Series CM. 1/50 B' on front. Back style 7		£1.20	—
			B 'J.M. Series 1/50' on front. 'Junior Member' back 9		£1.20	—
H2	P	50	*Foreign Scenes (c1925):			
			A 'Series C.M. 101-150.S' on front. Back style 7		£1.20	—
			B Nd S.101-S.150 on front. Back 4		£1.20	—
C	P	96	*Foreign Scenes, Nd 1/96D-96/96D. Back 6 (c1925)		£1.30	—
H2	P	50	*Foreign Scenes, Nd 1/50E-50/50E. Back 6 (c1925)		£1.20	—
H2	P	50	*Foreign Scenes, Nd 1/50F-50/50F. Back 6 (c1925)		£1.20	—
C	P	96	Footballers, Nd F.1-F.96. 'Casket' and 'Critic' back style 5 (c1925)		£7.50	—
C	P	96	Footballers, Nd F.97-F.192. 'Casket' and 'Critic' back styles (c1925)		£7.50	—
H	P	50	Football Teams, Nd F.193-F.242. ('Casket' and 'Critic') (c1925)		£18.00	—
C	P	96	*Footballers — 'Series F.A. 1/96' on front. Back 8 (c1925)		£5.50	—
C	P	96	*Footballers — 'Series F.B. 1/96' on front. Back 8 (c1925)		£5.50	—
C	P	96	*Footballers — 'Series F.C. 1/96' on front. Back 8 (c1925)		£5.50	—
H2	P	50	*Scenes — 'G. 1/50' on front. 'Junior Member'. Back 9 (c1925)		£1.50	—
H2	P	50	*Scenes — '1/50. H' on front. 'Junior Member'. Back 9 (c1925)		£1.20	—
H2	P	50	*Animals and Scenes, Nd I.1-I.50. Back style 6 (c1925)		£1.20	—

Size	*Print-ing*	*Number in set*		*Handbook reference*	*Price per card*	*Complete set*
H2	P	50	Famous Statues — 'J.C.M. 1 to 50 C' on front. Back style 6 (c1925)		£1.60	—
H2	P	50	*Scenes, Nd JCM 1/50D-JCM 50/50D (c1925):			
			A Back style 6		£1.30	—
			B Back style 9 ('Junior Member')		£1.30	—
B1	P	30	Child Studies, Nd J.M. No. 1-J.M. No. 30. 'Junior Member', back style 9 (c1925)		£3.50	—
B1	P	30	*Beauties, Nd J.M.1-J.M.30. 'Junior Member', back style 9 (c1925)		£2.25	—
H2	P	50	*Foreign Scenes — 'J.M. 1 to 50 A' on front. 'Junior Member', back style 9 (c1925)		£1.20	—
H2	P	50	British Empire Exhibition 'J.M. 1 to 50 B' on front (c1925)		£1.80	—
C	P	96	*Animals and Scenes — 'J.S. 1/96A'on front. 'Junior Member', back style 9 (c1925)		£1.00	—
H2	P	50	*Scenes, Nd S.1-S.50.' Junior Member', back 4 (c1925)		£1.20	—
H2	P	50	*Scenes, Nd S.51-S.100.' Junior Member', back 4 (c1925)		£1.20	—
B1	P	50	**Cathedrals and Abbeys, Nd S.J. 1-S.J. 50. Plain back (c1925)*	Ha.595-3	£2.30	—
B1	P	50	**British Castles. Nd S.J. 51-S.J. 100. Plain back (c1925)*	Ha.595-3	£2.30	—
H2	P	4	*Scenes, Nd V.1-V.4. 'Junior Member', back 4 (c1925)		£5.00	—
B			***COLOURED AND LETTERPRESS SERIES***			
A	C	50	British Empire Exhibition Series (c1928)		£2.50	£125.00
A	C	50	Builders of the British Empire (c1929)		£2.60	£130.00
A	C	50	Celebrities in Sport (c1930)		£4.00	£200.00
A	C	75	Cricketers Series (c1928)		£8.00	—
A	C	50	Dirt Track Riders (c1929)		£8.00	—
A	C	30	Drawing Made Easy (c1930)		£2.50	£75.00
A	C	52	The English and Welsh Counties (c1928)		£2.00	£105.00
A	C		Footballers Series (c1928):			
		50	A Captions in blue		£6.00	—
		100	B Captions in brown		£6.00	—
A	C	25	'King Lud' Problems (c1935)		£12.00	—
A	C	26	Maritime Flags (c1932)		£8.00	—
A	U	25	Photos of Football Stars (c1930)		£22.00	—
D	C	50	Railway Posters by Famous Artists (c1930)		£7.00	—
A	C	50	Sports Trophies (c1931)		£2.50	£125.00
A2	CP	51	*Views (c1930)	Ha.597	£1.10	£55.00
C			***1930s PHOTOGRAPHIC SERIES***			
	P		Beautiful Scotland (1939):	Ha.564-1		
D		28	A Small size		£1.00	£28.00
—		48	B Medium size (77 × 52mm)		25p	£12.00
—	P	48	The Bridges of Britain (77 × 52mm) (1938)		25p	£12.00
—	P	48	Britain from the Air (77 × 52mm) (1939)		25p	£12.00
—	P	48	British Railways (77 × 52mm) (1938)		60p	£30.00
	P		Coastwise (1939):	Ha.564-2		
D		28	A Small size		£1.00	£28.00
—		48	B Medium size (77 × 52mm)		25p	£12.00
D	P	54	Dirt Track Riders (1930):			
			A Descriptive back		£12.00	—
			* B Non-descriptive back		£20.00	—
—	P	48	Dogs (76 × 51mm) (1939)		35p	£17.50

J.A. PATTREIOUEX, Manchester *(continued)*

Size	*Print-ing*	*Number in set*		*Handbook reference*	*Price per card*	*Complete set*
	P		Flying (1938):	Ha.564-3		
D		28	A Small size		£1.50	—
		48	B Medium size (77 × 52mm)		40p	£20.00
A2	P	78	Footballers in Action (1934)		£2.50	—
—	P	48	Holiday Haunts by the Sea (77 × 52mm) (1937)		25p	£12.00
—	P	48	The Navy (1937):			
			A Large captions		50p	£24.00
			B Smaller captions		50p	£24.00
	P		Our Countryside (1938):	Ha.564-4		
D		28	A Small size		£1.25	£35.00
		48	B Medium size (77 × 52mm)		25p	£12.00
A2	P	54	Real Photographs of London (1936)		£2.00	—
D	P	28	Shots from the Films (1938)		£2.00	£55.00
—	P	48	Sights of Britain — 'Series of 48' (76 × 51 mm) (1936)		25p	£12.00
—	P	48	Sights of Britain — 'Second Series ...' (76 × 51mm) (1936):			
			A Large captions		25p	£12.00
			B Smaller captions		30p	£15.00
—	P	48	Sights of Britain — 'Third Series ...' (76 × 51mm) (1937)		25p	£12.00
—	P	48	Sights of London — 'First Series ...' (76 × 51mm) (1935)		50p	£25.00
—	P	12	Sights of London — 'Supplementary Series of 12 Jubilee Pictures' (76 × 51mm) (1935)		75p	£9.00
A2	P	54	Sporting Celebrities (1935)		£2.50	£135.00
—	P	96	Sporting Events and Stars (76 × 50mm) (1935)		£1.50	£150.00
A2	P	54	Views of Britain (1937)		£1.60	—
—	P	48	Winter Scenes (76 × 52mm) (1937)		30p	£15.00
D	***POST-1940 ISSUES***					
—	C	24	Cadet's Jackpot Jigsaws (90 × 65mm) (1969)		£1.50	—
—	C	24	Treasure Island (65 × 45mm) (1968)		£1.50	—

W. PEPPERDY

PRE-1919 ISSUES

A	C	30	*Army Pictures, Cartoons, etc (c1916)	H.12	£75.00	—

M. PEZARO & SON, London

PRE-1919 ISSUES

D	C	25	*Armies of the World (c1900):	H.43		
			A Cake Walk Cigarettes		£100.00	—
			B Nestor Virginia Cigarettes		£100.00	—
D	C	? 17	Song Titles Illustrated (c1900)	H.323	£130.00	—

GODFREY PHILLIPS LTD, London

40 page reference book available — £3.25

A PRE-1919 ISSUES

D1	C	25	*Actresses 'C' Series, Nd 101-125 (c1900):			
			A Blue Horseshoe design back		£27.00	—
			B Green back, 'Carriage' Cigarettes		£30.00	—
			C Blue back, 'Teapot' Cigarettes		£85.00	—
			D Blue back, 'Volunteer' Cigarettes		£85.00	—
			E Blue back, 'Derby' Cigarettes		£85.00	—
			F Blue back 'Ball of Beauty' Cigarettes		£85.00	—

GODFREY PHILLIPS LTD, London *(continued)*

Size	Printing	Number in set		Handbook reference	Price per card	Complete set
—	C	50	*Actresses — oval card (38 × 62mm) (1916):	H.324		
			A With name		£6.00	—
			B *Without Maker's and Actress's Name*		£5.00	£250.00
D	C	40	Animal Series (c1905)		£5.50	£220.00
D1	C	25	*Beauties, Nd B.801-825 (c1902)	H.325	£10.00	£250.00
A1	U	? 24	*Beauties, collotype — 'HUMPS' (c1895)	H.222	£70.00	—
A	C	30	*Beauties, 'Nymphs' (c1896)	H.326	£70.00	—
D			*Beauties — 'Plums' (1897):	H.186		
	BW	? 14	A Front in black and white		£130.00	—
	C	50	B Plum-coloured background		£55.00	—
	C	50	C Green background		£55.00	—
A1	C	50	Beautiful Women (c1905):	H.284		
			A Inscribed 'W.I. Series'		£9.00	—
			B Inscribed 'I.F. Series'		£9.00	—
—	C	50	Beautiful Women, Nd W.501-550 (55 × 75mm) (c1905)	H.284	£17.00	—
D1	C	25	*Boxer Rebellion — Sketches (1904)	H.46	£25.00	—
—	C	30	**British Beauties — Oval Card* (36 × 60mm) *Plain back (c1910)*	H.244	£2.50	£75.00
D	U	50	'British Beauties' photogravure (c1916)	H.327	£5.50	£275.00
—	PC	76	British Beauties (37 × 55mm) (c1916)		£2.60	£200.00
A	C	54	British Beauties Nd 1-54 (1914):	H.328		
			(a) Blue back, grey-black, glossy front		£2.25	£120.00
			(b) *Plain back, grey-black, glossy front*		£3.50	—
			(c) *Plain back, sepia, matt front*		£3.50	—
A	C	54	British Beauties Nd 55-108 (1914):	H.328		
			A Blue back, grey-black, semi-glossy front		£2.25	£120.00
			B Blue back, grey-black matt front		£2.25	£120.00
			C *Plain back, grey-black matt front*		£3.50	—
D1	C	30	British Butterflies, No. 1 issue (1911)		£4.50	£135.00
D1	U	25	British Warships, green photo style (1915)		£6.00	£150.00
L	U	25	British Warships, green photo style (1915)		£35.00	—
A1	P	80	British Warships, 'real photographic' (c1916)	H.329	£12.00	—
D1	C	50	*Busts of Famous People (1906):			
			A Pale green back, caption in black		£20.00	—
			B Brown back, caption in black		£30.00	—
			C Green back, caption in white		£6.00	£300.00
D1	C	25	*Chinese Series (c1910):	H.330		
			A Back in English		£6.00	£150.00
			B 'Volunteer' Cigarettes back		£7.00	£175.00
A	C	50	*Colonial Troops (1904)	H.40	£22.00	—
D1	C	30	Eggs, Nests and Birds, No. 1 issue (1912):			
			A Unnumbered	H.331	£6.00	£180.00
			B Numbered		£6.00	£180.00
D	C	25	First Aid Series, green back (1914)		£6.00	£150.00
A	C	13	*General Interest (c1895)	H.332	£40.00	£520.00
—	BW	100	*Guinea Gold Series, unnumbered (64 × 38mm) Inscribed 'Phillips' Guinea Gold', matt (1899)	H.333	£5.00	—
—	BW	90	*Guinea Gold Series, numbered 101-190 (68 × 41mm). Inscribed 'Smoke Phillips ...' (1900):			
			A Glossy		£4.00	—
			B Matt		£4.00	—
			*Guinea Gold Series, unnumbered (63 × 41mm) (c1900) Actresses:	H.333		
	BW	135	A Black front		£4.00	—
	U	100	B Brown front		£8.50	—

Size	*Print-ing*	*Number in set*		*Handbook reference*	*Price per card*	*Complete set*
	BW	26	Celebrities, Boer War		£4.50	—
D1	C	25	How to do it Series (1913)		£7.00	£175.00
D	C	25	Indian Series (1908)		£14.00	£350.00
K1	C	52	*Miniature Playing Cards (c1905)	H.334	£90.00	—
D1	C	30	Morse and Semaphore Signalling (1916):	H.335		
			'Morse Signalling' back		£8.00	£240.00
			'Semaphore Signalling' back		£8.00	£240.00
—	P	27	Real Photo Series — Admirals and Generals of the Great War. Cut-outs for buttonhole — 20 × 40mm (c1915)		£7.50	—
A	C	20	Russo-Japanese War Series (1904)	H.100	£130.00	—
		30	Semaphore Signalling — See 'Morse and Semaphore Signalling'			
D1	C	25	Sporting Series (c1910)		£17.00	—
D1	C	25	*Statues and Monuments (cut-outs) (1907):			
			A Provisional Patent No. 20736		£8.00	£200.00
			B Patent No. 20736		£8.00	£200.00
D	C	25	*Territorial Series (Nd 51-75) (1908)		£20.00	—
A1	C	25	*Types of British and Colonial Troops (1899)	H.76	£40.00	—
D1	C	25	*Types of British Soldiers (Nd M.651-75) (1900)	H.144	£16.00	£400.00
A	C	63	*War Photos (1916)	H.336	£8.00	—

B POST-1920 ISSUES

Size	*Print-ing*	*Number in set*		*Handbook reference*	*Price per card*	*Complete set*
A2	C	1	*Advertisement Card — 'Grand Cut' (1934)		—	£15.00
A2	C	1	*Advertisement Card — 'La Galbana Fours' (1934)		—	£15.00
A	C	50	Aircraft (1938)	Ha.598	£1.20	£60.00
A2	C	54	Aircraft — Series No. 1 (1938):			
			A Millhoff and Philips names at base		£4.00	—
			B Phillips and Associated Companies at base:			
			1 Front varnished		£2.50	£135.00
			2 Front matt		50p	£27.00
A2	U	50	*Animal Studies (Australia) (c1930)	Ha.538	£2.00	—
—	C	30	Animal Studies (61 × 53mm) (1936)		25p	£7.50
A2	C	50	Annuals (1939):			
			A Home issue		22p	£11.00
			B New Zealand issue (dates for planting 4-6 months later)		£1.00	£50.00
B	C	25	Arms of the English Sees (1924)		£4.40	£110.00
D	BW	50	Australian Sporting Celebrities (Australia) (1932)		£2.50	—
A	C	44	Beauties of Today, small — 'A Series of 44 ...' (1937)		£1.35	£60.00
A	C	50	Beauties of Today, small — 'A Series of 50 ...' (1938)	Ha.514	80p	£40.00
A2	P	54	Beauties of Today, small — 'A Series of Real Photographs ...' (1939)		£1.30	£70.00
A	C	36	Beauties of Today, small — 'A Series of 36 ... Second Series' (1940)		80p	£30.00
—	P		Beauties of Today, large (83 × 66mm) (c1938)			
		36	First arrangement, known as 'Series A'		£3.50	—
		36	Second arrangement, known as 'Series B'		£4.50	—
J2	P	36	Beauties of Today, extra-large, unnumbered (1937)		£1.50	£55.00
J2	P	36	Beauties of Today, extra-large — 'Second Series' (1938)		£1.25	£45.00
J2	P	36	Beauties of Today, extra-large — 'Third Series' (1938)		90p	£32.00
J2	P	36	Beauties of Today, extra-large — 'Fourth Series' (1938)		90p	£32.00
J2	P	36	Beauties of Today, extra-large — 'Fifth Series' (1938)		90p	£32.00

Size	*Printing*	*Number in set*		*Handbook reference*	*Price per card*	*Complete set*
J2	P	36	Beauties of Today, extra-large — 'Sixth Series' (1939)		90p	£32.00
J2	P	36	Beauties of Today, extra-large — Unmarked (1939):			
			A Back 'Godfrey Phillips Ltd'		90p	£32.00
			B Back 'Issued with B.D.V. Medium Cigarettes ...'		30p	£11.00
A2	BW	36	Beauties of the World — Stage, Cinema, Dancing Celebrities (1931)		£1.40	£50.00
A2	C	36	Beauties of the World — Series No. 2 — Stars of Stage and Screen (1933)		£1.50	£54.00
—	C	30	Beauty Spots of the Homeland (126 × 89mm) (1938)		50p	£15.00
A	C	50	Bird Painting (1938)		30p	£15.00
A	C	50	British Birds and Their Eggs (1936)		80p	£40.00
A	C	25	British Butterflies:	Ha.517-1		
			A Back in pale blue (1923)		90p	£22.50
			B Back in dark blue (1927)		80p	£20.00
			C 'Permacal' transfers (1936)		80p	£20.00
A2	C	25	British Orders of Chivalry and Valour (1939):	Ha.599		
			A Back 'Godfrey Phillips Ltd'		£1.60	£40.00
			B Back 'De Reszke Cigarettes' (no maker's name)		£1.60	£40.00
—	C	36	Characters Come to Life (61 × 53mm) (1938)		80p	£30.00
—	P	25	*Cinema Stars — Circular (57mm diam.) (1924)		£2.60	£65.00
A	P	52	Cinema Stars — Set 1 (c1925)	Ha.515-1A	£2.50	—
A2	U	30	Cinema Stars — Set 2 (c1928)	Ha.515-2	£2.20	—
A2	U	30	Cinema Stars — Set 3 (c1928)	Ha.515-3	£1.50	£45.00
A2	C	32	Cinema Stars — Set 4 (c1930)	Ha.515-4	£1.50	£48.00
A2	BW	32	Cinema Stars — Set 5 (c1930)	Ha.515-5	£1.50	£48.00
			Come to Life Series — see 'Zoo Studies'			
	C		Coronation of Their Majesties (1937):			
A2		50	A Small size		25p	£12.50
—		36	B Medium size (61 × 53mm)		25p	£9.00
—		24	C Postcard size (127 × 89mm)		£1.25	£30.00
	P		Cricketers (1924):			
K2		198	*A Miniature size, 'Pinnace' photos (Nd 16c-225c)		£8.00	—
D		192	B Small size, brown back (selected Nos)		£8.00	—
B1		? 58	*C Large size, 'Pinnace' photos		£35.00	—
B1		25	D Large size, brown back (selected Nos)		£20.00	—
—		? 165	*E *Cabinet size*		£35.00	—
D	C	25	Derby Winners and Jockeys (1923)		£3.40	£85.00
D1	C	25	Empire Industries (1927)	Ha.600	£1.00	£25.00
A2	C	50	*Evolution of the British Navy* (1930)		—	£90.00
			49 different (minus No 40)		£1.00	£50.00
D	C	25	Famous Boys (1924)		£2.40	£60.00
D	C	32	Famous Cricketers (1926)		£4.50	—
A	C	25	Famous Crowns (1938)		32p	£8.00
A2	C	50	Famous Footballers (1936)		£1.40	£70.00
—	C	36	Famous Love Scenes (60 × 53mm) (1939)		60p	£22.00
A2	C	50	Famous Minors (1936)		30p	£15.00
—	C	26	Famous Paintings (128 × 89mm) (1938)		£1.25	£32.00
D	C	25	Feathered Friends (1928)	Ha.516	£1.20	£30.00
A2	C	50	Film Favourites (1934)	Ha.517-2	50p	£25.00
D	BW	50	Film Stars (Australia) (1934)		£1.80	—
A2	C	50	Film Stars (1934)		60p	£30.00
—	C	24	*Film Stars — '... No. ... of a series of 24 cards ...' (128 × 89mm) (1934):			
			A Postcard format back		£2.60	£65.00
			B Back without postcard format		£4.00	—

GODFREY PHILLIPS LTD, London *(continued)*

Size	*Printing*	*Number in set*		*Handbook reference*	*Price per card*	*Complete set*
—	C	24	*Film Stars — '... No. ... of a series of cards', Nd 25-48 (128 × 89mm) (1935):			
			A Postcard format back		£3.00	—
			B Back without postcard format		£6.00	—
—	C	24	*Film Stars '... No. ... of a series of cards', vivid backgrounds (128 × 89mm) (1936):			
			A Postcard format back	Ha.517-3	£1.60	£40.00
			B Back without postcard format		£3.00	—
D	C	50	First Aid (1923)		£1.30	£65.00
D	C	25	*Fish (1924)		£2.20	£55.00
	C	30	Flower Studies (1937):			
—			A Medium size (61 × 53mm)		22p	£6.50
—			*B Postcard size (128 × 89mm)		70p	£21.00
	P		Footballers — 'Pinnace' photos (1922-24):			
K2			A Miniature size:			
(Prices shown apply to numbers 1 to 940, for numbers above 940 prices are doubled.)						
		112	1a 'Oval' design back, in brown		£2.50	—
		400	1b 'Oval' design back, in black		£1.25	—
		517	2 Double-lined oblong back		£1.25	—
		1109	3 Single-lined oblong back, address 'Photo'		£1.00	—
			4 Single-lined oblong back, address 'Pinnace' photos:			
		2462	a Name at head, team at base		£1.00	—
		? 1651	b Name at base, no team shown		£1.00	—
		? 217	c Team at head, name at base		£1.00	—
—			B Large size (83 × 59mm):			
		? 400	1 'Oval' design back		£3.00	—
		? 2000	2 Double-lined oblong back:			
			a Address 'Photo'		£3.00	—
			b Address 'Pinnace' photos		£3.00	—
		? 2462	3 Single-lined oblong back:			
			a Name at head, team at base		£3.00	—
			b Name at base, no team shown		£3.00	—
			c Team and name at base		£3.00	—
—		? 2462	C Cabinet size		£8.00	—
—	C	30	Garden Studies (128 × 89mm) (1938)		40p	£12.00
A2	C	25	Home Pets (1924)	Ha.540	£2.00	£50.00
A2	U	25	How to Build a Two Valve Set (1929)		£2.20	£55.00
D	C	25	How to Make a Valve Amplifier ..., Nd 26-50 (1924)		£2.40	£65.00
A	C	25	How to Make Your Own Wireless Set (1923)		£2.00	£50.00
A2	C	54	In the Public Eye (1935)		38p	£20.00
A2	C	50	International Caps (1936)		£1.40	£70.00
A2	C	37	Kings and Queens of England (1925):			
			Nos 1 and 4		£30.00	—
			Other numbers		£1.70	£60.00
A2	U	25	Lawn Tennis (1930)		£2.60	£65.00
K2	C	53	*Miniature Playing Cards (1932-34):			
			A Back with exchange scheme:			
			1 Buff. Offer for 'pack of playing cards'		50p	—
			2 Buff. Offer for 'playing cards, dominoes or chess'		50p	£25.00
			3 Buff. Offer for 'playing cards, dominoes or draughts'		50p	£25.00
			4 Lemon		60p	—
			5 White, with red over-printing		60p	—
			B *Blue scroll back, see Fig. 30, Plate 5, RB13*		50p	£25.00

Size	*Print-ing*	*Number in set*		*Handbook reference*	*Price per card*	*Complete set*
A2	C	25	Model Railways (1927)		£2.40	£60.00
D	C	50	Motor Cars at a Glance (1924)		£3.50	£175.00
D	C	20	Novelty Series (1924)		£9.00	—
A2	C	48	The 'Old Country' (1935)		60p	£30.00
A	C	25	Old Favourites (1924)	Ha.517-4	£1.40	£35.00
—	C	36	Old Masters (60 × 53mm) (1939)		30p	£11.00
A	U	36	Olympic Champions Amsterdam, 1928		£1.80	£65.00
A	C	25	Optical Illusions (1927)		£2.00	£50.00
	C		'Our Dogs' (1939):			
A2		36	A Small size (export)		£1.25	£45.00
—		30	B Medium size (60 × 53mm)		50p	£15.00
—		30	*C Postcard size (128 × 89mm)		£3.20	—
—	BW	48	'Our Favourites' (60 × 53mm) (1935)		25p	£12.50
—	C	30	Our Glorious Empire (128 × 89mm) (1939)		70p	£21.00
	C	30	'Our Puppies' (1936):			
—			A Medium size (60 × 53mm)		65p	£20.00
—			*B Postcard size (128 × 89mm)		£1.50	£45.00
A2	C	25	Personalities of Today (Caricatures) (1932)		£1.60	£40.00
A2	C	25	Popular Superstitions (1930)		£1.40	£35.00
A	C	25	Prizes for Needlework (1925)		£2.20	£55.00
D	C	25	Railway Engines (1924)		£2.60	£65.00
D	C	25	Red Indians (1927)	Ha.601	£2.60	£65.00
A	C	25	School Badges (1927)	Ha.543	£1.00	£25.00
A	C		Screen Stars (1936):			
		48	First arrangement, known as 'Series A':			
			i Frame embossed		90p	£45.00
			ii Frame not embossed		£1.40	£70.00
		48	Second arrangement, known as 'Series B'		90p	£45.00
A2	C		A Selection of B.D.V. Wonderful Gifts:			
		48	'... based on 1930 Budget' (1930)		£1.00	£50.00
		48	'... based on 1931 Budget' (1931)		£1.00	£50.00
		48	'... based on 1932 Budget' (1932)		£1.00	£50.00
D	C	25	Ships and Their Flags (1924)	Ha.602	£2.60	£65.00
—	C	36	Ships that have Made History (60 × 53mm) (1938)		40p	£15.00
—	C	48	Shots from the Films (60 × 53mm) (1934)		75p	£35.00
A2	C	50	Soccer Stars (1936)		£1.30	£65.00
A2	C	36	Soldiers of the King (1939):	Ha.603		
			A Inscribed 'This surface is adhesive'		£1.40	—
			B Without the above:			
			1 Thin card		70p	£25.00
			2 Thick card		70p	£25.00
	C		Special Jubilee Year Series (1935):			
—		20	A Medium size (60 × 53mm)		30p	£6.00
—		12	B Postcard size (128 × 89mm)		£2.00	£24.00
A2	U	30	Speed Champions (1930)		£1.65	£50.00
A2	U	36	Sporting Champions (1929)		£1.65	£60.00
	C	25	Sports (1923):			
			A White card		£3.40	—
			B Grey card		£3.40	—
A2	C	50	*Sportsmen — 'Spot the Winner' (1937):			
			A Inverted back		80p	£40.00
			B Normal back		£1.00	£50.00
A2	C		Stage and Cinema Beauties (1933):	Ha.572		
		35	First arrangement — known as 'Series A'		£1.15	£40.00
		35	Second arrangement — known as 'Series B'		£1.15	£40.00
A2	C	50	Stage and Cinema Beauties (1935)	Ha.517-5	£1.20	£60.00

GODFREY PHILLIPS LTD, London *(continued)*

Size	*Print-ing*	*Number in set*		*Handbook reference*	*Price per card*	*Complet se*
D	C	50	Stars of British Films (Australia) (1934):			
			A Back 'B.D.V. Cigarettes'		£1.60	—
			B Back 'Grey's Cigarettes ...'		£1.60	—
			C Back 'De Reszke Cigarettes'		£1.60	—
			D Back 'Godfrey Phillips (Aust)'		£1.60	—
A2	CP	54	Stars of the Screen — 'A Series of 54' (1934)		£1.10	£60.0
A2	C	48	Stars of the Screen — 'A Series of 48' (1936):			
			A Frame not embossed		90p	£45.0
			B Frame embossed		90p	£45.0
			C In strips of three, per strip		£2.50	£40.0
D	BW	38	Test Cricketers, 1932-1933 (Australia):			
			A 'Issued with Grey's Cigarettes'		£2.60	—
			B 'Issued with B.D.V. Cigarettes'		£2.60	—
			C Back 'Godfrey Phillips (Aust.)'		£2.60	—
A	U	25	The 1924 Cabinet (1924)		£1.60	£40.0
A	C	50	This Mechanized Age — First Series (1936):			
			A Inscribed 'This surface is adhesive'		25p	£12.5
			B Without the above		30p	£15.0
A	C	50	This Mechanized Age — Second Series (1937)		30p	£15.0
D2	C		Victorian Footballers (Australia) (1933):			
		50	1 'Series of 50':			
			A 'Godfrey Phillips (Aust.)'		£2.00	—
			B 'B.D.V. Cigarettes ...'		£2.00	—
			C 'Grey's Cigarettes'		£2.00	—
		75	2 'Series of 75':			
			D 'B.D.V. Cigarettes ...'		£2.00	—
D	BW	50	Victorian League and Association Footballers (Australia) (1934)		£2.00	—
A2	C	100	*Who's Who in Australian Sport (Australia) (1933)		£2.50	—
—	C	30	Zoo Studies — Come to Life Series (101 × 76mm) (1939)		£1.20	£36.0
			Spectacles for use with the above		—	£8.0

C SILKS. Known as 'the B.D.V. Silks'. All unbacked. Inscribed 'B.D.V. Cigarettes' or 'G.P.' (Godfre Phillips), or anonymous. Issued about 1910-25.

—	C	62	**Arms of Countries and Territories (73 × 50mm) — Anonymous*	Ha.504-12	£3.50	—
—	C	32	*Beauties — Modern Paintings (B.D.V.):	Ha.505-13		
			A Small size (70 × 46mm)		£10.00	—
			B Extra-large size (143 × 100mm)		£40.00	—
—	C	100	*Birds II (68 × 42mm) — B.D.V	Ha.505-2	£2.30	—
—	C	12	*Birds of the Tropics III — B.D.V.:	Ha.505-3		
			A Small size (71 × 47mm)		£11.00	—
			B Medium size (71 × 63mm)		£13.00	—
			C Extra-large size (150 × 100mm)		£17.00	—
—	U	24	**British Admirals (83 × 76mm) —Anonymous*	Ha.504-5	£5.00	—
—	C		**British Butterflies and Moths II —Anonymous:*	Ha.505-6		
		40	*Nos 1-40. Large size, 76 × 61mm*		£4.00	—
		10	*Nos 41-50. Medium size. 70 × 51mm*		£4.00	—
—	C	108	*British Naval Crests II:	Ha.504-4		
			A B.D.V., size 70 × 47mm		£1.80	—
			B *Anonymous, size 70 × 51mm*		£1.80	—
—	C	25	**Butterflies I (70 × 48mm) —Anonymous*	Ha.505-5	£9.00	—
—	C	47	Ceramic Art — B.D.V.:	Ha.505-16		
			A Small size (70 × 43mm)		£1.00	£47.0
			B Small size (70 × 48mm)		£1.00	—
			C Medium size (70 × 61mm)		£1.75	—

GODFREY PHILLIPS LTD, London *(continued)*

Size	*Print-ing*	*Number in set*		*Handbook reference*	*Price per card*	*Complete set*
—	C		*Clan Tartans:			
			A Small size (71 × 48mm):	Ha505-15		
		49	1 *Anonymous*		£1.00	£50.00
		65	2 B.D.V		£1.00	£65.00
		56	B Medium size (70 × 60mm) — B.D.V		£2.75	—
		12	C Extra-large size (150 × 100mm) B.D.V. (selected Nos.)		£5.00	—
—	C	108	**Colonial Army Badges (71 × 50mm) —Anonymous*	Ha.502-3	£1.50	—
—	C	17	County Cricket Badges (69 × 48mm):	Ha.505-8		
			A *Anonymous*		£17.00	—
			B B.D.V		£17.00	—
—	C	108	*Crests and Badges of the British Army II:	Ha.502-2		
			A1 *Small size* (70 × 48mm) Anonymous:			
			(a) *Numbered*		£1.00	£110.00
			(b) *Unnumbered*		£1.10	£120.00
			A2 Small size (70 × 48mm) — B.D.V		£1.00	£110.00
			A3 Medium size (70 × 60mm):			
			(a) *Anonymous*		£1.30	—
			(b) B.D.V		£1.50	—
—	C		**Flags —Set 4 —Anonymous:*	Ha.501-4		
		? 143	*A 'Long' size (82 × 53mm)*		£1.70	—
			B 'Short' size (70 × 48mm):			
		? 143	*1 First numbering arrangement (as A)*		£1.40	—
		? 108	*2 Second numbering arrangement*		90p	—
		? 113	*3 Third numbering arrangement*		90p	—
—	C		**Flags —Set 5 —Anonymous:*	Ha.501-5		
			A Small size (70 × 50mm):			
		20	*1 With caption*		£1.00	—
		6	*2 Without caption, flag 40 × 29mm*		£1.20	—
		? 6	*3 Without caption, flag 60 × 41mm*		£1.20	—
		? 8	*B Extra-large size (155 × 108mm)*		£14.00	—
—	C	18	**Flags —Set 6 —Anonymous:*	Ha.501-6		
			A Size 69 × 47mm		£1.00	£18.00
			B Size 71 × 51mm		£1.00	£18.00
—	C	20	**Flags —Set 7 (70 × 50mm) —Anonymous*	Ha.501-7	£1.00	—
—	C	50	**Flags — Set 9 — ('5th Series') (70 × 48mm) — Anonymous*	Ha.501-9	£1.60	£80.00
—	C		*Flags — Set 10:	Ha.501-10		
		120	*'7th Series' (70 × 48mm) —Anonymous*		80p	—
		120	*'10th Series' (70 × 62mm) —Anonymous*		£1.00	—
		120	*'12th Series' (70 × 48mm) —Anonymous*		90p	—
		65	'15th Series' (70 × 62mm) (selected Nos.) — B.D.V.		£1.10	—
		65	'16th Series' (70 × 62mm) (selected Nos.) — B.D.V.		£1.10	—
		132	'20th Series' (70 × 48 mm) — B.D.V. in brown or red		90p	—
		126	'25th Series' (70 × 48mm) — B.D.V. in brown or black		80p	—
		62	'25th Series' '(70 × 62mm) (selected Nos.) — B.D.V.		£2.75	—
		112	'26th Series' (70 × 48mm) — B.D.V. in brown or blue		80p	—
		70	'28th Series' (70 × 48mm) (selected Nos.) — B.D.V.		£1.00	—
–	C		*Flags — Set 12:	Ha.501-12		
		1	*A 'Let 'em all come' (70 × 46mm) —Anonymous*		—	£11.00
			B Allied Flags (grouped):			
		1	*Four Flags —Anonymous:*			
			1 Small size (70 × 46mm)		—	£9.00
			2 Extra-large size (163 × 120mm)		—	—

Size	*Print-ing*	*Number in set*		*Handbook reference*	*Price per card*	*Complete set*
		1	Seven Flags (165 × 116mm):			
			1 Anonymous		—	£9.00
			2 B.D.V. in brown or orange		—	£9.00
		1	Eight Flags (165 × 116mm) — B.D.V.		—	£32.00
—	C		*Flags — Set 13:	Ha.501-13		
		? 23	*A Size 163 × 114mm — Anonymous*		£1.75	—
		? 27	B Size 163 × 114mm — B.D.V. in brown, orange, blue, green or black		£1.75	—
		? 23	C Size 150 × 100mm — B.D.V.		£1.75	—
—	C	26	**Flags — Set 14 ('House Flags') (68 × 47mm) — Anonymous*	Ha.501-14	£7.00	—
—	C	25	*Flags — Set 15 (Pilot and Signal Flags) (70 × 50mm):	Ha.501-15		
			A Numbered 601-625 — Anonymous		£2.60	£65.00
			B Inscribed 'Series II' — B.D.V.		£1.80	£45.00
—	C		*Football Colours:	Ha.505-9		
		? 21	*A Anonymous, size 68 × 49mm*		£5.00	—
		? 86	B B.D.V., size 68 × 49mm		£4.50	—
		? 78	C B.D.V., size 150 × 100mm		£4.00	—
—	C	126	G.P. Territorial Badges (70 × 48mm)	Ha.502-12	£1.50	—
—	U	25	**Great War Leaders II (81 × 68mm) — Anonymous*	Ha.504-7	£4.50	—
—	U	? 53	**Great War Leaders III and Warships, sepia, black or blue on white or pink material (70 × 50mm) — Anonymous*	Ha.504-10	£6.00	—
—	C		*Great War Leaders IV and Celebrities:	Ha.504-11		
		3	*A Small size (70 × 48mm) — Anonymous*		£5.50	—
		4	B Small size (70 × 48mm) — B.D.V.		£5.50	—
		3	*C Medium size (70 × 63mm) — Anonymous*		£5.50	—
		2	D Medium size (70 × 63mm) — B. D.V.		£5.50	—
		? 18	E Extra-large size (150 × 100mm) — B.D.V.		£4.50	—
		? 4	*F Extra-large size (150 × 110mm) — Anonymous*		£5.00	£20.00
		? 1	G Extra-large size (150 × 110mm) — B.D.V.		—	£12.00
		? 26	*H Extra-large size (163 × 117mm) — Anonymous*		£4.50	—
		? 46	I Extra-large size (163 × 117mm) — B.D.V.		£4.50	—
—	C		Heraldic Series — B.D.V.:	Ha.504-17		
		25	A Small size (68 × 47mm)		£1.20	£30.00
		25	B Small size (68 × 43mm)		£1.20	£30.00
		25	C Medium size (68 × 60mm)		£3.00	—
		12	D Extra-large size (150 × 100mm) (selected Nos)		£5.00	£60.00
—	C	10	**Irish Patriots — Anonymous:*	Ha.505-11		
			A Small size (67 × 50mm)		£12.00	—
			B Large size (83 × 76mm)		£12.00	—
			C Extra-large size (152 × 110mm)		£17.00	—
—	C	1	*Irish Republican Stamp (70 × 50mm)	Ha.505-12	—	£1.75
—	C	54	**Naval Badges of Rank and Military Headdress (70 × 47mm) — Anonymous*	Ha.504-9	£5.50	—
—	C	40	*Old Masters — Set 1 (155 × 115mm) — B.D.V.	Ha.503-1	£28.00	—
—	C	20	*Old Masters — Set 2 (150 × 105mm):	Ha.503-2		
			A *Anonymous*		£4.00	—
			B B.D.V. wording above picture		£4.00	—
			C B.D.V. wording below picture		£5.00	—
—	C		*Old Masters — Set 3A (70 × 50mm):	Ha.503-3A		
		40	A B.D.V.		£2.75	—
		55	B *Anonymous*		£2.50	—
—	C	30	**Old Masters — Set 3B (70 × 50mm) — Anonymous*	Ha.503-3B	£2.50	—
—	C	120	**Old Masters — Set 4 (70 × 50mm) — Anonymous*	Ha.503-4	£1.80	—

Size	*Printing*	*Number in set*		*Handbook reference*	*Price per card*	*Complete set*
—	C		*Old Masters — Set 5 (70 × 50mm):	Ha.503-5		
		20	A *Unnumbered — Anonymous*		£2.60	—
		60	B Nd. 1-60 — B.D.V		£1.20	£72.00
		20	C *Nd. 101-120 — Anonymous:*			
			1 Numerals normal size		£1.60	—
			2 Numerals very small size		£1.60	£32.00
		20	D Nd. 101-120 — B.D.V.		£1.60	£32.00
—	C	50	*Old Masters — Set 6 (67 × 42mm) — B.D.V.	Ha.503-6	£1.20	£60.00
—	C	50	**Old Masters — Set 7, Nd. 301-350 (67 × 47mm) — Anonymous*	Ha.503-7	£2.00	—
—	C	50	**Orders of Chivalry I (70 × 48mm) — Anonymous*	Ha.504-14	£2.20	—
—	C	24	*Orders of Chivalry — Series 10 (70 × 50mm):	Ha.504-16		
			A Nd. 1-24 — B.D.V.		£1.60	£40.00
			B Nd. 401-424 — G.P		£1.80	£45.00
—	C	72	**Regimental Colours II (76 × 70mm) — Anonymous*	Ha.502-7	£4.00	—
—	C		*Regimental Colours and Crests III:	Ha.502-8		
			A Small size (70 × 51mm):			
		40	*1 Colours with faint backgrounds — Anonymous*		£1.00	—
		120	*2 Colours without backgrounds — Anonymous*		£1.20	—
		120	3 Colours without backgrounds — B.D.V.		£1.20	—
		120	B Extra-large size (165 × 120mm):			
			1 Anonymous — Unnumbered		£5.00	—
			2 B.D.V. — Numbered		£4.50	—
—	C	50	*Regimental Colours — Series 12 (70 × 50mm) — B.D.V.	Ha.502-11	£1.80	£90.00
—	C	10	**Religious Pictures — Anonymous:*	Ha.505-10		
			A Small size (67 × 50mm)		£18.00	—
			B Large size (83 × 76 mm)		£18.00	—
			C Extra-large size (155 × 110mm)		£27.00	—
—	C	75	*Town and City Arms — Series 30 (48 unnumbered, 27 numbered 49-75) — B.D.V.:	Ha.504-13		
			A Small size (70 × 50mm)		£1.80	—
			B Medium size (70 × 65mm)		£2.20	—
—	C	25	**Victoria Cross Heroes I (70 × 50mm) — Anonymous*	Ha.504-1	£9.00	—
—	C	? 25	**Victoria Cross Heroes II (70 × 50mm) — Anonymous*	Ha.504-2	£11.00	—
—	C	90	**War Pictures (70 × 48mm) — Anonymous*	Ha.504-8	£5.50	—
MISCELLANEOUS						
	BW		B.D.V. Package Issues (1932-34):			
		17	Boxers		£6.00	—
		54	Cricketers		£7.00	—
		67	Film Stars		£2.50	—
		132	Footballers		£3.50	—
		19	Jockeys		£3.50	—
		21	Speedway Riders		£8.00	—
		27	Sportsmen		£3.00	—
	BW		Sports Package Issues:			
		25	Cricketers (1948)		£7.00	—
		25	Cricketers (1951)		£7.00	—
		25	Footballers (1948)		£5.00	—
		50	Footballers (1950)		£5.00	—
		25	Footballers (1951)		£5.00	—
		25	Football & Rugby Players (1952)		£5.00	—
		25	Jockeys (1952)		£4.00	—
		25	Radio Stars (1949)		£2.60	—

GODFREY PHILLIPS LTD, London *(continued)*

Size	*Print-ing*	*Number in set*		*Handbook reference*	*Price per card*	*Complete set*
		50	Sportsmen (1948)		£3.50	—
		25	Sportsmen (1949)		£3.50	—
		25	Sportsmen (1953)		£3.50	—
		25	Sportsmen (1954)		£3.50	—
D	BW	1	Cricket Fixture Card (Radio Luxembourg) (1936)		—	£7.0
J2		20	'Private Seal' Wrestling Holds (export) (c1920)		£30.00	—
			Rugs (miscellaneous designs) (c1920)		£9.00	—
A	U	?	Stamp Cards (four colours, several wordings) (c1930)		£1.50	—

JOHN PLAYER & SONS, Nottingham

44 page reference book available — £3.25

A PRE-1919 ISSUES

A	C	25	*Actors and Actresses (1898)	H.337	£22.00	£550.0
A1	BW	50	*Actresses (c1897)	H.339	£22.00	—
A	C	7	*Advertisement Cards (1893-94)	H.338	From £260.00	—
J	C	10	Allied Cavalry or Regimental Uniforms:	H.340		
			Allied Cavalry (1914)		£8.00	£80.0
			Regimental Uniforms (1914)		£7.00	£70.0
A	C	50	Arms and Armour (1909)	H.273	£2.50	£125.0
A	C	25	Army Life (1910)	H.78	£1.80	£45.0
J	C	12	Artillery in Action (1917)		£3.50	£42.0
A	C	50	Badges and Flags of British Regiments (1904):	H.341		
			A Brown back, unnumbered		£2.50	£125.0
			B Brown back, numbered		£2.50	£125.0
A	C	50	Badges and Flags of British Regiments (1903):			
			A Green back, thick card		£2.50	£125.0
			B Green back, thin card		£2.50	£125.0
—	P	10	*Bookmarks — Authors (148 × 51mm) (1905)	H.342	£60.00	—
A	C	50	British Empire Series (1904):	H.343		
			A Grey-white card, matt		£1.20	£60.0
			B White card, semi-glossy		£1.40	£70.0
	C	25	British Livestock:	H.344		
A			A Small card (1915)		£1.80	£45.0
J			B Extra-large card, brown back (May 1916)		£2.80	£70.0
A	C	50	Butterflies and Moths (1904)	H.80	£1.80	£90.0
	C		Bygone Beauties:			
A		25	A Small card (1914)		£1.60	£40.0
J		10	B Extra-large card (1916)		£4.50	£45.0
—	U	? 28	*Cabinet Size Pictures, 1898-1900 (220 × 140mm):	Ha.476		
			A Plain back		£80.00	—
			B Printed back		£80.00	—
A	C	20	Castles, Abbeys etc (c1894):	H.345		
			A Without border		£28.00	£560.0
			B White border		£28.00	£560.0
A	C	50	Celebrated Bridges (1903)	H.346	£2.60	£130.0
A	C		Celebrated Gateways (1909):	H.347		
		50	A Thick card		£1.40	£70.0
		25	B Thinner card (26-50 only)		£1.60	—
A	C	25	Ceremonial and Court Dress (1911)	H.145	£1.80	£45.0
	C		Characters from Dickens:			
A		25	Small card, lst series (1912)		£2.40	£60.0
J		10	Extra-large card (1912)..	H.348	£5.50	£55.0
A	C	25	Characters from Dickens, 2nd series (1914)		£2.40	£60.0
A	C	25	Characters from Thackeray (1913)		£1.60	£40.0

Size	*Print-ing*	*Number in set*		*Handbook reference*	*Price per card*	*Complete set*
A	C	50	Cities of the World (1900):			
			A Grey-mauve on white back		£4.00	—
			B Grey-mauve on toned back		£4.00	—
			C Bright mauve on white back		£4.00	—
A	C	25	Colonial and Indian Army Badges (1916)		£1.40	£35.00
A	C	25	*Counties and Their Industries:	H.349		
			A Unnumbered (c1910)		£1.80	£45.00
			B Numbered (1914)		£1.80	£45.00
A	C	50	*Countries — Arms and Flags:			
			A Thick card (1905)		80p	£40.00
			B Thin Card (1912)		£1.00	£50.00
A	C	50	*Country Seats and Arms (1906)		80p	£40.00
A	C		*Country Seats and Arms, 2nd series (1907):			
		25	A Nd. 51-75 First printing		£1.40	£35.00
		50	B Nd. 51-100 Second printing		80p	£40.00
A	C	50	*Country Seats and Arms, 3rd series (1907)		80p	£40.00
	C		Cries of London:	H.350		
A		25	Small cards, 1st series (1913)		£2.00	£50.00
		10	Extra-large cards, 1st series (1912)		£4.50	£45.00
		10	Extra-large cards, 2nd series (1914)		£4.00	£40.00
A	C	25	Cries of London, 2nd series (1916)		£1.00	£25.00
A	C	25	Egyptian Kings and Queens, and Classical Deities (1911)		£1.60	£40.00
	C	10	Egyptian Sketches (1915)	H.351	£4.00	£40.00
A	C	25	*England's Military Heroes (1898):	H.352		
			A Wide card		£40.00	—
			A1 Wide card plain back		£40.00	—
			B Narrow card		£32.00	—
			B2 Narrow card, plain back		£30.00	—
A	C	25	England's Naval Heroes (1897):	H.353		
			A Wide card		£40.00	—
			B Narrow card		£24.00	£600.00
	C	25	England's Naval Heroes (1898), descriptions on back:	H.353		
			A Wide card		£40.00	—
			A2 Wide card, plain back		£40.00	—
			B Narrow card		£24.00	£600.00
			B2 Narrow card, plain back		£24.00	—
	C	25	Everyday Phrases by Tom Browne (1901):	H.354		
			A Thickcard		£15.00	£375.00
			B Thin card		£15.00	£375.00
	C	20	Famous Authors and Poets (1902):			
			A Wide card		£26.00	£520.00
			B Narrow card		£20.00	£400.00
	C	10	Famous Paintings (1913)	H.355	£3.50	£35.00
	C	50	Fishes of the World (1903)	H.66	£2.20	£110.00
	C	50	Gallery of Beauty (1896):	H.356		
			A Wide Card:			
			I Set of 50		£22.00	—
			II 5 Alternative Pictures		£50.00	—
			B Narrow Card:			
			I Set of 50		£20.00	—
			II 5 Alternative Pictures		£50.00	—
	C	25	Gems of British Scenery (1914)		80p	£20.00
	C	25	Highland Clans (1908)		£3.20	£80.00
	C	10	Historic Ships (1910):			
			A Thick card		£4.50	£45.00
			B Thin card		£4.50	£45.00

JOHN PLAYER & SONS, Nottingham *(continued)*

Size	*Print-ing*	*Number in set*		*Handbook reference*	*Price per card*	*Complete set*
A	C	50	Life on Board a Man of War in 1805 and 1905 (1905)	H.38	£2.20	£110.0
A	C	50	Military Series (1900)		£17.00	£850.0
A	C	25	Miniatures (1916)		44p	£11.0
A	C	25	Napoleon (1915)	H.364	£1.60	£40.0
	C		Nature Series:			
A		50	Small card (1908)		£1.30	£65.0
J		10	Extra-large card (Birds) (1908)		£12.00	-
J		10	Extra-large card (Animals) (1913)		£4.50	£45.0
A	C	50	Old England's Defenders (1898)		£17.00	£850.0
A	C	25	Players — Past and Present (1916)		80p	£20.0
A	C	25	Polar Exploration (1915)		£1.60	£40.0
A	C	25	Polar Exploration, 2nd series (1916)		£1.60	£40.0
A	C	25	Products of the World:			
			A Thick card (1909)		60p	£15.0
			B Thin card (1908)		£1.20	£30.0
A	C	50	*Regimental Colours and Cap Badges (1907)		£1.20	£60.0
A	C	50	*Regimental Colours and Cap Badges — Territorial Regiments (1910):			
			A Blue back		£1.20	£60.0
			B Brown back		£1.20	£60.0
J	C	10	Regimental Uniforms — See 'Allied Cavalry'			
A	C	50	Regimental Uniforms (1-50):			
			A Blue back (Jul. 1912)		£1.80	£90.0
			B Brown back (Jul. 1914)		£2.00	£100.0
A	C	50	Regimental Uniforms (51-100) (1914)		£1.40	£70.0
A	C	50	Riders of the World:	H.358		
			A Thick grey card (1905)		£1.60	£80.0
			B Thinner white card (1914)		£1.60	£80.0
—	P	6	The Royal Family (101 × 154mm) (1902)	H.359	—	£270.0
—	P	? 30	Rulers and Views (101 × 154mm) (1902)	H.363	£80.00	-
A	C	25	Shakespearian Series (1914)		£1.00	£25.0
A	C	25	Ships' Figureheads (1912):			
			A Numerals 'sans serif'		£1.60	£40.0
			B Numerals with serif		£1.40	£35.0
A	BW	? 148	Stereoscopic Series (c1900)	H.357	£80.00	-
A	C	25	Those Pearls of Heaven (1914)		80p	£20.0
A	BW	66	Transvaal Series (1902):	H.360		
			A Black front		£5.00	-
			B Violet-black front		£5.00	-
A	C	50	Useful Plants and Fruit (1904)	H.361	£2.20	£110.0
A	C	25	Victoria Cross (1914)		£1.60	£40.0
A	C	50	Wild Animals of the World (1902):	H.77		
			A 'John Player & Sons Ltd.'		£3.00	£150.0
			B 'John Player & Sons, Branch, Nottingham'		£4.00	-
			C1 As B, 'Branch' omitted but showing traces of some or all of the letters		£4.00	-
			C2 As B. New printing with 'Branch' omitted		£3.00	£150.0
A2	C	45	Wild Animals of the World, narrow card (1902):	H.77		
			A 'John Player & Sons Ltd.'		£5.00	£225.0
			B 'John Player & Sons, Branch, Nottingham'		£6.00	-
			C1 As B, 'Branch' omitted but showing traces of some or all of the letters		£5.00	-
			C2 As B. New printing with 'Branch' omitted		£5.00	£225.0
A	C	50	Wonders of the Deep (1904)	H.365	£1.60	£80.0
A	C	25	Wonders of the World, blue back (1913)	H.362	80p	£20.0

Size	*Print-ing*	*Number in set*		*Handbook reference*	*Price per card*	*Complete set*
J	C	10	Wooden Walls (1909):			
			A Thick card		£5.50	£55.00
			B Thin card		£5.50	£55.00
A	C	25	Wrestling and Ju-Jitsu (blue back) (1911)	H.467	£1.40	£35.00
B	***POST-1920 ISSUES.***		Series with I.T.C. Clause.			
	C	1	*Advertisement Card (Sailor) (c1930):			
A			A Small size		—	£4.50
B			B Large size		—	£20.00
A	C	50	Aeroplanes (1935):			
			A Home issue — titled 'Aeroplanes (Civil)'		90p	£45.00
			B Irish issue — titled 'Aeroplanes'		£1.30	£65.00
A	C	50	Aircraft of the Royal Air Force (1938)		90p	£45.00
A	C	50	Animals of the Countryside (1934):			
			A Home issue — adhesive		22p	£11.00
			B Irish issue — non-adhesive, green numerals overprinted		£1.00	—
B	C	25	Aquarium Studies (1932)		£1.80	£45.00
B	C	25	Architectural Beauties (1927)		£2.00	£50.00
A	C	50	Army Corps and Divisional Signs, 1914-1918 (1924)		32p	£16.00
A	C	100	Army Corps and Divisional Signs, 1914-1918, '2nd Series' (1925):			
			Nos. 51-100		32p	£16.00
			Nos. 101-150		32p	£16.00
A	U	50	Association Cup Winners (1930)		£1.60	£80.00
	C		Aviary and Cage Birds:			
A		50	A Small size (1933):			
			1 Cards		90p	£45.00
			2 Transfers		40p	£20.00
B		25	B Large size (1935)		£3.00	£75.00
A	C	50	Birds and Their Young (1937):			
			A Home issue — adhesive		20p	£10.00
			B Irish issue — 1 Adhesive		£1.00	—
			2 Non-adhesive		£1.00	—
A	C	25	Boxing (1934)		£6.00	—
A	C	50	Boy Scout and Girl Guide Patrol Signs and Emblems (1933):			
			A Cards		40p	£20.00
			B Transfers		30p	£15.00
B	C	25	British Butterflies (1934)		£3.80	£95.00
A	C	25	British Live Stock (blue back) (1923)	H.344	£2.20	£55.00
B	C	25	British Naval Craft (1939)		70p	£17.50
A	C	20	British Pedigree Stock (1925)		£2.50	£50.00
B	C	25	British Regalia (1937)		£1.20	£30.00
A	C	50	Butterflies (1932):			
			A Cards		£1.10	£55.00
			B Transfers		40p	£20.00
B	C	24	Cats (1936)		£6.50	—
B	C	25	Championship Golf Courses (1936)		£7.00	£175.00
A	C	50	Characters from Dickens (1923)	H.348	£1.40	£70.00
B	C	25	Characters from Fiction (1933)		£3.00	£75.00
B	C	20	Clocks — Old and New (1928)		£4.50	£90.00
A	C	50	Coronation Series Ceremonial Dress (1937)		28p	£14.00
B	C	25	Country Sports (1930)		£5.00	£125.00
A	C	50	Cricketers, 1930 (1930)		£1.30	£65.00
A	C	50	Cricketers, 1934 (1934)		90p	£45.00

JOHN PLAYER & SONS, Nottingham *(continued)*

Size	*Print-ing*	*Number in set*		*Handbook reference*	*Price per card*	*Complete set*
A	C	50	Cricketers, 1938 (1938)		80p	£40.00
A	C	50	Cricketers, Caricatures by 'Rip' (1926)		£1.40	£70.00
A	C	50	Curious Beaks (1929)		80p	£40.00
A	C	50	Cycling (1939):			
			A Home issue — adhesive		80p	£40.00
			B Irish issue — 1 Adhesive		£1.20	—
			2 Non-adhesive		£1.20	—
	C		Dandies (1932):			
A		50	A Small size		35p	£17.50
B		25	B Large size		£1.80	£45.00
A	C	50	Derby and Grand National Winners (1933):			
			A Cards		£1.60	£80.00
			B Transfers		50p	£25.00
	C		Dogs (1924) — Scenic backgrounds:			
A		50	A Small size		90p	£45.00
J		12	B Extra-large size		£2.50	£30.00
	C		Dogs — Heads:			
A		50	A Small size — Home issue (1929)		90p	£45.00
A		25	B Small size — Irish issue, 'A Series of 25' (1927)		£2.00	£50.00
A		25	C Small size — Irish issue, '2nd Series of 25' (1929)		£2.00	£50.00
B		20	D Large size — Home issue, 'A Series of 20' (1926)		£2.25	£45.00
B		20	E Large size — Home issue, '2nd Series of 20' (1928)		£2.25	£45.00
	C		Dogs — Full length:			
A		50	A Small size (1931):			
			1 Cards		70p	£35.00
			2 Transfers		40p	£20.00
B		25	B Large size (1933)		£2.20	£55.00
A	C	50	Dogs' Heads (silver-grey backgrounds) (1940)		£2.80	—
A	C	50	Drum Banners and Cap Badges (1924):			
			A Base panel joining vertical framelines		80p	£40.00
			B Fractional space between the above		70p	£35.00
B	BW	25	Fables of Aesop (1927)		£2.40	£60.00
B	C	25	Famous Beauties (1937)		£1.60	£40.00
A	C	50	Famous Irish-Bred Horses (1936)		£3.00	£150.00
A	C	50	Famous Irish Greyhounds (1935)		£5.00	—
A	C	50	Film Stars — 'Series of 50' (1934)		£1.00	£50.00
A	C	50	Film Stars — 'Second Series ...':			
			A Home issue — Album 'price one penny' (1934)		80p	£40.00
			B Irish issue — Album offer without price (1935)		£1.50	£75.00
A	C	50	Film Stars:			
			A Home issue — titled 'Film Stars — Third Series ...' (1938)		70p	£35.00
			B Irish issue — titled 'Screen Celebrities' (1939)		£1.50	—
B	BW	25	Film Stars — Large size (1934):			
			A Home issue — with album offer		£2.60	£65.00
			B Irish issue — without album offer		£6.00	—
A	C	50	Fire-Fighting Appliances (1930)		£1.50	£75.00
A	C	50	Flags of the League of Nations (1928)		40p	£20.00
A	C	50	Football Caricatures by 'Mac' (1927)		£1.20	£60.00
A	C	50	Football Caricatures by 'Rip' (1926)		£1.20	£60.00
A	C	50	Footballers, 1928 (1928)		£1.20	£60.00
A	C	25	Footballers, 1928-9 — '2nd Series' (1929)		£1.20	£30.00

JOHN PLAYER & SONS, Nottingham *(continued)*

Size	*Printing*	*Number in set*		*Handbook reference*	*Price per card*	*Complete set*
	C		Fresh-Water Fishes:			
A		50	A Small size, Home issue:			
			1 Pink card (1933)		£1.00	£50.00
			2 White card (1934)		£1.30	£65.00
B		25	B Large size, Home issue — adhesive (1935)		£2.40	£60.00
B		25	C Large size, Irish issue — non-adhesive (1935)		£5.00	£125.00
A	C	25	From Plantation to Smoker (1926)		32p	£8.00
	C		Game Birds and Wild Fowl:			
A		50	A Small size (1927)		£1.40	£70.00
B		25	B Large size (1928)		£4.00	£100.00
	C		Gilbert and Sullivan — 'A Series of ...':			
A		50	A Small size (1925)		£1.10	£55.00
		25	B Extra-large size (1926)		£3.00	£75.00
	C		Gilbert and Sullivan — '2nd Series of ...':			
A		50	A Small size (1927)		£1.10	£55.00
B		25	B Large size (1928)		£3.20	£80.00
B	C	25	Golf (1939)		£7.50	—
A	C	25	Hidden Beauties (1929)		24p	£6.00
A	C	50	Hints on Association Football (1934)		50p	£25.00
	C		History of Naval Dress:			
A		50	A Small size (1930)		£1.10	£55.00
B		25	B Large size (1929)		£1.80	£45.00
A	C	50	International Air Liners:			
			A Home issue — Album 'price one penny' (1936)		45p	£22.50
			B Irish issue — Album offer without price (1937)		£1.00	£50.00
A	C	25	Irish Place Names — 'A Series of 25' (1927)		£2.00	£50.00
A	C	25	Irish Place Names — '2nd Series of 25' (1929)		£2.00	£50.00
	C	50	Kings and Queens of England (1935):			
A			A Small size		£1.20	£60.00
B			B Large size		£2.50	£125.00
A	C	25	Live Stock (1925)		£3.00	£75.00
A	C	50	Military Head-Dress (1931)		£1.00	£50.00
A	C	50	Military Uniforms of the British Empire Overseas (1938)		80p	£40.00
A	C	50	Modern Naval Craft (1939):			
			A Home issue — adhesive		40p	£20.00
			B Irish issue — non-adhesive		£1.00	—
A	C	50	Motor Cars — 'A Series of 50' (1936):			
			A Home issue — Album 'price one penny'		£1.30	£65.00
			B Irish issue — Album offer without price		£2.00	—
A	C	50	Motor Cars — 'Second Series ...' (1937)		£1.00	£50.00
B	U	20	Mount Everest (1925)		£2.50	£50.00
A	C	50	National Flags and Arms:			
			A Home issue — Album 'price one penny' (1936)		40p	£20.00
			B Irish issue — Album offer without price (1937)		£1.00	£50.00
B	C	25	The Nation's Shrines (1929)		£2.00	£50.00
	C		Natural History:			
A		50	A Small size (1924)		30p	£15.00
		12	B Extra-large size — 'A Series of 12' (1923)		£1.25	£15.00
		12	C Extra-large size — '2nd Series of 12' (1924)		£1.25	£15.00
B	C	24	A Nature Calendar (1930)		£2.80	£70.00
B	C	25	'Old Hunting Prints' (1938)		£2.60	£65.00
B	C	25	Old Naval Prints (1936)		£2.40	£60.00
B	BW	25	Old Sporting Prints (1924)		£2.80	£70.00
B	C	25	Picturesque Bridges (1929)		£2.60	£65.00
B	C	25	Picturesque Cottages (1929)		£2.60	£65.00

JOHN PLAYER & SONS, Nottingham *(continued)*

Size	*Print-ing*	*Number in set*		*Handbook reference*	*Price per card*	*Complete set*
B	C	25	Picturesque London (1931)		£3.20	£80.00
B	C	25	Portals of the Past (1930)		£2.20	£55.00
A	C	50	Poultry (1931):			
			A Cards		£1.50	£75.00
			B Transfers		40p	£20.00
A	C	50	Products of the World — Scenes only (1928)		25p	£12.50
A	C	25	Racehorses (1926)		£5.00	£125.00
A	U	40	Racing Caricatures (1925)		75p	£30.00
B	C	25	Racing Yachts (1938)		£3.20	£80.00
A	C	50	RAF Badges (1937):			
			A Without motto		60p	£30.00
			B With motto		60p	£30.00
A	C	50	Regimental Standards and Cap Badges (1930)		70p	£35.00
—	C	1	The Royal Family (55 × 66mm) (1937)		—	£2.50
			Screen Celebrities — see Film Stars			
A	C	50	Sea Fishes:			
			A Home issue — Album 'price one penny' (1935)		30p	£15.00
			B Irish issue — Album offer without price (1937)		£1.00	—
A	C	50	A Sectional Map of Ireland (1932)		£2.20	—
B	C	20	Ship-Models (1926)		£2.50	£50.00
B	C	25	Ships' Figure-Heads (1931)		£1.80	£45.00
A	C	50	Speedway Riders (1937)		£1.50	£75.00
A	C	50	Straight Line Caricatures (1926)		50p	£25.00
A	C	25	Struggle for Existence (1923)		32p	£8.00
A	C	50	Tennis (1936)		80p	£40.00
B	C	25	Treasures of Britain (1931)		£1.60	£40.00
A	C	25	Treasures of Ireland (1930)		£1.80	£45.00
B	C	25	Types of Horses (1939)		£3.40	£85.00
A	C	50	Uniforms of the Territorial Army (Oct. 1939)		70p	£35.00
A	C	90	War Decorations and Medals (1927)		70p	£65.00
	C		Wild Animals:			
A		50	A Small size — 'Wild Animals' Heads' (1931)		60p	£30.00
A		25	B Small transfers, number in series not stated (1931)		£1.50	—
A		50	C Small transfers — 'A Series of 50' (1931)		40p	£20.00
B		25	D Large size — 'Wild Animals — A Series of ...' (1927)		£1.60	£40.00
B		25	E Large size — 'Wild Animals — 2nd Series ...' (1932)		£1.60	£40.00
	C		Wild Birds:			
A		50	A Small size (1932):			
			1 Cards		40p	£20.00
			2 Transfers		35p	£17.50
B		25	B Large size (1934)		£2.40	£60.00
B	C	25	Wild Fowl (1937)		£2.80	£70.00
A	C	25	Wonders of the World (grey back) (1926)	H.362	£1.40	£35.00
A	C	25	Wrestling and Ju-Jitsu (grey back) (1925)	H.467	£1.40	£35.00
A	C	26	Your Initials (transfers) (1932)		60p	£16.00
B	C	25	Zoo Babies (1938)		50p	£12.50
C	***POST-1940 ISSUES***					
G	C	30	African Wildlife (1990)		40p	£12.00
—	BW	9	Basket Ball Fixtures (114 × 71mm) (1972)		£5.00	—
G	C	32	Britain's Endangered Wildlife:			
			A Grandee Issue (1984)		25p	£8.00
			B Doncella Issue (1984)		30p	£9.00
H2	C	30	Britain's Maritime History (1989)		40p	£12.00

JOHN PLAYER & SONS, Nottingham *(continued)*

Size	*Print-ing*	*Number in set*		*Handbook reference*	*Price per card*	*Complete set*
G	C	30	Britain's Nocturnal Wildlife:			
			A Grandee Issue (1987)		27p	£8.00
			B Doncella Issue (1987)		40p	£12.00
G	C	30	Britain's Wayside Wildlife (1988)		30p	£9.00
G	C	30	Britain's Wild Flowers:			
			A Grandee Issue (1986)		25p	£7.50
			B Doncella Issue (1986)		40p	£12.00
G	C	32	British Birds (1980)		50p	£16.00
G	C	32	British Butterflies:			
			A Grandee Issue (1983)		40p	£13.00
			B Doncella Issue (1984)		34p	£11.00
G	C	30	British Mammals:			
			A Grandee Issue (1982):			
			1 Imperial Tobacco Ltd		27p	£8.00
			2 Imperial Group PLC		30p	£9.00
			B Doncella Issue (1983)		40p	£12.00
G	C	32	Country Houses and Castles (1981)		20p	£6.50
—	U	116	Corsair Game (63 × 38mm) (1965)		90p	—
H2	C	32	Exploration of Space (1983)		20p	£6.50
G	C	28	Famous MG Marques (1981)		80p	£22.00
G	C	24	The Golden Age of Flying (1977)		25p	£6.00
G	C	1	The Golden Age of Flying Completion Offer (1977)		—	£3.50
G	C	24	The Golden Age of Motoring (1975):			
			A With set completion offer		£3.50	—
			B Without set completion offer		27p	£6.50
G	C	24	The Golden Age of Sail (1978)		25p	£6.00
G	C	1	The Golden Age of Sail Completion Offer (1978)		—	£3.50
G	C	24	The Golden Age of Steam (1976)		25p	£6.00
G	C	1	The Golden Age of Steam Completion Offer (1976)		—	£3.50
G	U	7	Grandee Limericks (1977)		£8.00	—
H2	C	30	History of Britain's Railways (1987)		33p	£10.00
H2	C	30	History of British Aviation (1988)		60p	£18.00
H2	C	30	History of Motor Racing (1986):			
			A Imperial Tobacco Ltd		70p	£20.00
			B Imperial Group PLC		70p	£20.00
G	C	24	History of the VC (1980)		80p	£20.00
G	C	1	History of the VC completion offer (1980)		—	£5.00
—	BW	5	Jubilee Issue (70 × 55mm) (1960)		£1.40	£7.00
G	C	30	The Living Ocean:			
			A Grandee Issue (1985)		25p	£7.50
			B Doncella Issue (1985)		40p	£12.00
H2	C	32	Myths and Legends (1982)		90p	£30.00
G	C	24	Napoleonic Uniforms (1979)		20p	£5.00
G	C	1	Napoleonic Uniforms Completion Offer (1979)		—	£3.50
G	C	7	Panama Puzzles (1975)		£6.00	—
G	BW	6	Play Ladbroke Spot-Ball (1975)		£6.00	—
—	U	4	Tom Thumb Record Breakers (82 × 65mm) (1976)		£6.00	—
G	C	25	Top Dogs (1979)		80p	£20.00
H2	C	32	Wonders of the Ancient World (1984)		40p	£12.50
H2	C	30	Wonders of the Modern World (1985)		30p	£9.00
G	C	6	World of Gardening (1976)		£8.00	—
D	***UNISSUED SERIES***					
A	C	25	Birds and Their Young, 1st series (c1955)		24p	£6.00
A	C	25	Birds and Their Young, 2nd series (c1955)		16p	£4.00
A	C	25	Cries of London, '2nd Series ...' (black back) (1916)		£5.00	—
A	C	50	Decorations and Medals (c1940)		£1.90	£95.00

JOHN PLAYER & SONS, Nottingham *(continued)*

Size	*Printing*	*Number in set*		*Handbook reference*	*Price per card*	*Complete set*
A	C	50	Dogs' Heads by Biegel (c1955)		60p	£30.00
B	C	25	Dogs — Pairs and Groups (c1955)		£1.20	£30.00
A	C	50	Shipping (c1955)		£1.40	£75.00
E	***MISCELLANEOUS***					
B	BW	1	Advertisement Card — Wants List (1936)		—	£1.00
A	C	1	Card Scheme — Joker Card (c1935)		—	£5.00
—	C	?	Football Fixture Folders (1946-61)		£12.00	—
—	C	8	Snap Cards (93 × 65mm) (c1930)		£6.50	—

JAS. PLAYFAIR & CO., London

PRE-1919 ISSUE

A	C	25	How to Keep Fit — Sandow Exercises (c1912)	H.136	£32.00	—

THE PREMIER TOBACCO MANUFACTURERS LTD, London

POST-1920 ISSUES

D	U	48	Eminent Stage and Screen Personalities (1936)	Ha.569	£1.50	—
K2	C	52	*Miniature Playing Cards (c1935)		£7.00	—
—	BW		Stage and Screen Personalities (57 × 35mm) (1937):			
		100	A Back in grey		£1.30	—
		50	B Back in brown (Nos. 51-100)		£1.80	—

PRITCHARD & BURTON LTD, London

PRE-1919 ISSUES

A2	C	50	*Actors and Actresses — 'FROGA B and C' (c1900):	H.20		
			A Blue back		£18.00	—
			B Grey-black back		£40.00	—
A	C	15	*Beauties 'PAC' (c1900)	H.2	£55.00	—
D	BW	20	*Boer War Cartoons (1900)	H.42	£80.00	—
A1	C		*Flags and Flags with Soldiers (c1902):	H.41		
			A Flagstaff Draped:			
		30	1st printing		£14.00	£420.00
		15	2nd printing		£20.00	—
		15	B Flagstaff not Draped (Flags only)		£20.00	—
D	U	25	*Holiday Resorts and Views (c1902)	H.366	£16.00	—
A	C	40	*Home Colonial Regiments (c1901):	H.69		
			20 Caption in blue		£45.00	—
			20 Caption in brown		£45.00	—
D	U	25	*Royalty series (1902)	H.367	£20.00	—
D	U	25	*South African Series (1901)	H.368	£17.00	—
A2	C	25	*Star Girls (c1900)	H.30	£130.00	—

G. PRUDHOE, Darlington

PRE-1919 ISSUES

C	C	30	*Army Pictures, Cartoons, etc (c1916)	Ha.12	£75.00	—

JAMES QUINTON LTD, London

PRE-1919 ISSUE

A	C	26	*Actresses — 'FROGA A' (c1900)	H.20	£130.00	—

RAY & CO. LTD, London

PRE-1919 ISSUES

A	BW	25	War Series — 1-25 — Battleships (c1915)		£11.00	—

RAY & CO. LTD, London *(continued)*

Size	*Printing*	*Number in set*		*Handbook reference*	*Price per card*	*Complete set*
A	C	75	War Series — 26-100 — British and Foreign Uniforms (c1915)		£8.00	—
A	C	24	War Series — 101-124 — British and Dominion Uniforms (c1915)		£18.00	—

RAYMOND REVUEBAR, London

POST-1940 ISSUE

—	P	25	Revuebar Striptease Artists (72 × 46mm) (1960)		£12.00	—

RECORD CIGARETTE CO., London

POST-1920 ISSUE

—	U	? 34	The 'Talkie' Cigarette Card — (gramophone record on reverse) (70mm square) (c1935)		£35.00	—

J. REDFORD & CO., London

PRE-1919 ISSUES

A	BW	20	*Actresses — 'BLARM' (c1900)	H.23	£65.00	—
A2	C	25	*Armies of the World (c1901)	H.43	£50.00	—
A2	C	25	*Beauties — 'GRACC' (c1899)	H.59	£85.00	—
A2	C	30	*Colonial Troops (c1902)	H.40	£50.00	—
D	C	? 24	*Nautical Expressions (c1900)	H.174	£80.00	—
D2	C	40	*Naval and Military Phrases (c1904)	H.14	£50.00	—
A	C	25	Picture Series (c1905)	H.369	£65.00	—
A	C	25	Sports and Pastimes Series 1 (c1905)	H.225	£70.00	—
D1	BW	50	Stage Artistes of the Day (c1908)	H.370	£14.00	£700.00

RELIANCE TOBACCO MFG. CO. LTD

POST-1920 ISSUES

A2	C	24	British Birds (c1935)	Ha.604	£4.00	—
A2	C	35	*Famous Stars* (c1935)	Ha.572	£4.00	—

RICHARDS & WARD

PRE-1919 ISSUE

A1	P	? 11	*Beauties — 'Topsy Cigarettes' (c1900)	H.371	£175.00	—

A. S. RICHARDSON, Luton

POST-1920 ISSUE

—	U	12	*Manikin Cards (79 × 51mm) (c1920)	Ha.481	£70.00	—

THE RICHMOND CAVENDISH CO. LTD, London

PRE-1919 ISSUES

A2	C	26	*Actresses — 'FROGA A' (c1900)	H.20	£26.00	—
D2	BW	28	*Actresses — 'PILPI I' (c1902)	H.195	£13.00	—
D	P	50	*Actresses 'PILPI II' (c1902)	H.196	£8.50	—
A	U		*Actresses Photogravure, 'Smoke Pioneer Cigarettes' back (c1905):	H.372		
		50	I Reading bottom to top		£6.00	£300.00
		? 179	IIA Reading top to bottom. Different subjects		£6.00	—
		? 13	B Plain back		£10.00	—

THE RICHMOND CAVENDISH CO. LTD, London *(continued)*

Size	Print-ing	Number in set		Handbook reference	Price per card	Complete set
A	C	14	*Beauties 'AMBS' (1899):	H.373		
			A Verses 'The Absent-minded Beggar' back (4 verses and 4 choruses)		£45.00	—
			B Verses 'Soldiers of the Queen' back (3 verses and 1 chorus)		£45.00	—
A	C	52	*Beauties — 'ROBRI' playing card inset (c1898)	H.374	£45.00	—
—	C	40	*Medals (34 × 72mm) (c1900)	H.200	£16.00	£640.00
A2	C	20	Music Hall Artistes (c1902)	H.202	£38.00	—
A	C	12	*Pretty Girl Series — 'RASH' (c1900)	H.8	£38.00	£230.00
A	C	20	*Yachts (c1900):	H.204		
			A Gold on black back		£60.00	—
			B Black on white back		£60.00	—

R. ROBERTS & SONS, London

PRE-1919 ISSUES

A2	C	26	*Actresses — 'FROGA A' (c1900)	H.20	£55.00	—
A	C	25	*Armies of the World (c1900):	H.43		
			A 'Fine Old Virginia' back		£45.00	—
			B Plain back		£45.00	—
A2	C	50	*Beauties — 'CHOAB' (c1900):	H.21		
			1-25 without borders to back		£65.00	—
			26-50 with borders to back		£85.00	—
A2	C	50	*Colonial Troops (c1902):	H.40		
			1-30 'Fine Old Virginia'		£40.00	—
			31-50 'Bobs Cigarettes'		£40.00	—
A	BW	28	*Dominoes (c1905)		£80.00	—
K1	C	52	*Miniature Playing Cards (c1905)	H.334	£50.00	—
D2	C	? 24	*Nautical Expressions (c1900):	H.174		
			A 'Navy Cut Cigarettes' on front		£55.00	—
			B Firm's name only on front		£55.00	—
A2	C	70	Stories without words (c1905)		£50.00	—
A2	C	25	*Types of British and Colonial Troops (c1900)	H.76	£45.00	—

ROBINSON & BARNSDALE LTD, London

PRE-1919 ISSUES

—	C	1	*Advertisement Card — Soldier, 'Colin Campbell Cigars' (29 × 75mm) (c1897)		—	£110.00
—	BW	? 24	*Actresses, 'Colin Campbell Cigars' (c1898):	H.375		
			A Size 43 × 70mm		£130.00	—
			B Officially cut narrow — 32 × 70mm		£130.00	—
A	P	? 28	*Actresses, 'Cupola' Cigarettes (c1898)	H.376	£140.00	—
A1	P		*Beauties — collotype (c1895):	H.377		
		? 5	A 'Our Golden Beauties' back in black		£130.00	—
		? 10	B 'Nana' back in red on white		£130.00	—
		? 10	C 'Nana' back in vermillion on cream		£130.00	—
A	C	? 1	*Beauties — 'Blush of Day' (c1898)	H.378	£130.00	—
—	C	? 13	*Beauties — 'Highest Honors' (44 × 73mm) (c1895)	H.379	£180.00	—

E. ROBINSON & SONS LTD, Stockport

A PRE-1919 ISSUES

A1	C	10	*Beauties 'ROBRI' (c1900)	H.374	£60.00	—
A	BW	? 38	Derbyshire and the Peak (c1905)	H.380	£90.00	—
A2	C	25	Egyptian Studies (c1914)		£22.00	—
A	C	6	Medals and Decorations of Great Britain (c1905)	Ha.484	£130.00	—

E. ROBINSON & SONS LTD, Stockport *(continued)*

Size	Printing	Number in set		Handbook reference	Price per card	Complete set
A2	C	40	Nature Studies (c1912)		£20.00	£800.00
A2	C	25	Regimental Mascots (1916)		£60.00	—
A2	C	25	Wild Flowers (c1915)		£18.00	£450.00
B	***POST-1920 ISSUE***					
A	C	25	King Lud Problems (c1934)		£16.00	—

ROMAN STAR CIGARS

PRE-1919 ISSUES

C	C	? 26	*Actresses 'FROGA A' (c1900)	H.20	£120.00	—
A	C	25	*Beauties 'BOCCA' (c1900)	H.39	£120.00	—

ROTHMAN'S LTD, London

A	***POST-1920 ISSUES***					
	C		Beauties of the Cinema (1939):	Ha.605		
D1		40	A Small size		£1.25	£50.00
—		24	B Circular cards, 64mm diam:			
			1 Varnished		£3.50	£85.00
			2 Unvarnished		£3.50	£85.00
A2	P	24	Cinema Stars — Small size (c1925)		£1.00	£25.00
B	P	25	Cinema Stars — Large size (c1925)		90p	£22.50
C	U	36	Landmarks in Empire History (c1936)		£1.00	£36.00
D1	U	50	Modern Inventions (1935)		£1.00	£50.00
B2	P	54	New Zealand (c1930)		80p	£43.00
D1	U	24	Prominent Screen Favourites (1934)	Ha.568	80p	£20.00
A2	BW	50	'Punch Jokes' (c1935)		50p	£25.00
B	***POST-1940 ISSUES***					
—	C	30	Country Living (Consulate) (112 × 102mm) (1973)		—	£15.00
A1	C	5	Rare Banknotes (1970)		£3.00	£15.00
C	***MISCELLANEOUS***					
—	C	6	Diamond Jubilee Folders (127 × 95mm) (1950)		£12.00	—
C2	C	50	International Football Stars (unissued) (1984)		—	—
		?	Metal Charms (c1930)		£3.00	—

WM. RUDDELL LTD, Dublin and Liverpool

POST-1920 ISSUES

K	U	?	*Couplet Cards (c1925)		£11.00	—
D	C	25	Grand Opera Series (1924)		£7.00	£175.00
A2	C	25	Rod and Gun (1924)		£6.00	£150.00
D	C	50	Songs that will Live for Ever (c1925)		£3.20	£160.00

I. RUTTER & CO., Mitcham

PRE-1919 ISSUES

D	BW	15	*Actresses — 'RUTAN' (c1900):	H.381		
			A Rubber-stamped on plain back		£60.00	—
			B Red printed back		£50.00	—
			C *Plain back*		£35.00	—
A	BW	1	Advertisement Card 'Tobacco Bloom' (1899)	Ha.485	—	£350.00
A	BW	7	*Boer War Celebrities (c1901)	H.382	£45.00	—
D1	C	54	*Comic Phrases (c1905)	H.223	£16.00	—

I. RUTTER & CO., Mitcham *(continued)*

Size	*Print-ing*	*Number in set*		*Handbook reference*	*Price per card*	*Complete set*
A	BW	20	Cricketers Series (1901)	H.29	£250.00	—
C	C		*Flags and Flags with Soldiers (c1902):	H.41		
		15	A Flagstaff Draped, 2nd printing		£24.00	—
		15	B Flagstaff not Draped (Flags only)			
			(a) white back		£24.00	—
			(b) cream back		£24.00	—
C	C	24	*Girls, Flags and Arms of Countries (c1900):	H.383		
			A Blue back		£35.00	—
			B *Plain back*		£25.00	—
A	C	25	Proverbs (c1905)	H.384	£40.00	—
A	C	25	*Shadowgraphs (c1905)	H.44	£35.00	—

S.D.V. TOBACCO CO. LTD, Liverpool

PRE-1919 ISSUES

A	BW	16	British Royal Family (c1901)	H.28	£180.00	—

ST. DUNSTAN'S, London

POST-1920 ISSUE

—	C	6	Famous Posters (folders) (65 × 41mm) (1923)	Ha.606	£22.00	—

ST. PETERSBURG CIGARETTE CO. LTD, Portsmouth

PRE-1919 ISSUES

A	BW	? 11	Footballers (c1900)	H.410	£225.00	—

SALMON & GLUCKSTEIN LTD, London

A PRE-1919 ISSUES

—	C	1	*Advertisement Card ('Snake Charmer' Cigarettes) (73 × 107mm) (c1897)		—	£400.00
C	C	15	*Billiard Terms (c1905):			
			A Small numerals		£50.00	—
			B Larger numerals		£50.00	—
A	C	12	British Queens (c1897)	Ha.480	£45.00	—
—	C	30	*Castles, Abbeys and Houses (76 × 73mm) (c1906):			
			A Brown back		£17.00	—
			B Red back		£23.00	—
C	C	32	*Characters from Dickens (c1903)	H.385	£25.00	—
A	C	25	Coronation Series (1911)		£9.00	£225.00
—	U	25	*Famous Pictures — Brown photogravure (57 × 76mm) (c1910)	H.386	£9.00	£225.00
—	U	25	*Famous Pictures — Green photogravure (58 × 76mm) (c1910)	H.387	£8.00	£200.00
A2	C	6	Her Most Gracious Majesty Queen Victoria (1897):	H.388		
			A Thin card		£50.00	£300.00
			B Thick card		£50.00	£300.00
A	C	50	The Great White City (c1908)		£11.00	£550.00
C	C	40	Heroes of the Transvaal War (1901)	H.389	£15.00	£600.00
C	C	30	*Music Hall Celebrities (c1902)		£50.00	—
—	C	? 26	*Occupations (64 × 18mm) (c1898)	H.390	£350.00	—
C	C	20	'Owners and Jockeys' Series (c1900)	H.392	£60.00	—
—	C	48	*The Post in Various Countries (41 × 66mm) (c1900)	H.391	£23.00	—
A2	C	6	*Pretty Girl Series — 'RASH' (c1900)	H.8	£65.00	—

SALMON & GLUCKSTEIN LTD, London *(continued)*

Size	*Print-ing*	*Number in set*		*Handbook reference*	*Price per card*	*Complete set*
—	C	22	Shakespearian Series (c1902):	H.393		
			A Large format, frame line back (38 × 69mm) ...		£32.00	—
			B Re-drawn, small format, no frame line back (37 × 66mm) ...		£32.00	—
A	C	25	*Star Girls (c1900):	H.30		
			A Red back ...		£120.00	—
			B Brown back, different setting ...		£120.00	—
A	C	25	Traditions of the Army and Navy (c1917):			
			A Large numerals ...		£11.00	£275.00
			B Smaller numerals, back redrawn ...		£12.00	£300.00
B POST-1920 ISSUES						
D2	C	25	Magical Series (1923) ...		£5.00	£125.00
A2	C	25	Wireless Explained (1923) ...		£5.00	£125.00
C SILKS						
—	C	50	*Pottery Types (paper-backed) (83 × 55mm) (c1915):			
			A Numbered on front and back ...		£3.50	—
			B Numbered on back only ...		£3.50	—

W. SANDORIDES & CO. LTD, London

POST-1920 ISSUES

	U	25	Aquarium Studies from the London Zoo (1925):	Ha.607		
C2			A Small size:			
			1 Small lettering on back ...		£3.00	£75.00
			2 Larger lettering on back ...		£3.00	£75.00
B1			B Large size ...		£3.00	£75.00
	C	25	Cinema Celebrities (1924):	Ha.530		
C2			A Small size ...		£2.60	£65.00
—			B Extra-large size (109 × 67mm) ...		£4.00	£100.00
	C	25	Cinema Stars (export) (c1924):	Ha.530		
C2			A Small size, with firm's name at base of back ...		£6.00	—
C2			B Small size, 'Issued with Lucana Cigarettes ...		£6.00	—
C2			C Small size, 'Issued with Big Gun Cigarettes ...'		£8.00	—
—			D Extra-large size (109 × 67mm) 'Issued with Big Gun Cigarettes ...		£2.40	£60.00
—			E Extra-large size (109 × 67mm) issued with Lucana 66 ...		£7.00	—
	U	50	Famous Racecourses (1926) — 'Lucana':	Ha.608		
C2			A Small size ...		£2.50	£125.00
B1			B Large size ...		£3.50	£175.00
C2	U	50	Famous Racehorses (1923):	Ha.609		
			1A Back in light brown ...		£2.50	£125.00
			1B Back in dark brown ...		£2.50	£125.00
			2 As 1A, with blue label added, inscribed 'Issued with Sandorides Big Gun Cigarettes ...' ...		£12.00	—
A	C	25	Sports & Pastimes — Series 1 — 'Big Gun Cigarettes (c1924) ...	H.225	£12.00	—

SANSOM'S CIGAR STORES, London

PRE-1919 ISSUE

—	P	? 2	*London Views (52 × 37mm) (c1915) ...		£200.00	—

NICHOLAS SARONY & CO., London

A PRE-1919 ISSUE

—	U	? 2	Boer War Scenes (67 × 45mm) (c1901) ...	H.394	£200.00	—

NICHOLAS SARONY & CO., London *(continued)*

Size	*Printing*	*Number in set*		*Handbook reference*	*Price per card*	*Complete set*
B	***POST-1920 ISSUES***					
	C	50	Around the Mediterranean (1926):	Ha.610		
C2			A Small size		90p	£45.00
B1			B Large size		£1.00	£50.00
	U	25	Celebrities and Their Autographs, Nd 1-25 (1923):			
C1			A Small size		80p	£20.00
B1			B Large size		80p	£20.00
	U	25	Celebrities and Their Autographs, Nd 26-50 (1924):			
C1			A Small size:			
			1 Small numerals		80p	£20.00
			2 Large numerals		80p	£20.00
B1			B Large size:			
			1 Small numerals		80p	£20.00
			2 Large numerals		80p	£20.00
	U	25	Celebrities and Their Autographs. Nd 51-75 (1924):			
C1			A Small size		80p	£20.00
B1			B Large size		80p	£20.00
	U	25	Celebrities and Their Autographs, Nd 76-100 (1925):			
C1			A Small size		80p	£20.00
B1			B Large size		80p	£20.00
A2	U	50	Cinema Stars — Set 7 (1933)	Ha.515-7	£1.20	£60.00
—	U		Cinema Stars — Postcard size (137 × 85mm):			
		38	'of a Series of 38 Cinema Stars' (1929)		£9.00	—
		42	'of a second Series of 42 Cinema Stars' (c1930)		£4.50	£190.00
		50	'of a third Series of 50 Cinema Stars' (c1930)		£4.50	£225.00
		42	'of a fourth Series of 42 Cinema Stars' (c1931)		£4.50	£190.00
		25	'of a fifth Series of 25 Cinema Stars' (c1931)		£4.50	£110.00
D	U	25	Cinema Studies (1929)		£1.00	£25.00
	C	25	A Day on the Airway (1928):			
C2			A Small size		90p	£22.50
B2			B Large size		£1.00	£25.00
A2	P	54	Life at Whipsnade Zoo (1934)	Ha.556	55p	£30.00
	BW	25	Links with the Past — First 25 subjects, Nd 1-25 (1925):			
C1			A Small size		36p	£9.00
B			B Large size		30p	£7.50
	BW	25	Links with the Past — Second 25 subjects (1926):			
C			A Home issue, Nd 26-50:			
			1 Small size		28p	£7.00
B			2 Large size, descriptive back		24p	£6.00
B			3 Large size, advertisement back		£1.60	—
			B Sydney issue, Nd 1-25:			
C			1 Small size		60p	£15.00
B			2 Large size		60p	£15.00
			C Christchurch issue, Nd 1-25:			
C			1 Small size		50p	£12.50
B			2 Large size		40p	£10.00
	BW	25	Museum Series (1927):			
			A Home issue:			
C2			1 Small size		30p	£7.50
B			2 Large size, descriptive back		30p	£7.50
B			3 Large size, advertisement back		60p	£15.00
B			B Sydney issue, large size		50p	£12.50
			C Christchurch issue:			
C2			1 Small size		50p	£12.50
B			2 Large size		50p	£12.50

NICHOLAS SARONY & CO., London *(continued)*

Size	*Printing*	*Number in set*		*Handbook reference*	*Price per card*	*Complete set*
	P	36	National Types of Beauty (1928):	Ha.558		
A2			A Small size		30p	£11.00
—			B Medium size (76 × 51mm)		30p	£11.00
	C	15	Origin of Games (1923):			
A			A Small size		£3.30	£50.00
B2			B Large size		£3.30	£50.00
	C	50	'Saronicks' (1929):	Ha.557		
D2			A Small size		30p	£15.00
—			B Medium size (76 × 51 mm)		30p	£15.00
	C	50	Ships of All Ages (1929):			
D			A Small size		60p	£30.00
—			B Medium size (76 × 52mm)		70p	£35.00
D	C	25	Tennis Strokes (1923)		£2.60	£65.00

T. S. SAUNT, Leicester

PRE-1919 ISSUE

D	C	30	*Army Pictures, Cartoons etc (c1916)	H.12	£75.00	—

SCOTTISH CO-OPERATIVE WHOLESALE SOCIETY LTD, Glasgow ('S.C.W.S.')

POST-1920 ISSUES

A2	C	25	Burns (1924):	Ha.611		
			A Printed back:			
			1 White card		£2.00	—
			2 Cream card		£1.20	£30.00
			*B Plain back		£6.00	—
[illegible]	C	20	Dogs (1925)	H.211	£10.00	—
A2	C	25	Dwellings of All Nations (1924):	Ha.612		
			A Printed back:			
			1 White card		£3.50	—
			2 Cream card		£2.00	£50.00
			*B Plain back		£6.00	—
B	C	25	Famous Pictures (1924)		£7.00	—
A2	C	25	Famous Pictures — Glasgow Gallery (1927):			
			A Non-adhesive back		£2.20	£55.00
			B Adhesive back		£1.40	£35.00
A2	C	25	Famous Pictures — London Galleries (1927):			
			A Non-adhesive back		£2.20	£55.00
			B Adhesive back		£1.40	£35.00
2	C	50	Feathered Favourites (1926):			
			A Grey borders		£2.00	£100.00
			B White borders:			
			1 Non-adhesiveback		£2.00	£100.00
			2 Adhesive back		£1.40	£70.00
	C	25	Racial Types (1925)		£8.00	£200.00
2	C	50	Triumphs of Engineering (1926):			
			A Brown border		£2.00	£100.00
			B White border		£2.00	—
2	C	50	Wireless (1924)		£3.20	£160.00

ELBY'S TOBACCO STORES, Cirencester

OST-1920 ISSUE

-	U	12	'Manikin' Cards (79 × 51mm) (c1920)		£70.00	—

SHARPE & SNOWDEN, London

Size	Printing	Number in set		Handbook reference	Price per card	Complete set
PRE-1919 ISSUES						
A	U	? 1	*Views of England (c1905)		£130.00	—
A	U	? 21	*Views of London (c1905)	H.395	£130.00	—

W.J. SHEPHERD, London

Size	Printing	Number in set		Handbook reference	Price per card	Complete set
PRE-1919 ISSUES						
A	U	25	*Beauties — 'FECKSA' (c1900)	H.58	£85.00	—

SHORT'S, London

Size	Printing	Number in set		Handbook reference	Price per card	Complete set
POST-1920 ISSUE						
—	BW		*Short's House Views (c1925):	Ha.562		
		? 13	1 Numbered (75 × 60mm)		£50.00	—
		? 8	2 Unnumbered (77 × 69mm)		£40.00	—

JOHN SINCLAIR LTD, Newcastle-on-Tyne

Size	Printing	Number in set		Handbook reference	Price per card	Complete set
A PRE-1919 ISSUES						
D2	U	? 69	*Actresses (42 × 63 mm) (c1900)	H.396	£65.00	—
D	P	? 52	Football Favourites (c1910)		£80.00	—
A	BW	4	*North Country Celebrities (c1905)	H.397	£60.00	£240.00
D	P	? 55	Northern Gems (c1902)		£55.00	—
A	C	50	Picture Puzzles and Riddles (c1910)		£22.00	—
A	C	50	Trick Series (c1910)		£22.00	—
D2	C	50	World's Coinage (c1915)	H.398	£17.00	£850.00
B POST-1920 ISSUES						
—	P		*Birds (1924):	Ha.613		
C		? 30	A Small size, back 'Specimen Cigarette Card'		£6.00	—
C		48	B Small size, descriptive back:			
			1 White front		£1.80	—
			2 Pinkish front		£1.80	—
—		50	C Large size (78 × 58mm)		£5.00	—
A	C	50	British Sea Dogs (1926)		£4.00	£200.00
	P		Champion Dogs — 'A Series of ...' (1938):			
A2		54	A Small size		75p	£40.00
B2		52	B Large size		75p	£40.00
	P		Champion Dogs — '2nd Series ...' (1939):			
A2		54	A Small size		£2.50	£130.00
B2		52	B Large size		£3.00	—
A2	P	50	English and Scottish Football Stars (1935)		£1.20	£60.00
A	P	54	Film Stars — 'A Series of 54 Real Photos' (1934)		£1.60	£85.00
A	P	54	Film Stars — 'A Series of Real Photos', Nd 1-54 (1937)		£1.40	£75.00
326	A	P	54 Film Stars — 'A Series of Real Photos', Nd 55-108 (1937)		£1.20	£65.00
	P		*Flowers and Plants (1924):	Ha.614		
C		? 24	A Small size, back 'Specimen Cigarette Card'		£6.00	—
C		96	B Small size, descriptive back:			
			1 White front		£2.00	—
			2 Pinkish front		£2.00	—
—		? 48	C Large size, 78 × 58mm		£6.00	—
A	P	54	Radio Favourites (1935)		£1.50	£80.00
K2	C	53	Rubicon Cards (miniature playing cards) (c1935)		£6.00	—
A	BW	50	Well-Known Footballers — North Eastern Counties (1938)		£1.20	£60.00
A	BW	50	Well-Known Footballers — Scottish (1938)		£1.20	£60.00

OHN SINCLAIR LTD, Newcastle-on-Tyne *(continued)*

ize	*Print-ing*	*Number in set*		*Handbook reference*	*Price per card*	*Complete set*
			SILKS			
—	C		**Flags — Set 2 (70 × 52mm) (unbacked and anonymous) (c1915):*	Ha.501-2		
		? 12	*A Numbered Nos 25-36*		£14.00	—
			B Unnumbered:			
		? 24	*1 Caption in red*		£8.00	—
		? 24	*2 Caption in myrtle-green*		£6.50	—
		? 20	*3 Caption in bright green*		£6.50	—
		? 23	*4 Caption in blue*		£8.00	—
		? 25	*5 Caption in black*		£10.00	—
—	C		**Flags — Set 11 (unbacked and anonymous) (c1915):*	Ha.501-11		
		50	*'Fourth Series' (49 × 70mm)*		£6.00	—
		50	*'Fifth Series' (49 × 70mm)*		£6.00	—
		50	*'Sixth Series':*			
			1 Nos 1-25 (49 × 70mm)		£7.00	—
			2 Nos 26-50 (68 × 80mm)		£7.00	—
		? 10	*'Seventh Series' (115 × 145mm)*		£45.00	—
—	C	? 1	The Allies (140 × 100mm) (Numbered 37) (c1915)		—	£35.00
—	C	50	*Regimental Badges I (paper backed) (70 × 52mm) (c1915)	Ha.502-1	£5.00	—
—	C	? 24	**Regimental Colours II (unbacked and anonymous) (c1915):*	Ha.502-7		
			1 Nos 38-49 (No. 49 not seen) (76 × 70mm)		£13.00	—
			2 Nos 50-61 (65 × 51mm)		£13.00	—

OBERT SINCLAIR TOBACCO CO. LTD, Newcastle-on-Tyne

			PRE-1919 ISSUE			
2	U	28	Dominoes (c1900)		£50.00	—
	BW	? 4	*Footballers (c1900)	H.399	£200.00	—
	C	12	*Policemen of the World (c1899)	H.164	£130.00	—
			POST-1920 ISSUES			
2	C		Billiards by Willie Smith (1928):			
		10	1 First set of 10		£7.00	£70.00
		15	2 Second Set of 15		£8.00	£120.00
		3	3 Third Set of 25 (Nos 26-28 only issued)		£12.00	£36.00
	C	12	The 'Smiler' Series (1924):			
			A Small size (inscribed '... 24 cards'),		£6.00	—
			B Large size		£10.00	—
			SILKS. Unbacked silks, inscribed with initials 'R.S.' in circle.			
-	C	4	*Battleships and Crests (73 × 102mm) (c1915)	Ha.499-1	£50.00	—
-	C	? 9	*Flags (70 × 51 mm) (c1915)	Ha.499-2	£26.00	—
-	C	? 6	*Great War Area — Cathedrals and Churches (140 × 102mm) (c1915)	Ha.499-3	£38.00	—
-	C	? 10	*Great War Heroes (70 × 51 mm) (c1915)	Ha.499-4	£32.00	—
-	C	1	*Red Cross Nurse (73 × 102mm) (c1915)	Ha.499-5	—	£50.00
-	C	? 5	*Regimental Badges (70 × 51 mm) (c1915)	Ha.499-6	£26.00	—

. SINFIELD, Scarborough

			RE-1919 ISSUE			
	U	? 24	*Beauties — 'HUMPS' (c1900)	H.222	£200.00	—

INGLETON & COLE LTD, Shrewsbury

			PRE-1919 ISSUES			
	C	50	*Atlantic Liners (1910)		£17.00	£850.00

SINGLETON & COLE LTD, Shrewsbury *(continued)*

Size	*Printing*	*Number in set*		*Handbook reference*	*Price per card*	*Complete set*
D1	BW	50	*Celebrities — Boer War Period (c1901):	H.400		
			25 Actresses		£17.00	£425.00
			25 Boer War Celebrities		£17.00	£425.00
A	BW	35	Famous Officers — Hero Series (1915):			
			A1 'Famous Officers' on back toned card		£14.00	£490.00
			A2 'Famous Officers' thin white card		£35.00	—
			B 'Hero Series' on back		£175.00	—
D1	BW	50	*Footballers (c1905)		£80.00	—
C	C	40	*Kings and Queens (1902)	H.157	£18.00	—
A	C	25	Maxims of Success (c1905):	H.401		
			A Orange border		£25.00	—
			B Lemon yellow border		£125.00	—
A	BW		Orient Royal Mail Line (c1905):	H.402		
		8	A 'Orient-Pacific Line' Manager's back		£45.00	—
		8	B 'Orient Royal Mail Line' Singleton and Cole back		£45.00	—
		? 12	C 'Orient Line' Manager's back		£45.00	—
A	C	25	Wallace Jones — Keep Fit System (c1910)		£20.00	—
B	***POST-1920 ISSUES***					
A	C	25	Bonzo Series (1928)		£6.00	£150.00
A2	BW	35	Famous Boxers (1930):			
			A Numbered		£12.00	—
			B Unnumbered		£40.00	—
A2	BW	25	Famous Film Stars (1930)		£8.00	—
—	U	12	'Manikin' Cards (79 × 51mm) (c1920)	H.481	£70.00	—
C	***SILKS***					
—	C	110	Crests and Badges of the British Army (paper-backed) (66 × 40mm) (c1915)	Ha.502-2	£4.00	—

F. & J. SMITH, Glasgow

36 page reference book available — £3.25

Size	*Printing*	*Number in set*		*Handbook reference*	*Price per card*	*Complete set*
A	***PRE-1919 ISSUES***					
A	C	25	*Advertisement Cards (1899)	H.403	£200.00	—
A	C	50	Battlefields of Great Britain (1913)	Ha.475	£12.00	£600.00
A1	BW	25	*Boer War Series 'Studio' Cigarettes back (1900)		£60.00	—
A	C	50	*Boer War Series (1900)		£24.00	—
D	BW		*Champions of Sport (1902):	H.404		
		50	Red back. Numbered		£60.00	—
		50	Blue back. Unnumbered		£70.00	—
A	U	50	Cricketers (1912)		£13.00	£650.00
A	U	20	Cricketers, 2nd Series, Nd 51-70 (1912)		£30.00	£600.00
A	U	50	Derby Winners (1913)		£11.00	£550.00
A	C	50	Famous Explorers (1911)		£11.00	£550.00
D	U	120	*Footballers, brown back (1902)		£25.00	—
A	U	50	*Footballers, blue back Nd 1-52 (Nos 1 and 13 not issued) (1910):			
			A Black portrait		£10.00	—
			B Brown portrait		£10.00	—
A	U	50	*Footballers, blue back. Nd 55-104 (Nos 53 and 54 not issued) (1910):			
			A Black portrait		£10.00	—
			B Brown portrait		£10.00	—
A	U	150	*Footballers, yellow frame line (1914):			
			A Pale blue back		£10.00	—
			B Deep blue back		£10.00	—

F. & J. SMITH, Glasgow *(continued)*

Size	*Printing*	*Number in set*		*Handbook reference*	*Price per card*	*Complete set*
A	C	50	Football Club Records, 1913 to 1917 (1918)		£12.00	£600.00
A	C	50	Fowls, Pigeons and Dogs (1908)	H.64	£8.00	£400.00
A	C		*Medals:	H.71		
		20	A Unnumbered — thick card (1902)		£12.00	£240.00
		50	B Numbered. 'F. & J. Smith' thick card (1902)		£8.00	£400.00
		50	C Numbered. 'The Imperial Tobacco Co.' very thin card (1903)		£32.00	—
		50	D Numbered. 'The Imperial Tobacco Company' thin card (1906)		£9.00	£450.00
A	C	50	Naval Dress and Badges:	H.172		
			A Descriptive back (1911)		£9.00	£450.00
			B Non-descriptive back (1914)		£9.00	£450.00
A	C	50	*Phil May Sketches, blue-grey back (1908)	H.72	£8.00	£400.00
A	C	40	Races of Mankind (1900):	Ha.483		
			A Series title on front		£45.00	—
			*B Without series title		£60.00	—
A	C	25	Shadowgraphs (1915)	H.466	£5.00	£125.00
A	C	50	*A Tour Round the World:			
			A Script Advertisement back (1904)		£22.00	—
			B Post-card format back (1905)		£40.00	—
A	C	50	A Tour Round the World (titled series) (1906)	H.75	£8.00	£400.00
A	BW	25	War Incidents (1914):	H.405		
			A White back		£6.00	£150.00
			B Toned back		£6.00	£150.00
A	BW	25	War Incidents, 2nd series (1915):	H.405		
			A White back		£6.00	£150.00
			B Toned back		£6.00	£150.00
B	***POST-1920 ISSUES***					
A	C	25	'Cinema Stars' (1920)	Ha.615	£7.00	£175.00
A	C	50	Football Club Records, 1921-22 (1922)		£12.00	£600.00
A	C	25	Holiday Resorts (1925)		£7.00	£175.00
A	C	50	Nations of the World (1923)	H.454	£5.50	£275.00
A	C	50	Phil May Sketches (brown back) (1924)	Ha.72	£5.00	£250.00
A	C	25	Prominent Rugby Players (1924)		£9.00	£225.00

SNELL & CO., Plymouth and Devonport

PRE-1919 ISSUE

A	BW	25	*Boer War Celebrities — 'STEW' (c1901)	H.105	£130.00	—

SOCIETE JOB, London (and Paris)

A	***PRE-1919 ISSUES***					
D	BW	25	*Dogs (1911)	H.406	£18.00	£450.00
D	BW	25	*Liners (1912)	H.407	£30.00	—
D	BW	25	*Racehorses — 1908-09 Winners (1909)	H.408	£18.00	£450.00
B	***POST-1920 ISSUES***					
A	C	25	British Lighthouses (c1925)		£5.00	£125.00
—	U		*Cinema Stars (c1926):	Ha.616		
		48	A Unnumbered size (58 × 45mm):			
			1 Complete Set		—	£60.00
			2 46 different (minus Love, Milovanoff)		80p	£36.00
		43	B Unnumbered size (58 × 36mm)		£3.00	—
		?	C Numbered		£4.00	—

SOCIETE JOB, London (and Paris) *(continued)*

Size	Printing	Number in set		Handbook reference	Price per card	Complete set
D1	C	52	*Miniature Playing Cards (c1925)		£7.00	—
A2	C	25	Orders of Chivalry (1924)		£3.00	£75.00
A2	C	25	Orders of Chivalry (Second series) (1927)		£3.00	£75.00
A2	C	3	Orders of Chivalry (unnumbered) (1927)		£8.00	£24.00

LEON SOROKO, London

POST-1920 ISSUE

—	U	6	Jubilee series (1935):			
			A Small size (75 × 41mm)		£25.00	—
			B Large size (83 × 73mm)		£25.00	—

SOUTH WALES TOB. MFG CO. LTD, Newport and London

PRE-1919 ISSUES

A	BW	? 91	Game of Numbers (c1910)		£60.00	—
A	U	25	*Views of London (c1910)	H.409	£22.00	£550.00

SOUTH WALES TOBACCO CO. (1913) LTD, Newport

PRE-1919 ISSUE

D	C	30	*Army Pictures, Cartoons, etc. (c1916)	H.12	£75.00	—

S.E. SOUTHGATE & SON, London

PRE-1919 ISSUE

A1	C	25	*Types of British and Colonial Troops (c1900)	H.76	£100.00	—

T. SPALTON, Macclesfield

PRE-1919 ISSUE

D	C	30	*Army Pictures, cartoons etc (c1916)	H.12	£75.00	—

SPIRO VALLERI & CO

PRE-1919 ISSUE

A	BW	? 10	Noted Footballers (c1905)		£250.00	—

G. STANDLEY, Newbury

POST-1920 ISSUE

—	U	12	'Manikin' Cards (79 × 51mm) (c1920)	Ha.481	£70.00	—

A. & A.E. STAPLETON, Hastings

POST-1920 ISSUE

—	U	12	*'Manikin' Cards (79 × 51mm) (c1920)	Ha.481	£70.00	—

H. STEVENS & CO., Salisbury

POST-1920 ISSUES

A1	C	20	*Dogs (1923)	H.211	£8.00	—
A1	U	25	*Zoo series (1926)	Ha.588	£5.50	—

A. STEVENSON, Middleton

PRE-1919 ISSUE

A	U	50	War Portraits (1916)	H.86	£65.00	—

ALBERT STOCKWELL, Porthcawl

Size	Printing	Number in set		Handbook reference	Price per card	Complete set
			PRE-1919 ISSUE			
D	C	30	*Army Pictures, Cartoons, etc (c1916).	H.12	£75.00	—

STRATHMORE TOBACCO CO. LTD, London

Size	Printing	Number in set		Handbook reference	Price per card	Complete set
			POST-1920 ISSUE			
—	U	25	British Aircraft (76 × 50mm) (1938)		£2.40	£60.00

TADDY & CO., London

2 page reference book available — £3.25

Size	Printing	Number in set		Handbook reference	Price per card	Complete set
			PRE-1919 ISSUES			
—	U	? 72	*Actresses — collotype (40 × 70mm) (c1897)	H.411	£90.00	—
A	C	25	*Actresses — with flowers (c1900)		£80.00	—
A	BW	37	Admirals and Generals — The War (c1915):			
			A 25 Commoner Cards	H.412	£13.00	—
			B 12 Scarce Cards (Nos 8, 9, 10, 13, 14, 17, 18, 21, 22, 23, 24, 25)		£40.00	—
A	BW	25	Admirals and Generals — The War (South African printing) (c1915)		£35.00	—
A	C	25	Autographs (c1910)	H.413	£16.00	£400.00
A	C	20	Boer Leaders: (c1901)			
			A White back		£17.00	£340.00
			B Cream back		£17.00	—
A	C	50	British Medals and Decorations — Series 2 (c1905)		£10.00	£500.00
A	C	50	British Medals and Ribbons (c1903)		£10.00	£500.00
A	C	20	*Clowns and Circus Artistes (c1915)	H.414	£700.00	—
A2	C	30	Coronation series (1902):			
			A Grained card		£20.00	£600.00
			B Smooth card		£20.00	£600.00
A	BW	238	County Cricketers (c1907)	H.415	£40.00	—
A	C	50	Dogs (c1900)	Ha.487	£22.00	—
A	U	5	*English Royalty — collotype (c1898)	H.416	£500.00	—
A	C	25	Famous Actors — Famous Actresses (c1903)		£16.00	£400.00
A	BW	50	Famous Horses and Cattle (c1912)		£95.00	—
A2	C	25	Famous Jockeys (c1905):	H.417		
			A Without frame line — blue title		£26.00	£650.00
			B With frame line — brown title		£24.00	£600.00
A	BW	50	Footballers (export issue) (c1906)	H.418	£65.00	—
A	C	25	'Heraldry' series (c1910)		£16.00	£400.00
A	C	25	Honours and Ribbons (c1910)		£18.00	£450.00
A	C	10	Klondyke series (c1900)		£60.00	£600.00
A	BW	60	Leading Members of the Legislative Assembly (export issue) (c1900)		£500.00	—
A	C	25	*Natives of the World (c1900)	H.419	£55.00	—
A	C	25	Orders of Chivalry (c1911)	H.301	£16.00	£400.00
A	C	25	Orders of Chivalry, second series (c1912)	H.301	£22.00	£550.00
A	BW		Prominent Footballers — Grapnel and/or Imperial back:	H.420		
		? 595	A without 'Myrtle Grove' footnote (1907)		£11.00	—
		? 405	B with 'Myrtle Grove' footnote (1908-9)		£11.00	—
A	BW	? 375	Prominent Footballers — London Mixture back (1913-14)	H.420	£30.00	—
—	C	20	*Royalty, Actresses, Soldiers (39 × 72mm) (c1898)	H.421	£180.00	—
A	C	25	'Royalty' series (c1908)		£17.00	£425.00
A	C	25	*Russo-Japanese War (1-25) (1904)		£16.00	£400.00
A	C	25	*Russo-Japanese War (26-50) (1904)		£22.00	£550.00

TADDY & CO., London *(continued)*

Size	Printing	Number in set		Handbook reference	Price per card	Complete set
A	BW	16	South African Cricket Team 1907	H.422	£60.00	—
A	BW	26	South African Football Team 1906-07	H.423	£22.00	—
A	C	25	Sports and Pastimes — Series 1 (c1912)	H.225	£17.00	£425.00
A	C	25	Territorial Regiments — Series 1 (1908)		£18.00	£450.00
A	C	25	Thames series (c1903)		£32.00	£800.00
C	C	20	Victoria Cross Heroes (1-20) (c1900)		£55.00	—
C	C	20	Victoria Cross Heroes (21-40) (c1900)		£55.00	—
A	C	20	VC Heroes — Boer War (41-60) (1901):			
			A White back		£16.00	—
			B Toned back		£16.00	£320.00
A	C	20	VC Heroes — Boer War (61-80) (1901):			
			A White back		£16.00	—
			B Toned back		£16.00	£320.00
A	C	20	VC Heroes — Boer War (81-100) (1902):			
			A White back		£18.00	—
			B Toned back		£18.00	£360.00
A	C	25	Victoria Cross Heroes (101-125) (1905)		£50.00	—
A2	BW	2	*Wrestlers (c1908)	H.424	£300.00	—

TADDY & CO., London and Grimsby

POST-1940 ISSUES

—	C	8	Advertisement Cards, three sizes (1980)		60p	£5.00
A	C	26	Motor Cars, including checklist (1980):			
			A 'Clown Cigarettes' back		40p	£10.00
			B 'Myrtle Grove Cigarettes' back		40p	£10.00
A	C	26	Railway Locomotives including checklist (1980):			
			A 'Clown Cigarettes' back		40p	£10.00
			B 'Myrtle Grove Cigarettes' back		40p	£10.00

W. & M. TAYLOR, Dublin

PRE-1919 ISSUES

A	C	8	European War series (c1915):	H.129		
			A 'Bendigo Cigarettes' back		£45.00	—
			B 'Tipperary Cigarettes' back		£45.00	—
A	U	25	*War series — 'Muratti II' (c1915):	H.290		
			A 'Bendigo Cigarettes' back		£60.00	—
			B 'Tipperary Cigarettes' back		£14.00	£350.00

TAYLOR WOOD, Newcastle

PRE-1919 ISSUE

C	C	18	Motor Cycle series (c1914)	Ha.469	£70.00	—

TEOFANI & CO. LTD, London

A POST-1920 HOME ISSUES

Cards inscribed with Teofani's name.

A2	C	24	Past and Present — Series A — The Army (1938):			
			A With framelines		£2.00	£50.00
			B Without framelines		£1.50	£36.00
A2	C	24	Past and Present — Series B — Weapons of War (1939)		80p	£20.00
A2	C	4	Past and Present — Series C — Transport (1940)		£4.00	—

B POST-1920 EXPORT ISSUES

Cards mostly without Teofani's name.

Size	*Printing*	*Number in set*		*Handbook reference*	*Price per card*	*Complete set*
C2	U	25	Aquarium Studies from the London Zoo ('Lucana' cards with green label added, inscribed 'Issued with Teofani Windsor Cigarettes') (c1925)	Ha.607	£11.00	—
D1	U	50	Cinema Celebrities (c1928):	Ha.617		
			A 'Presented with Broadway Novelties'		£5.00	—
			B 'Presented with these well-known choice cigarettes'		£3.50	—
	C	25	Cinema Stars (c1928):	Ha.530		
			1 *Anonymous printings:*			
C2			A *Small size*		£6.50	—
			B *Extra-large size (109 × 67mm)*		£6.50	—
			2 Teofani printings:			
C2			A Small size — 'Issued with Blue Band Cigarettes		£7.00	—
C2			B Small size — 'Three Star Cigarettes'		£7.00	—
C2			C Small size — 'Three Star Magnums'		£6.50	—
—			D Extra-large size (109 × 67mm) — 'Three Star Magnums'		£6.50	—
D	U	25	*Famous Boxers — 'Issued with The 'Favourite Magnums ...' (c1925)	Ha.579	£8.00	—
C2	P	32	Famous British Ships and Officers — 'Issued with these High Grade Cigarettes' (1934)		£2.80	£90.00
B1	U	50	Famous Racecourses ('Lucana' cards with mauve label added, inscribed 'Issued with The Favourite Cigarettes' (c1926)	Ha.608	£15.00	—
A	U	? 24	Famous Racehorses (c1925)		£12.00	—
—	BW	12	**Film Actors and Actresses (56 × 31mm) (plain back)* (1936)	Ha.618	80p	£10.00
C2	C	20	*Great Inventors (c1924)*	H.213	£4.50	—
A	C	20	**Head Dresses of Various Nations (plain back)* (c1925)	Ha.619-1	£12.00	—
—	BW	12	**London Views (57 × 31mm) (plain back)* (c1936)	Ha.620	50p	£6.00
D2	U	48	*Modern Movie Stars and Cinema Celebrities* (1934)	Ha.569	90p	£45.00
A	C	50	**Natives in Costume (plain back)* (c1925)	Ha.619-2	£14.00	—
C	U	50	Public Schools and Colleges — 'Issued with these Fine Cigarettes' (c1924)	Ha.575	£3.60	—
D	C	50	Ships and Their Flags — 'Issued with these well-known cigarettes' (c1925)	Ha.602	£2.60	£130.00
A	C	25	Sports and Pastimes Series I — 'Smoke these cigarettes always' (c1925)	H.225	£14.00	—
—	P	22	**Teofani Gems I — Series of 22 (53 × 35mm) (plain back)* (c1925)	Ha.621-1	£3.00	—
—	P	28	**Teofani Gems II — Series of 28 (53 × 35mm) (plain back)* (c1925)	Ha.621-2	£1.00	—
—	P	36	**Teofani Gems III — Series of 36 (53 × 35mm) (plain back)* (c1925)	Ha.621-3	£3.00	—
—	P	2	Teofani Gems — Unnumbered (53 × 35mm) (plain back) (c1925)		£3.00	£6.00
A2	P	36	Views of the British Empire — 'Issued with these Famous Cigarettes' (c1928):			
			A Front in black and white		£1.00	£36.00
			B Front in light brown		£1.00	£36.00
C	U	50	Views of London — 'Issued with these World Famous Cigarettes' (c1925)	Ha.577	£2.20	—
C2	U	24	*Well-Known Racehorses* (c1924)	Ha.609	£6.00	—
A	C	50	**World's Smokers (plain back)* (c1925)	Ha.619-3	£14.00	—
C	U	50	Zoological Studies (c1924)	Ha.578	£3.50	—

TETLEY & SONS LTD, Leeds

Size	*Print-ing*	*Number in set*		*Handbook reference*	*Price per card*	*Complete set*
PRE-1919 ISSUES						
A2	C	1	*'The Allies' (grouped flags) (c1915)	H.425	—	£225.00
A	U	50	War Portraits (c1916)	H.86	£65.00	—
D	C	25	World's Coinage (1914)	H.398	£50.00	—

THEMANS & CO., Manchester

A PRE-1919 ISSUES						
A	C	? 2	*Advertisement card with Riddles (c1913)	H.426	£200.00	—
A1	C	? 1	Allied Flags ('United Strength' in centre) (c1915)	Ha.486	£350.00	—
A	—	55	Dominoes (Sunspot brand issue) (c1914)		£80.00	—
C	C	18	Motor Cycle series (c1914)	Ha.469	£65.00	—
A	U	50	*War Portraits (1916)	H.86	£40.00	—
—		14	War Posters (63 × 41 mm) (c1916)		£150.00	—
B SILKS						
			Anonymous silks with blue border, plain board backing. Reported also to have been issued with firm's name rubber stamped on backing.			
—	C		**Miscellaneous Subjects* (c1915):	Ha.500		
		? 8	*Series B1 — Flags (50 × 66mm)*		£10.00	—
		? 3	*Series B2 — Flags (50 × 66mm)*		£10.00	—
		? 12	*Series B3 — Regimental Badges (50 × 66mm)*		£7.00	—
		? 7	*Series B5 — British Views and Scenes (50 × 66mm)*		£20.00	—
		? 48	*Series B6 — Film Stars (50 × 66mm)*		£10.00	—
		? 2	*Series C1 — Flags (65 × 55mm)*		£10.00	—
		? 3	*Series C2 — Flags (70 × 65mm)*		£10.00	—
		? 4	*Series C3 — Regimental Badges (64 × 77mm)*		£10.00	—
		? 2	*Series C4 — Crests of Warships (64 × 77mm)*		£10.00	—
		? 1	*Series D1 — Royal Standard (138 × 89mm)*		£15.00	—
		? 1	*Series D2 — Shield of Flags (138 × 89mm)*		£15.00	—
		? 1	*Series D3 — Regimental Badge (138 × 89mm)*		£15.00	—
		? 1	*Series D5 — British Views and Scenes (138 × 89mm)*		£20.00	—
		? 14	*Series D6 — Film Stars (138 × 89mm)*		£10.00	—

THOMSON & PORTEOUS, Edinburgh

PRE-1919 ISSUES						
D2	C	50	Arms of British Towns (c1905)		£13.00	£650.00
A	BW	25	*Boer War Celebrities — 'STEW' (c1901)	H.105	£50.00	—
A	C	20	European War series (c1915)	H.129	£12.00	£240.00
A	C	25	*Shadowgraphs (c1905)	H.44	£34.00	—
A	C	41	VC Heroes (c1915):	H.427		
			Ai Name on back — Luntin Cigarettes		£11.00	£500.00
			Aii As above, but No. 6 Type B		—	£450.00
			B *Without Maker's Name*		£11.00	£450.00

TOBACCO SUPPLY SYNDICATE, London (T.S.S.)

PRE-1919 ISSUE						
D	C	? 24	*Nautical Expressions (c1900)	H.174	£80.00	—

TURKISH MONOPOLY CIGARETTE CO. LTD

PRE-1919 ISSUE						
—	C	? 13	*Scenes from the Boer War (113 × 68mm, folded in three) (c1901)	Ha.478	£120.00	—

UNITED KINGDOM TOBACCO CO., London

Size	Printing	Number in set		Handbook reference	Price per card	Complete set
POST-1920 ISSUES						
A	C	50	Aircraft — 'The Greys Cigarettes' (1938)	Ha.598	£1.20	£60.00
—	U	48	Beautiful Britain — 'The Greys Cigarettes' (140 × 90mm) (1929)		£1.40	£70.00
—	U	48	Beautiful Britain — Second series 'The Greys Cigarettes' (140 × 90mm) (1929)		£1.40	£70.00
A2	C	25	British Orders of Chivalry and Valour — 'The Greys Cigarettes' (1936)	Ha.599	£1.40	£35.00
A	U	24	Chinese Scenes (1933)		75p	£18.00
A2	U	32	Cinema Stars — Set 4 (1933)	Ha.515-4	£1.50	£50.00
A2	U	50	Cinema Stars — Set 7 (1934):	Ha.515-7		
			A *Anonymous back*		£1.80	£90.00
			B Back with firm's name		£1.50	£75.00
A2	C	36	Officers Full Dress (1936)		£1.70	£60.00
A2	C	36	Soldiers of the King — 'The Greys Cigarettes' (1937)	Ha.603	£1.70	£60.00

UNITED SERVICES MANUFACTURING CO. LTD, London

A POST-1920 ISSUES						
A1	C	50	Ancient Warriors (1938)		£1.50	£75.00
A1	BW	50	Bathing Belles (1939)	Ha.592	50p	£25.00
D	U	100	Interesting Personalities (1935)		£2.20	—
D	U	50	Popular Footballers (1936)		£3.50	—
D	U	50	Popular Screen Stars (1937)		£3.50	—
B POST-1940 ISSUE						
A	C	25	Ancient Warriors (1954)		£3.50	—

UNITED TOBACCONISTS' ASSOCIATION LTD

PRE-1919 ISSUES						
A	C	? 9	*Actresses — 'MUTA' (c1900)	H.265	£130.00	—
A2	C	12	*Pretty Girl Series 'RASH' (c1900)	H.8	£150.00	—

WALKER'S TOBACCO CO. LTD, Liverpool

PRE-1919 ISSUE						
A	BW	28	*Dominoes 'Old Monk' issue (1908)		£55.00	—
POST-1920 ISSUES						
C	P	60	*British Beauty Spots (c1925)	Ha.553	£15.00	—
D2	U	28	*Dominoes 'W.T.C.' Monogram back (c1925)	Ha.535-2	£4.00	—
A2	P	32	Film Stars — 'Tatley's Cigarettes' (1936)	Ha.623	—	£70.00
			31 Different (minus Lombard)		£1.50	£46.00
A2	P	48	*Film Stars — Walker's name at base (1937)	Ha.623	£4.50	—

WALTERS TOBACCO CO. LTD, London

POST-1920 ISSUE						
B	U	6	Angling Information (wording only) (1939)	Ha.624	£1.50	£9.00

E.T. WATERMAN, Coventry

PRE-1919 ISSUE						
D	C	30	*Army Pictures, Cartoons, etc. (1916)	H.12	£75.00	—

WEBB & RASSELL, Reigate

PRE-1919 ISSUE						
A	U	50	War Portraits (1916)	H.86	£65.00	—

H.C. WEBSTER (Q.V. Cigars)

Size	Printing	Number in set		Handbook reference	Price per card	Complete set
PRE-1919 ISSUE						
—	BW	? 7	*Barnum and Bailey's Circus (60 × 42mm) (c1900)	H.428	£150.00	—

HENRY WELFARE & CO., London

Size	Printing	Number in set		Handbook reference	Price per card	Complete set
PRE-1919 ISSUE						
D	P	? 22	Prominent Politicians (c1911)	H.429	£70.00	—

WESTMINSTER TOBACCO CO. LTD, London

Size	Printing	Number in set		Handbook reference	Price per card	Complete set
POST-1920 ISSUES						
			Inscribed 'Issued by the Successors in the United Kingdom to the Westminster Tobacco Co., Ltd. ...'. For other issues see Section II Foreign Cards.			
A2	P	36	Australia — 'First Series' (1932)		25p	£9.00
A2	P	48	British Royal and Ancient Buildings (1925):			
			A Unnumbered, without descriptive text		80p	£40.00
			B Numbered, with descriptive text		60p	£30.00
A2	P	48	British Royal and Ancient Buildings — 'A Second Series ...' (1926)		30p	£15.00
A2	P	36	Canada — 'First Series' (1927)		60p	£22.00
A2	P	36	Canada — 'Second Series' (1928)		60p	£22.00
A2	P	48	Indian Empire — 'First Series' (1926)		30p	£15.00
A2	P	48	Indian Empire — 'Second Series' (1927)		30p	£15.00
A2	P	36	New Zealand — 'First Series' (1929)		30p	£11.00
A2	P	36	New Zealand — 'Second Series' (1930)		25p	£9.00
A2	P	36	South Africa — 'First Series' (1930)		50p	£18.00
A2	P	36	South Africa — 'Second Series' (1931)		50p	£18.00
NOT ISSUED						
A2	P	36	*Australia, Seond Series, plain back* (1933)		25p	£9.00

WHALE & CO.

Size	Printing	Number in set		Handbook reference	Price per card	Complete set
PRE-1919 ISSUE						
A	C	13	Conundrums (c1900)	H.232	£150.00	—

M. WHITE & CO., London

Size	Printing	Number in set		Handbook reference	Price per card	Complete set
PRE-1919 ISSUE						
—	BW	20	*Actresses — 'BLARM' (c1900)	H.23	£130.00	—

WHITFIELD'S, Walsall

Size	Printing	Number in set		Handbook reference	Price per card	Complete set
PRE-1919 ISSUE						
D	C	30	*Army Pictures, Cartoons etc. (c1916)	H.12	£75.00	—

WHITFORD & SONS, Evesham

Size	Printing	Number in set		Handbook reference	Price per card	Complete set
POST-1920 ISSUE						
C2	C	20	*Inventors series (c1924)	H.213	£40.00	—

WHOLESALE TOBACCO SUPPLY CO., London ('Hawser' Cigarettes)

Size	Printing	Number in set		Handbook reference	Price per card	Complete set
PRE-1919 ISSUES						
A	C	25	Armies of the World (c1902)	H.43	£65.00	—
A	C	40	Army Pictures (c1902)	H.69	£80.00	—

P. WHYTE, England

Size	Print-ing	Number in set		Handbook reference	Price per card	Complete set
PRE-1919 ISSUE						
D	C	30	*Army Pictures, Cartoons, etc. (1916)	H.12	£75.00	—

W. WILLIAMS & CO., Chester

Size	Print-ing	Number in set		Handbook reference	Price per card	Complete set
A PRE-1919 ISSUES						
A	BW	25	*Boer War Celebrities 'STEW' (c1901)	H.105	£60.00	—
A	C	50	Interesting Buildings (c1910)	H.70	£12.00	£600.00
A	BW	12	Views of Chester (c1910)	H.430	£25.00	£300.00
A	BW	12	Views of Chester — As It Was (c1910):	H.430		
			A Toned card		£27.00	£325.00
			B Bleuté card		£27.00	—
B POST-1920 ISSUES						
A	U	30	Aristocrats of the Turf (c1925)	Ha.554	£6.50	£195.00
A	U	36	Aristocrats of the Turf 2nd series (c1925)		£14.00	—
A	C	25	Boxing (c1924)	H.311	£8.00	£200.00

W.D. & H.O. WILLS, Bristol

200 page reference book available — £10.00

Size	Print-ing	Number in set		Handbook reference	Price per card	Complete set
A PERIOD TO 1902 — INCLUDING SERIES ISSUED ABROAD.						
A	U		*Actresses — collotype (c1894):	H.431		
		25	A 'Wills' Cigarettes'		£80.00	—
		43	B 'Wills's Cigarettes'		£80.00	—
A	C	? 9	*Actresses, brown type-set back (c1895)	H.432	£750.00	—
A	C	52	*Actresses, brown scroll back, with PC inset (c1898)		£15.00	£825.00
A	C	52	*Actresses, grey scroll back (c1897):	H.433		
			A Without PC inset		£15.00	£825.00
			B With PC inset		£15.00	£825.00
A	U		*Actresses and Beauties — collotype, 'Three Castles' and 'Firefly' front (c1895):	H.434		
		? 86	Actresses		£90.00	—
		? 32	Beauties		£90.00	—
A	C		*Advertisement Cards:	H.435		
		?4	1888 issue (tobacco packets)		£800.00	—
		? 1	1889-90 issue (serving maid)		£650.00	—
		? 11	1890-93 issues (tobacco packings)		£600.00	—
		? 3	1893 issue (various backs) (showcards)		£300.00	—
		? 6	1893-94 issue (posters)		£300.00	—
	C	50	*Animals and Birds in Fancy Costumes (c1896)	H.436	£45.00	—
	U	? 17	*Beauties — collotype (c1894):	H.437		
			A 'W.D. & H.O. Wills' Cigarettes'		£100.00	—
			B 'Firefly' Cigarettes		£100.00	—
1	C	? 9	*Beauties ('Girl Studies'), type-set back (c1895)	H.438	£750.00	—
	C		*Beauties, brown backs (c1897):	H.439		
		52	A With PC inset — scroll back		£15.00	£825.00
		10	B As A, 10 additional pictures		£45.00	—
		? 48	C 'Wills' Cigarettes' front, scroll back		£140.00	—
		? 35	D 'Wills' Cigarettes' front, type-set back		£175.00	—
	C	52	*Beauties, miniature cards, PC inset, grey scroll back (c1896)		£24.00	—
	C	50	Builders of the Empire (1898):			
			A White card		£6.00	£300.00
			B Cream card		£6.00	£300.00
	C	60	Coronation Series (1902):			
			A 'Wide arrow' type back		£5.00	£300.00
			B 'Narrow arrow' type back		£5.00	£300.00

W.D. & H.O. WILLS, Bristol *(continued)*

Size	*Print-ing*	*Number in set*		*Handbook reference*	*Price per card*	*Complet[e] se[t]*
A	C	50	*Cricketers (1896)	H.440	£60.00	–
A	C		Cricketer series, 1901:			
		50	A With Vignette		£22.00	–
		25	B Without Vignette		£22.00	–
A	C		*Double Meaning (1898):			
		50	A Without PC inset		£9.00	£450.0
		52	B With PC inset		£9.00	£470.0
A	C	50	Japanese series (c1900)	H.441	£35.00	–
	C		*Kings and Queens:	H.442		
A1		50	A Short card (1897):			
			a Grey back, thin card		£5.00	£250.0
			b Grey back, thick card		£5.00	£250.0
			c Brown back		£9.00	–
A			B Standard size card (1902):			
		51	a Blue-grey back with 5 substitute titles		£5.50	£280.0
		50	b Grey back, different design, thinner card		£11.00	–
A	C		*Locomotive Engines and Rolling Stock:	H.443		
		50	A Without ITC Clause (1901)		£7.00	£350.0
		7	B As A, 7 additional cards (1901)		£20.00	–
			C With ITC Clause — See B Period			
A	C	50	*Medals: (1902)	H.71		
			A White card		£2.50	£125.0
			B Toned card		£2.50	£125.0
A	C	25	*National Costumes (c1895)		£180.00	–
A	C	? 8	*National Types (c1893)		£600.00	–
A	C	20	Our Gallant Grenadiers (c1901):	H.163		
			A Deep grey on toned card		£28.00	–
			B Blue-grey on bluish card		£28.00	–
A	C	50	Seaside Resorts (1899)		£9.00	£450.0
A	C		*Ships:	H.444		
		25	A Without 'Wills' on front (1895):			
			a 'Three Castles' back		£28.00	£700.0
			b Grey scroll back		£28.00	£700.0
		50	B With 'Wills' on front, dark grey back (1896)		£18.00	–
		100	C Green scroll back on brown card (1898-1902):			
			i 1898-25 subjects as A		£17.00	–
			ii 1898-50 subjects as B		£17.00	–
			iii 1902-25 additional subjects		£17.00	–
A	C		*Soldiers of the World (1895-7):	H.445		
			A Without PC inset:			
		100	a With 'Ld.' back, thick card		£6.50	£650.0
		100	b With 'Ld.' back, thin card		£7.00	–
		100	c Without 'Ld.' back, thin card		£6.50	£650.0
		1	Additional card (as c) 'England, Drummer Boy'		—	£100.0
		52	B With PC inset		£22.00	£1150.0
A	C	50	*Soldiers and Sailors (c1894):	H.446		
			A Grey back		£40.00	–
			B Blue back		£40.00	–
A	C	50	Sports of All Nations (1900)		£9.00	£450.0
A	BW		Transvaal series:	H.360		
		50	A With black border (1899)		£8.00	–
		66	Bi Without black border (1900-01)		£1.75	£115.0
		258	Bii Intermediate cards — additions and alternatives (1900-01)		£1.75	–
		66	C Final 66 subjects, as issued with 'Capstan' back (*see B Period*) (1902).			

Size	*Print-ing*	*Number in set*		*Handbook reference*	*Price per card*	*Complete set*
A	C		'Vanity Fair' series (1902):	H.447		
		50	1st series		£5.00	£250.00
		50	2nd series		£5.00	£250.00
		50	Unnumbered — 43 subjects as in 1st and 2nd, 7 new subjects		£5.00	£250.00
A	C		Wild Animals of the World (c1900):	H.77		
		50	A Green scroll back		£5.00	£250.00
		52	B Grey back, PC inset		£11.00	£570.00
		? 7	C Text back		£30.00	—

B PERIOD 1902-1919 — HOME ISSUES I.E. SERIES BEARING IMPERIAL TOBACCO CO. ('I.T.C.') CLAUSE

A	C	50	Allied Army Leaders (1917)		£1.50	£75.00
A	C	50	Alpine Flowers (1913)		90p	£45.00
A	C	50	Arms of the Bishopric (1907)		90p	£45.00
A	C	50	Arms of the British Empire (1910)		80p	£40.00
A	C	50	Arms of Companies (1913)		80p	£40.00
A	C	50	Arms of Foreign Cities (1912):			
			A White card		80p	£40.00
			B Cream card		90p	—
			C As A, with 'Mark'		£1.00	—
A	C	50	Aviation (1910)		£1.60	£80.00
A	C	50	Billiards (1909)		£1.60	£80.00
A	C	50	*Borough Arms (1-50):			
			A Scroll back, unnumbered (1904)	H.448	£1.00	£50.00
			B Scroll back, numbered on front (1904)		£10.00	—
			C Descriptive back, numbered on back (1905)		£1.00	£50.00
			D 2nd Edition — 1-50 (1906)		70p	£35.00
A	C	50	*Borough Arms (51-100):			
			A 2nd Series (1905)		70p	£35.00
			B 2nd Edition, 51-100 (1906)		70p	£35.00
A	C	50	*Borough Arms (101-150):			
			A 3rd Series, Album clause in grey (1905)		90p	£45.00
			B 3rd Series, Album clause in red (1905)		70p	£35.00
			C 2nd Edition, 101-150 (1906)		70p	£35.00
A	C	50	*Borough Arms (151-200), 4th series (1905)		70p	£35.00
A	C	24	*Britain's Part in the War (1917)		90p	£22.00
A	C	50	British Birds (1917)		£1.10	£55.00
A	C	1	*Calendar for 1911 (1910)		—	£14.00
A	C	1	*Calendar for 1912 (1911)		—	£8.00
B	U	25	Celebrated Pictures (1916):			
			A Deep brown back		£2.00	£50.00
			B Yellow-brown back		£1.80	£45.00
B	U	25	Celebrated Pictures, 2nd Series (1916)		£2.20	£55.00
A	C	50	Celebrated Ships (1911)		£1.00	£50.00
A	C	50	The Coronation Series (1911)		£1.00	£50.00
A	C	50	Cricketers (1908):			
			A 1-25 'Wills' S' at top front		£6.00	£150.00
			B 1-50 'Wills's' at top front		£6.00	£300.00
B	C	25	Dogs (1914)		£3.00	£75.00
B	C	25	Dogs, 2nd Series (1915)		£3.00	£75.00
A	C	50	Famous Inventions (1915)		£1.00	£50.00
A	C	50	First Aid:			
			A Without Album Clause (1913)		£1.00	£50.00
			B With Album Clause (1915)		£1.00	£50.00
A	C	50	Fish & Bait (1910)	H.65	£1.60	£80.00
A	U	66	*Football Series (1902)	H.81	£6.00	—

Size	*Printing*	*Number in set*		*Handbook reference*	*Price per card*	*Complete set*
A	C	50	Garden Life (1914)	H.449	70p	£35.00
A	C	50	Gems of Belgian Architecture (1915)		60p	£30.00
A	C	50	Gems of French Architecture (1917):			
			A White card		£1.20	£60.00
			B Bleuté card		£1.40	—
			C Rough brown card		£1.40	—
A	C	50	Gems of Russian Architecture (1916)		60p	£30.00
A	C	50	Historic Events (1912)	H.464	£1.10	£55.00
A	C	50	*Locomotive Engines and Rolling Stock, with I.T.C. Clause (1902)		£7.00	£350.00
			For issue without I T. C. Clause see Period A.			
A	C	50	Military Motors (1916):			
			A Without 'Passed by Censor'		£1.60	£80.00
			B With 'Passed by Censor'		£1.60	£80.00
A	C	50	Mining (1916)	H.450	£1.00	£50.00
A	C	50	Musical Celebrities (1911)		£2.50	£125.00
A	C	50	Musical Celebrities — Second Series (1916):	H.465		
			Set of 50 with 8 substituted cards		£3.00	£150.00
			8 original cards (later substituted)		£200.00	—
A	C	50	Naval Dress & Badges (1909)	H.172	£2.00	£100.00
A	C	50	Nelson Series (1905)		£2.80	£140.00
A	C	50	Old English Garden Flowers (1910)		90p	£45.00
A	C	50	Old English Garden Flowers, 2nd Series (1913)		90p	£45.00
A	C	50	Overseas Dominions (Australia) (1915)	H.451	60p	£30.00
A	C	50	Overseas Dominions (Canada) (1914)		60p	£30.00
A	C	50	Physical Culture (1914)		90p	£45.00
A	U	100	*Portraits of European Royalty (1908):			
			Nos. 1-50		£1.20	£60.00
			Nos. 51-100		£1.20	£60.00
B	U	25	Punch Cartoons (1916):			
			A Toned card		£3.40	£85.00
			B Glossy white card		£6.00	—
B	U	25	Punch Cartoons — Second Series (1917)		£16.00	—
A	C	12	Recruiting Posters (1915)	H.452	£7.00	£85.00
A	C	50	Roses (1912)		£1.10	£55.00
A	C	50	Roses, 2nd Series (1914)		£1.00	£50.00
A	C	50	School Arms (1906)		70p	£35.00
A	C	50	Signalling Series (1911)	H.453	£1.20	£60.00
A	C	50	Time and Money in Different Countries (1906)	H.454	£1.40	£70.00
A	BW	66	Transvaal Series, 'Capstan' back (1902)	H.360	£5.50	£365.00
			For other 'Transvaal Series' see A Period.			
A	C	25	The World's Dreadnoughts (1910)		£2.60	£65.00

C POST-1920 ISSUES

Home issues, i.e. series with I.T.C. Clause.

A	C		Air Raid Precautions (1938):	Ha.544		
		50	A Home issue — adhesive back		50p	£25.00
		40	B Irish issue — non-adhesive back		£1.00	—
A	C	48	Animalloys (sectional) (1934)		30p	£15.00
B	C	25	Animals and Their Furs (1929)		£1.80	£45.00
B	C	25	Arms of the British Empire — 'First Series' (1931)		£1.60	£40.00
B	C	25	Arms of the British Empire — 'Second Series' (1932)		£1.60	£40.00
B	C	42	Arms of Oxford and Cambridge Colleges (1922)		£1.30	£55.00
B	C	25	Arms of Public Schools — '1st Series' (1933)		£1.60	£40.00
B	C	25	Arms of Public Schools — '2nd Series' (1934)		£1.60	£40.00
B	C	25	Arms of Universities (1923)		£1.40	£35.00
A	C	50	Association Footballers 'Frameline' back (1935)		£1.00	£50.00

Size	*Printing*	*Number in set*		*Handbook reference*	*Price per card*	*Complete set*
	C	50	Association Footballers — 'No frameline' back (1939):			
			A Home issue — adhesive back		£1.00	£50.00
			B Irish issue — non-adhesive back		£1.80	£90.00
	C	25	Auction Bridge (1926)		£2.00	£50.00
	C	25	Beautiful Homes (1930)		£2.40	£60.00
	C	50	British Butterflies (1927)		90p	£45.00
	C	25	British Castles (1925)		£2.20	£55.00
	C	25	British School of Painting (1927)		£1.20	£30.00
-	BW	48	British Sporting Personalities (66 × 52mm) (1937)		75p	£36.00
	C	40	Butterflies and Moths (1938)		80p	£32.00
	C	25	Cathedrals (1933)		£2.60	£65.00
	C	25	Cinema Stars — 'First Series' (1928)		£1.60	£40.00
	C	25	Cinema Stars — 'Second Series' (1928)		£1.60	£40.00
	U	50	Cinema Stars — 'Third Series' (1931)		£1.80	£90.00
	C	50	Cricketers, 1928 (1928)		£1.80	£90.00
	C	50	Cricketers — '2nd Series' (1929)		£1.60	£80.00
	C	50	Dogs — Light backgrounds (1937):			
			A Home issue — adhesive back		50p	£25.00
			B Irish issue — non-adhesive back		£1.00	£50.00
	C		Do You Know:			
		50	'A Series of 50' (1922)		40p	£20.00
		50	'2nd Series of 50' (1924)		40p	£20.00
		50	'3rd Series of 50' (1926)		40p	£20.00
		50	'4th Series of 50' (1933)		45p	£22.50
	C	50	Engineering Wonders (1927)		70p	£35.00
	C	50	English Period Costumes (1929)		90p	£45.00
	C	25	English Period Costumes (1927)		£2.40	£60.00
	C	40	Famous British Authors (1937)		£1.50	£60.00
	C	30	Famous British Liners — 'First Series' (1934)		£3.50	—
	C	30	Famous British Liners — 'Second Series' (1935)		£3.00	£90.00
	C	25	Famous Golfers (1930)		£15.00	—
	C		A Famous Picture — (sectional):			
		48	Series No. 1 — 'Between Two Fires' (1930)		30p	£15.00
		48	Series No. 2 — 'The Boyhood of Raleigh' (1930)		30p	£15.00
		48	Series No. 3 — 'Mother and Son' (1931)		30p	£15.00
		48	'The Toast' (1931):			
			A Home issue — Series No. 4		50p	£24.00
			B Irish issue — Series No. 1		£1.80	—
		48	'The Laughing Cavalier' (1931):			
			A Home issue — Series No. 5:			
			1 No stop after numeral		35p	£17.50
			2 Full stop after numeral		35p	£17.50
			B Irish issue — Series No. 2		£1.80	—
		49	Series No. 6 — 'And When did you Last See Your Father?' (1932)		90p	£45.00
	C	25	Flags of the Empire (1926)		£1.00	£25.00
	C	25	Flags of the Empire — '2nd Series' (1929)		£1.00	£25.00
	C	50	Flower Culture in Pots (1925)		40p	£20.00
	C	30	Flowering Shrubs (1935)		£1.00	£30.00
	C	50	Flowering Trees and Shrubs (1924)		70p	£35.00
	C	50	Garden Flowers (1933)		50p	£25.00
	C	50	Garden Flowers by Richard Sudell (1939):			
			A Home issue — four brands quoted at base		25p	£12.50
			B Irish issue — no brands at base		40p	£20.00
	C	40	Garden Flowers — New Varieties — 'A Series' (1938)		60p	£24.00
	C	40	Garden Flowers — New Varieties — '2nd Series' (1939)		50p	£20.00

Size	*Print-ing*	*Number in set*		*Handbook reference*	*Price per card*	*Comple s*
A	C	50	Garden Hints (1938):			
			A Home issue — Albums 'one penny each'		17p	£8.5
			B Irish issue — Album offer without price		30p	£15.0
A	C	50	Gardening Hints (1923)		25p	£12.5
B	C	25	Golfing (1924)		£8.00	-
B	C	25	Heraldic Signs and Their Origin (1925)		£1.80	£45.0
A2	P	54	Homeland Events (1932)		32p	£17.0
A	C	50	Household Hints (1927)		32p	£16.0
A	C	50	Household Hints — '2nd Series' (1930)		40p	£20.0
A	C	50	Household Hints (1936):			
			A Home issue — Albums 'one penny each'		16p	£8.0
			B Irish issue — Album offer without price		30p	£15.0
A	BW	50	Hurlers (1927)		£1.30	£65.0
A	C	25	Irish Beauty Spots (1929)		£4.00	-
A	C	25	Irish Holiday Resorts (1930)		£4.00	-
A	C	50	Irish Industries (1937):			
			A Back 'This surface is adhesive ...'		£3.00	-
			B Back 'Ask your retailer ...'		£1.00	£50.0
A	U	25	Irish Rugby Internationals (1928)		£7.50	-
A	C	50	Irish Sportsmen (1935)		£3.00	-
B	C	40	The King's Art Treasures (1938)		30p	£12.0
B	C	25	Lawn Tennis, 1931 (1931)		£6.00	-
A	C	50	Life in the Royal Navy (1939)		22p	£11.0
A	C	50	Life in the Tree Tops (1925)		30p	£15.0
A	C	50	Lucky Charms (1923)		40p	£20.0
A	C	50	Merchant Ships of the World (1924)		£1.00	£50.0
K2	C	53	*Miniature Playing Cards (1932-34):			
			A Home issue, blue back — 'narrow 52' (2 printings)		50p	£25.0
			B Home issue, blue back — 'wide 52' (4 printings)		50p	£25.0
			C Home issue, pink back (3 printings)		60p	-
			D Irish issue, blue back (7 printings)		£1.00	-
B	C	25	Modern Architecture (1931)		£1.40	£35.0
B	U	30	Modern British Sculpture (1928)		£1.30	£40.0
B	C	25	Old Furniture — '1st Series' (1923)		£2.80	£70.0
B	C	25	Old Furniture — '2nd Series' (1924)		£2.80	£70.0
B	C	40	Old Inns — 'A Series of 40' (1936)		£2.75	£110.0
B	C	40	Old Inns — 'Second Series of 40' (1939)		£1.50	£60.0
B	C	25	Old London (1929)		£3.00	£75.0
B	C	30	Old Pottery and Porcelain (1934)		£1.10	£33.0
B	C	25	Old Silver (1924)		£2.40	£60.0
B	C	25	Old Sundials (1928)		£2.60	£65.0
A	BW	50	Our King and Queen (1937)		20p	£10.0
B	C	25	Public Schools (1927)		£2.40	£60.0
B	C	40	Racehorses and Jockeys, 1938 (1939)		£1.75	£70.0
A	C	50	Radio Celebrities — 'A Series ...' (1934):			
			A Home issue — back 'This surface ...'		70p	£35.0
			B Irish issue — back 'Note. This surface ...'		£1.50	-
A	C	50	Radio Celebrities — 'Second Series — (1935):			
			A Home issue — back 'This surface ...'		50p	£25.0
			B Irish issue — back 'Note. This surface ...'		£1.00	-
A	C	50	Railway Engines (1924)		90p	£45.0
A	C	50	Railway Engines (1936):			
			A Home issue — back 'This surface ...'		90p	£45.0
			B Irish issue — back 'Note. This surface ...'		£1.40	£70.0

.D. & H.O. WILLS, Bristol *(continued)*

ze	*Printing*	*Number in set*		*Handbook reference*	*Price per card*	*Complete set*
	C	50	Railway Equipment (1939)		22p	£11.00
	C	50	Railway Locomotives (1930)		£1.40	£70.00
	C	50	The Reign of H. M. King George V (1935)		50p	£25.00
	C	25	Rigs of Ships (1929)		£3.40	£85.00
	C	50	Romance of the Heavens (1928):			
			A Thin card		50p	£25.00
			B Thick card		50p	£25.00
	C	50	Roses (1926)		80p	£40.00
	C	40	Roses (1936)		£1.25	£50.00
	BW	48	Round Europe (66 × 52mm) (1937)		30p	£15.00
	C	50	Rugby Internationals (1929)		£1.20	£60.00
	C	50	Safety First (1934):			
			A Home issue — 'This surface ...'		80p	£40.00
			B Irish issue — 'Note. This surface ...'		£1.50	—
	C	50	The Sea-Shore (1938):			
			A Home issue — special album offer		22p	£11.00
			B Irish issue — general album offer		70p	£35.00
	U	40	Shannon Electric Power Scheme (1931)		£1.50	£60.00
	U	50	Ships' Badges (1925)		60p	£30.00
	C	50	Speed (1930)		£1.20	£60.00
	C	50	Speed (1938):			
			A Home issue — four brands quoted at base		30p	£15.00
			B Irish issue — no brands at base		70p	£35.00
	C	50	Strange Craft (1931)		£1.00	£50.00
	C	40	Trees (1937)		£1.50	£60.00
	C	25	University Hoods and Gowns (1926)		£2.40	£60.00
	C	50	Wild Flowers (1923):			
			A With dots in side panels		50p	£25.00
			B Without dots in side panels		50p	£25.00
	C	50	Wild Flowers — 'Series of 50' (1936):			
			A Home issue — back 'This surface ...'		30p	£15.00
			B Irish issue — back 'Note. This surface ...'		70p	—
	C	50	Wild Flowers — '2nd Series.' (1937):			
			A Home issue — adhesive back		20p	£10.00
			B Irish issue — non-adhesive back		60p	£30.00
	C	50	Wonders of the Past (1926)		50p	£25.00
	C	50	Wonders of the Sea (1928)		40p	£20.00
POST-1940 ISSUES						
	C	30	Britain's Motoring History (1991)		£1.20	£36.00
	C	6	Britain's Motoring History (1991) Beer Mats		£1.00	—
	C	30	British Aviation (1994)		£1.00	£30.00
	C	6	British Aviation (1994) Beer Mats		35p	£2.00
	C	30	Classic Sports Cars (1996)		£1.00	—
	C	30	Donington Collection (1993)		£1.20	£36.00
	C	6	Donington Collection (1993) Beer Mats		£1.00	—
	BW	48	Familiar Phrases (1986)		£1.00	£50.00
	C	30	History of Britain's Railways (1987)		£1.20	£36.00
	C	30	History of Motor Racing (1987)		£1.50	—
	C	30	In Search of Steam (1992)		£1.20	£36.00
	C	6	In Search of Steam (1992) Beer Mats		£1.00	—
	BW	5	Pica Punchline (1984)		£1.20	£6.00
	U	144	Punch Lines (1983)		60p	—
	U	288	Punch Lines (1983)		60p	—
	U	48	Ring the Changes (1985):			
			A With 'Wills' name		£1.00	—
			B Without 'Wills' Name		£1.00	—

W.D. & H.O. WILLS, Bristol *(continued)*

Size	Print-ing	Number in set		Handbook reference	Price per card	Comple s
—	C	12	Russ Abbot Advertising Cards (80 × 47mm) (1993)		£1.25	–
G2	C	30	Soldiers of Waterloo (1995)		£1.00	£30.0
G2	BW	10	Spot the Shot (1986)		£2.50	–
G2	C	30	The Tank Story (1997)		£1.00	–
—	C	56	Wonders of the World (1986):			
			A Size 90 × 47mm		50p	£28.0
			B Size 80 × 47mm		70p	–
			C Size 80 × 35mm		90p	–
C1	C	36	World of Firearms (1982)		25p	£9.0
C1	C	36	World of Speed (1981)		25p	£9.0
E	***UNISSUED SERIES***					
A	P	50	Gems of Italian Architecture (1960) (reprint)		70p	£35.0
A	C	50	Life in the Hedgerow (c1950)		50p	£25.0
A	C	50	Life of King Edward VIII (1936)		—	£800.0
A	C	25	Pond and Aquarium 1st Series (c1950)		32p	£8.0
A	C	25	Pond and Aquarium 2nd Series (c1950)		32p	£8.0
B	C	40	Puppies (c1950)		—	–
A	C	50	Waterloo(c1916)		£90.00	–
F	***MISCELLANEOUS***					
B	BW	1	Advertisement Card — Wants List (1935)		—	50
—	—	? 8	Boer War Medallions (c1901)		£80.00	–
—	C	12	The British Empire (133 × 101mm) (c1930)		£7.00	–
—	C	12	Cities of Britain (133 × 101mm) (c1930)		£7.00	–
	C	6	Flags of the Allies (shaped) (c1915)		£12.00	–
—	C	32	Happy Families (non-insert) (91 × 63mm) (c1935)		£4.00	–
—	C	12	Industries of Britain (133 × 101mm) (c1930)		£7.00	–
—	—	1	Pinchbeck Medallion (1897)		£100.00	–
			Three Castles Sailing Ship Model advertisement cards (1965):			
A	C	1	A View from Stern:			
			I. Three Castles Cigarettes		—	£4.0
			II. In the eighteenth century		—	£1.5
A	C	1	B Views from Bows:			
			I. Three Castles Filter		—	£1.5
			II. Three Castles Filter magnum		—	£1.5
A	BW	1	C Sailing Ship Black Line Drawing		—	£5.0
A	BW	1	D Three Castles Shield Black Line Drawing		—	£5.0
—	C		200th Anniversary Presentation Packs (2 sets of Playing Cards) (1986)		—	£80.0

WILSON & CO., Ely

PRE-1919 ISSUE

A	C	50	War Portraits (1916)	H.86	£65.00	–

W. WILSON, Birmingham

PRE-1919 ISSUES

D	C	30	*Army Pictures. Cartoons, etc (1916)	H.12	£75.00	–

HENRI WINTERMANS (UK) LTD

POST-1940 ISSUES

G	C	30	Disappearing Rain Forest (1991)		40p	£12.0
G	C	30	Wonders of Nature (1992)		40p	£12.0

A. & M. WIX, London and Johannesburg

Size	Printing	Number in set		Handbook reference	Price per card	Complete set
POST-1920 ISSUES						
–	—		Cinema Cavalcade (50 coloured, 200 black and white; sizes — 70 small, 110 large, 70 extra-large):			
		250	'A Series of 250 ...' ('Max Cigarettes') (1939)		90p	—
		250	'2nd Series of 250 ...' ('Max Cigarettes') (1940)		90p	£225.00
A2	C	100	Film Favourites — 'Series of 100 ...' (c1937)	Ha.581-1	£2.00	—
A2	C	100	Film Favourites — '2nd Series of 100 ...' (c1938)	Ha.581-2	£2.00	—
A2	C	100	Film Favourites — '3rd Series of 100 ...' (c1939)	Ha.581-3	£1.00	£100.00
1	C	100	*Men of Destiny (folders) (P.O. Box 5764, Johannesburg) (c1935)		£2.00	—
–	C	250	Speed Through the Ages (171 small, 79 large) (1938):	Ha.583		
			A Back in English and Afrikaans		32p	£80.00
			B Back in English		40p	£100.00
–	C	250	This Age of Power and Wonder (170 small, 80 large) ('Max Cigarettes') (c1935)		30p	£75.00

. WIX & SONS LTD, London

Size	Printing	Number in set		Handbook reference	Price per card	Complete set
POST-1920 ISSUES						
	C	50	Builders of Empire — 'Kensitas' (1937)		32p	£16.00
2	C	50	Coronation (1937):			
			A J. Wix back:			
			1. Linen finish		25p	£12.50
			2. Varnished		32p	£16.00
			B 'Kensitas' back		25p	£12.50
	C		Henry:	Ha.625		
			'A Series of ...' (1935):			
1		50	A Large size		60p	£30.00
–		25	B Extra-large size		£2.60	£65.00
			'2nd Series ...' (1935):			
1		50	A Large size		90p	£45.00
–		25	B Extra-large size		£2.80	£70.00
1		50	3rd Series (1936)		70p	£35.00
1		50	4th Series (1936)		70p	£35.00
1		50	5th Series (1936)		60p	£30.00
	U	25	Love Scenes from Famous Films — 'First Series' (1932):			
2			A Small size		£2.60	£65.00
1			B Large size		£2.60	£65.00
–			C Extra-large size (127 × 88mm)		£4.50	—
	U	19	Love Scenes from Famous Films — 'Second Series' (1932) (Nos. 5, 9, 13, 20, 23, 24 withdrawn):			
2			A Small size		£2.50	£50.00
1			B Large size		£3.00	£60.00
			C Extra-large size (127 × 88mm)		£6.50	—
2	C	53	**Miniature Playing Cards (anonymous)* (c1935):	Ha.535-3A		
			A Scroll design:			
			1 Red back		18p	£9.00
			2 Blue back		25p	£12.50
			B Ship design:			
			1 Red border — Nelson's 'Victory'		30p	£15.00
			2 Black border — Drake's 'Revenge'		30p	£15.00
		25	Scenes from Famous Films — 'Third Series' (1933):			
2			A Small size		£2.60	£65.00
–			B Extra-large size (127 × 88mm)		£6.00	—

J. WIX & SONS LTD, London *(continued)*

Size	*Printing*	*Number in set*		*Handbook reference*	*Price per card*	*Complete set*
B	***SILKS***					
—	C	48	British Empire Flags — 'Kensitas' (78 × 54mm) (1933)	Ha.496-4		
			A Inscribed 'Printed in U.S.A.'		80p	£40.00
			B Without the above		80p	£40.00
—	C	60	Kensitas Flowers — 'First Series', small (68 × 40mm) (1934):	Ha.496-1		
			1 Back of folder plain		£3.00	—
			2 Back of folder printed in green:			
			(a) Centre oval, 19mm deep		£3.00	—
			(b) Centre oval, 22mm deep		£3.00	—
			(c) As (b), inscribed washable ...' below number		£3.00	—
—	C	60	Kensitas Flowers — 'First Series', medium (76 × 55mm) (1934):	Ha.496-1		
			A Back of folder plain		£4.50	—
			B Back of folder printed in green		£4.50	—
	C	30	Kensitas Flowers — 'First Series' Extra-large (138 × 96mm) (1934):	Ha.496-1		
			A Back of folder plain		£40.00	—
			B Back of folder printed in green		£40.00	—
—	C	40	Kensitas Flowers — 'Second Series' (1935):	Ha.496-2		
			A Small size, 68 × 40mm		£5.00	—
			B Medium size, 76 × 55mm		£6.00	—
	C	60	National Flags — 'Kensitas' (78 × 54mm) (1934)	Ha.496-3	£1.00	£60.00
C	***POST-1940 ISSUES***					
			Ken-cards (102 × 118mm):			
		12	Series 1. Starters/Snacks (1969)		—	£5.00
		12	Series 2. Main Courses (1969)		—	£5.00
		12	Series 3. Desserts (1969)		—	£5.00
		12	Series 4. Motoring (1969)		—	£5.00
		12	Series 5. Gardening (1969)		—	£5.00
		12	Series 6. Do It Yourself (1969)		—	£5.00
		12	Series 7. Home Hints (1969)		—	£5.00
		12	Series 8. Fishing (1969)		—	£5.00
D	***MISCELLANEOUS***					
—	C	80	Bridge Favours and Place Cards (diecut) (1937)		£12.00	—
—	C	50	Bridge Hands (140 × 105mm) (1930)		£12.00	—
		42	Card Tricks by Jasper Maskelyne (c1938):	Ha.535-3B		
			A Size 70 × 34mm		£3.00	—
			B Size 70 × 41mm		£3.00	—
	U		Jenkynisms:			
			A 'The K4's' Series (75-78 × 65mm) (c1932):			
		101	I. Known as 1st Series		80p	—
		50	II. Known as 2nd Series		80p	£40.00
		30	III. Known as 3rd Series		80p	—
		1	IV. Known as 4th Series		—	£2.00
			B The Red Bordered series (2 sizes for each series) (c1932):			
		20	I. Series of Quotations		£3.00	—
		? 43	II. 'Today's Jenkynisms'		£3.00	—

WOOD BROS., England

PRE-1919 ISSUE

—	BW	28	Dominoes (63 × 29mm) (c1910)		£60.00	—

'. WOOD, Cleckheaton

'ze	Print-ing	Number in set		Handbook reference	Price per card	Complete set
RE-1919 ISSUE						
	C	30	*Army Pictures, Cartoons, etc (1916)	H.12	£75.00	—

OHN J. WOODS, London

RE-1919 ISSUE						
	BW	? 21	*Views of London (c1905)	H.395	£130.00	—

V. H. & J. WOODS LTD., Preston

PRE-1919 ISSUE						
	C	25	*Types of Volunteers and Yeomanry (c1902)	H.455	£24.00	£600.00
POST-1920 ISSUES						
2	U	25	Aesop's Fables (c1932)	Ha.518	£1.60	£40.00
2	P	50	Modern Motor Cars (c1936)		£4.50	£225.00
	C	25	Romance of the Royal Mail (c1933)		£1.00	£25.00

. & E. WOOLF

RE-1919 ISSUE						
	U	? 3	*Beauties 'KEWA' (c1900)	H.139	£200.00	—

I. H. WOOLLER, London

RE-1919 ISSUE						
	—	25	Beauties 'BOCCA' (c1900)		£200.00	—

'. E. YEOMANS & SONS LTD., Derby

RE-1919 ISSUES						
-	C	72	Beautiful Women (75 × 55mm) (c1900)	Ha.284	£150.00	—
	U	50	War Portraits (1916)		£65.00	—

OHN YOUNG & SONS LTD., Bolton

RE-1919 ISSUES						
2	C	12	Naval Skits (c1904)	H.457	£130.00	—
2	C	12	*Russo-Japanese Series (1904)	H.456	£70.00	—

ANONYMOUS SERIES

Size	Printing	Number in set		Handbook reference	Price per card	Complete set
A			***PRE-1919 ISSUES. WITH LETTERPRESS ON BACK OF CARD***			
A2	C	20	Animal Series: See Hill			
			A 'The cigarettes with which ...' back			
			B Space at back			
A	U	? 40	*Beauties — 'KEW A' 'England Expects ...' back	H.139	£100.00	—
D	BW	25	*Boxers, green back See Cohen Weenen			
A1	C	? 3	*Celebrities — Coloured. 1902 Calendar back		—	—
D	C	? 2	*Celebrities — 'GAINSBOROUGH I', 1902 Calendar back, gilt border to front. See Cohen Weenen	H.90		
A2	C	20	*Interesting Buildings and Views, 1902 Calendar back	Ha.96	—	—
D2	C	? 1	*Nations, 1902 Calendar back	Ha.97		
A	C	25	*Types of British Soldiers, 'General Favourite Onyx' back	H.144	—	—
D	C	25	V.C. Heroes (Nos. 51-75 — See Cohen Weenen)			
A	C	41	V.C. Heroes — 'Pure Virginia Cigarettes' — Dobson Molle & Co. Ltd. — Printers		£8.00	—
D	U	50	*War Series (Cohen Weenen — Nos. 1-50)	H.103		
A	C	41	V.C. Heroes — See Thomson and Porteous	H.427		
B			***PRE-1919 ISSUES. WITH PLAIN BACK***			
A	U	25	*Actors and Actresses — 'FROGA C'	H.20	£12.00	—
D2	U	? 5	*Actresses — 'Anglo'	Ha.185	£50.00	—
	U		*Actresses — 'ANGOOD':	H.187		
		? 13	A Brown tinted —			
			i. Thick board		—	—
			ii. Thin board		—	—
		? 1	B Green tinted		—	—
		? 10	C Black tinted		£30.00	—
A1	BW	20	*Actresses — 'BLARM'	H.23	£10.00	—
D	U	20	*Actresses — Chocolate tinted. See Hill	H.207		
A	C	? 19	*Actresses — 'DAVAN':	Ha.124		
			A Portrait in red only		—	—
			B Portrait in colour		—	—
D	BW	12	*Actresses — 'FRAN'. See Drapkin	H.175		
A	U	26	*Actresses — 'FROGA A'	H.20	£12.00	—
A1	BW	? 15	*Actresses — 'HAGG B'	H.24	£10.00	—
A	BW	15	*Actresses — 'RUTAN' See Rutter	H.381		
—	C	50	*Actresses Oval Card (as Phillips)	Ha.324		
A1	U		*Actresses and Beauties — Collotype (See Ogden)	H.306		
C	C	20	*Animal Series. See Hill			
—	C	? 12	*Arms of Cambridge Colleges (17 × 25mm). See Kuit	H.458		
—	C	? 12	*Arms of Companies (30 × 33mm). See Kuit	H.459		
A2	BW	? 13	*Battleships. See Hill	H.208		
A	C	? 14	*Beauties — 'BOCCA'	H.39	£14.00	—
A		50	*Beauties — 'CHOAB':	H.21		
	U		A Unicoloured		£12.00	—
	C		B Coloured		£10.00	—
A			*Beauties — 'FECKSA':	H.58		
	U	50	A Plum-coloured front		£9.00	—
	C	? 6	B Coloured front		£20.00	—
D2	U	? 18	*Beauties — 'FENA'	H.148	£45.00	—
A2	C	25	*Beauties — 'GRACC'	H.59	£14.00	—
A	C	26	*Beauties — 'HOL'	H.192	£10.00	—
A	U	? 41	*Beauties 'KEWA'	H.139	—	—

ANONYMOUS SERIES *(continued)*

Size	Printing	Number in set		Handbook reference	Price per card	Complete set
—	C	30	*Beauties — Oval card (36 × 60mm.) (See Phillips)*	H.244		
A	U	? 17	*Beauties — Collotype*	Ha.278	—	—
D1	U		*Bewlay's War Series:*	Ha.477		
		12	1. Front without captions		—	—
		? 1	2. Front with captions		—	—
A2	BW	20	*Boer War Cartoons*	H.42	£20.00	—
A	C	? 25	*Boer War and General Interest:*	H.13		
			A Plain cream back		£40.00	—
			B Brown Leaf Design back		£40.00	—
			C Green Leaf Design back		£40.00	—
			D Green Daisy Design back		—	—
A2	BW	? 16	*Boer War Celebrities — 'CAG'*	H.79	—	—
A		? 8	Boer War Celebrities 'RUTTER':	Ha.382		
	BW		A Front in Black and White		£25.00	—
			B Front in light orange brown		£25.00	—
D2	BW	20	*Boer War Generals — 'CLAM'*	H.61	£16.00	—
A1	BW	? 12	*Boer War Generals — 'FLAC'*	H.47	£16.00	—
D	C	25	*Boxer Rebellion — Sketches (1904)*	H.46	£12.00	—
A	C	54	*British Beauties (Phillips) (1-54)*	H.328		
A	C	54	*British Beauties (Phillips) (55-108) Matt*	H.328		
A	C	12	British Queens	Ha.480	£20.00	—
A	BW	16	*British Royal Family*	H.28	£10.00	—
A	C	45	*Celebrities — Coloured (Cohen Weenen)*	H.89		
D	C	39	*Celebrities — 'GAINSBOROUGH I'. See Cohen Weenen*	H.90		
D	BW	? 147	*Celebrities — 'GAINSBOROUGH II'. See Cohen Weenen*	H.91		
A1	P	36	*Celebrities of the Great War (1916). See Major Drapkin & Co*			
A	BW	? 12	Celebrities of the Great War	Ha.236	—	—
A	C		*Colonial Troops:*	H.40		
		30	A Cream card		—	—
		50	B White card		£15.00	—
A	BW	20	Cricketers Series	H.29	£175.00	—
A	C	50	Dogs (as Taddy)	Ha.487	£22.00	—
A	C	25	*England's Military Heroes. See Player:*	H.352		
			A Wide card			
			B Narrow card			
A	C	25	*England's Naval Heroes. See Player:*	H.353		
			A Wide card			
			B Narrow card			
A	C	20	*The European War Series*	H.129	£6.00	—
A	C		*Flags, Arms and Types of Nations:*	H.115		
		24	A Numbered		£7.00	—
		? 1	B Unnumbered		—	—
A	C		*Flags and Flags with Soldiers:*	H.41	—	—
		30	A Flagstaff Draped		£7.00	—
		15	B Flagstaff not Draped (Flags only)		£7.00	—
A1	C	30	*Flags of Nations. See Cope*	H.114		
A1	C	24	*Girls, Flags and Arms of Countries. See Rutter*	H.383		
A	C	40	*Home and Colonial Regiments:*	H.69		
			20. Caption in blue		—	—
			20. Caption in brown		£7.00	—
A	C	52	*Japanese Series, P.C. Inset. See Muratti*			
A1	P	? 2	*King Edward and Queen Alexandra*	H.460	£18.00	—
C	C	20	*National Flag Series. See Hill*			

ANONYMOUS SERIES *(continued)*

Size	*Print-ing*	*Number in set*		*Handbook reference*	*Price per card*	*Complete set*
D	C	20	**Nations, gilt border. See Cohen Weenen*	H.97		
D	C	40	**Naval and Military Phrases:*	H.14		
			A Plain front (no border)		£8.00	—
			B Front with gilt border		—	—
—	U	? 1	**Portraits. See Drapkin & Millhoff (48 × 36mm)*	H.461		
A	U	? 47	**Pretty Girl Series — 'BAGG'*	H.45	£15.00	—
A2	C	12	**Pretty Girl Series 'RASH' (c1897)*	H.8	£16.00	—
A1	C	20	**Prince of Wales Series. See Hill*	H.22	£12.00	—
D	C	30	**Proverbs*	H.15	£10.00	—
A	BW	19	*Russo-Japanese Series*	Ha.184	£20.00	—
A	C	20	*Russo-Japanese War Series*	H.100	£20.00	—
A	C	10	*Scenes from San Toy. See Richard Lloyd*	H.462		
A	C	25	*Sports and Pastimes Series No. 1*	H.225	£7.00	—
A	C	25	**Star Girls*	H.30	£12.00	—
A1	BW	? 28	**Statuary (Hill A-D)*	H.218		
A	C	25	**Types of British and Colonial Troops*	H.76	—	—
A2	C	25	**Types of British Soldiers*	H.144	£10.00	—
—	U	? 21	*Views and Yachts (narrow, abt. 63 × 30mm)*	Ha.262-2	£50.00	—
D	BW	12	**Views of the World. See Drapkin*	H.176		
D	BW	8	**Warships. See Drapkin*	H.463		
D			**War Series:*	Ha.103		
	U	? 1	*A Front in brown*		—	—
	BW	? 2	*B Front in black and white*		—	—

C POST-1920 ISSUES. WITH LETTERPRESS ON BACK

	C	25	*Cinema Stars — see Teofani:*	Ha.530		
C2			*A Small size*			
—			*B Extra-large size (109 × 67mm)*			
A2	U	50	*Cinema Stars — Set 7 — see United Kingdom Tobacco Co*	Ha.515-7		
D2	C	25	*Cinema Stars — Set 8 — see Moustafa*	Ha.515-8		
A2	C	50	*Evolution of the British Navy — see Godfrey Phillips*			
A2	BW	40	*Famous Film Stars, text in Arabic (two series) — see Hill*			
A2	C	50	*Famous Footballers — see Godfrey Phillips*			
A2	C	35	*Famous Stars — see Reliance Tobacco Mfg. Co.*	Ha.572		
C2	C	20	*Great Inventors — see Teofani*	H.213		
D2	U	48	*Modern Movie Stars and Cinema Celebrities — see Teofani*	Ha.569		
D2	C	25	*Pictures of World Interest — see Moustafa*			
C2	U	24	*Well-Known Racehorses — see Teofani*	Ha.609		

D POST-1920 ISSUES. WITH DESIGNS ON BACK

A	BW	25	*Careless Moments (1922)*		80p	£20.00
D2	U	28	**Dominoes ("W.T.C." monogram back) — see Walker's Tobacco Co.*	Ha.535-2		
—	C	53	**Miniature Playing Cards (68 × 42mm) (red back, black cat trade mark in centre) — see Carreras*	Ha.535-1		
K2	C	53	**Miniature Playing Cards (blue scroll back) — see Godfrey Phillips*			
K2	C	53	**Miniature Playing Cards — see J. Wix:*	Ha.535-3		
			A Scroll design:			
			1 Red back			
			2 Blue back			
			B Ship design:			
			2 Black border — Drake's "Revenge"			

ANONYMOUS SERIES *(continued)*

Size	Printing	Number in set		Handbook reference	Price per card	Complete set
	C		**Playing Cards and Dominoes — see Carreras:*	Ha.535-1		
C		52	*A Small size:*			
			1 Numbered			
			2 Unnumbered			
—		26	*B Large size (77 × 69mm):*			
			1 Numbered			
			2 Unnumbered			

E POST-1920 ISSUES. WITH PLAIN BACK

Size	Printing	Number in set		Handbook reference	Price per card	Complete set
A2	P	36	*Australia. Second Series — see Westminster*			
A2	P	18	**Beauties — see Marcovitch*	Ha.627		
A1	P	60	**British Beauty Spots — see Coudens*	Ha.553		
B1	P	50	**British Castles, Nd. S.J.51-S.J.100 — see Pattreiouex*	Ha.595-3		
—	C	108	**British Naval Crests (74 × 52mm)*	Ha.504-4	—	—
D2	CP	50	**Camera Studies — see Moustafa*			
B1	P	50	**Cathedrals and Abbeys. Nd. S.J.1-S.J.50 — see Pattreiouex*	Ha.595-3		
A	C	25	**Charming Portraits — see Continental Cigarette Factory*	Ha.549		
A2	U	30	**Cinema Stars — Set 3*	Ha.515- 3	—	—
A2	U	30	**Cinema Stars — Set 6*	Ha.515-6	65p	£20.00
—	C	110	**Crests and Badges of the British Army (74 × 52mm):*	Ha.502-2		
			(a) Numbered		—	—
			(b) Unnumbered		—	—
—	BW	12	**Film Actors and Actresses (56 × 31mm) — see Teofani*	Ha.618		
A	C	20	**Head Dresses of Various Nations — see Teofani*	Ha.619-1		
A	—	20	**Inventors and Their Inventions — see Hill*	H.213		
—	C	? 9	**Irish Views (68 × 67mm) — see Lambkin*	Ha.585		
—	BW	12	**London Views (57 × 31mm) — see Teofani*	Ha.620		
A	C	50	**Natives in Costume — see Teofani*	Ha.619-2		
—	P	30	**Photographs (Animal Studies) (64 × 41mm)*	Ha.541	£1.50	—
—	C	? 48	**Regimental Colours II (76 × 70mm)*	Ha.502-7	£12.00	—
—	P	22	**Teofani Gems I — Series of 22 (53 × 35mm) — see Teofani*	Ha.621-1		
—	P	28	**Teofani Gems II — Series of 28 (53 × 35mm) see Teofani*	Ha.621-2		
—	P	36	**Teofani Gems III — Series of 36 (53 × 35mm) — see Teofani*	Ha.621-3		
A	C	50	**World's Smokers — see Teofani*	Ha.619-3		

F POST-1920 ISSUES. ANONYMOUS SERIES — Silks and Other Novelty Issues

For Anonymous Metal Plaques — see International Tobacco Co.
For Anonymous Metal Charms — see Rothman's.
For Anonymous Miniature Rugs — see Godfrey Phillips.
For Anonymous Lace Motifs — see Carreras.
For Anonymous Woven Silks — see Anstie and J. Wix.
For Anonymous Printed Silks with Blue Borders — see Themans.

Anonymous ordinary printed British silks which are found unbacked are listed below, with cross-reference to issuing firms. Entries marked § are only anonymous when the paper backings are missing, and in these cases the indication applies only to the silks without backings.

	Handbook reference
**Arms of Countries and Territories see Phillips*	Ha.504-12
**Battleship Crests I — see Morris§*	Ha.504-3
**British Admirals — see Phillips*	Ha.504-5

ANONYMOUS SERIES *(continued)*

Size	*Print-ing*	*Number in set*		*Handbook reference*	*Price per card*	*Complete set*
			**British Butterflies and Moths II — see Phillips*	Ha.505-6		
			**British Naval Crests II — see Phillips*	Ha.504-4		
			**Butterflies I — see Phillips*	Ha.505-5		
			**Butterflies and Moths III — see Leaf*	Ha.505-7		
			**Clan Tartans — see Phillips*	Ha505-15		
			**Colonial Army Badges — see Phillips*	Ha.502-3		
			County Cricket Badges — see Phillips	Ha.505		
			**Crests and Badges of the British Army II — see Phillips and Singleton & Cole§*	Ha.502-2		
			**English Flowers — see Morris§*	Ha.505-4		
			**English and Foreign Birds I — see Morris§*	Ha.505-1		
			**Flags — Set 1 — see Gallaher§*	Ha.501-1		
			**Flags — Set 2 — see Muratti*	Ha.501-2		
			**Flags — Set 3 — see Muratti§*	Ha.501-3		
			**Flags — Set 4 — see Phillips*	Ha.501-4		
			**Flags — Set 5 — see Phillips*	Ha.501-5		
			**Flags — Set 6 — see Phillips*	Ha.501-6		
			**Flags — Set 7 — see Phillips*	Ha.501-7		
			**Flags — Set 8 — see Muratti§*	Ha.501-8		
			**Flags — Set 9 — see Phillips*	Ha.501-9		
			**Flags — Set 10 (7th, 10th and 12th Series) — see Phillips*	Ha501-10		
			**Flags — Set 11 (Fourth to Seventh Series) — see John Sinclair*	Ha.501-11		
			**Flags — Set 12 ("Let 'em all come" and Allies grouped Flags) — see Phillips*	Ha.501-12		
			**Flags — Set 13 — see Phillips*	Ha.501-13		
			**Flags — Set 14 (House Flags) — see Phillips*	Ha.501-14		
			**Flags — Set 15 (Pilot and Signal Flags) — see Phillips*	Ha.501 -15		
			**Football Colours — see Phillips*	Ha.505-9		
			**Great War Leaders I — see Muratti§*	Ha.504-6		
			**Great War Leaders II — see Phillips*	Ha.504-7		
			**Great War Leaders III and Warships — see Phillips*	Ha.504-10		
			**Great War Leaders IV and Celebrities — see Phillips*	Ha.504-11		
			**Irish Patriots — see Phillips*	Ha.505-11		
			**Naval Badges of Rank and Military Headdress — see Phillips*	Ha.504-9		
			**Old Masters — Set 2 — see Phillips*	Ha.503-2		
			**Old Masters — Set 3A — see Phillips*	Ha.503-3A		
			**Old Masters — Set 3B — see Phillips*	Ha.503-3B		
			**Old Masters — Set 4 — see Phillips*	Ha.503-4		
			**Old Masters — Set 5 — see Phillips*	Ha.503-5		
			**Old Masters — Set 7 — see Phillips*	Ha.503-7		
			**Old Pottery — see Lea§*	Ha.505-14		
			**Orders of Chivalry I — see Phillips*	Ha.504-14		
			**Orders of Chivalry II — see Murray§*	Ha.504-15		
			**Pottery Types — see Salmon & Gluckstein§ (see RB21/311)*			
			**Regimental Badges I — see Muratti§ and John Sinclair§*	Ha.502-1		
			**Regiment Colours I — see Muratti§*	Ha.502-6		
			**Regimental Colours II — see Phillips and John Sinclair*	Ha.502-7		
			**Regimental Colours III — see Phillips*	Ha.502-8		
			**Regimental Colours IV — see Morris*	Ha.502-9		
			**Regimental Colours V — see Muratti§*	Ha.502-10		
			**Regimental Colours & Badges of the Indian Army — see Drapkin§*	Ha.502-5		
			**Regimental Crests and Badges III — see Lea§*	Ha.502-4		
			**Religious Pictures — see Phillips*	Ha.505-10		
			**Victoria Cross Heroes I — see Phillips*	Ha.504-1		
			**Victoria Cross Heroes II — see Phillips and Cohen Weenen§*	Ha.504-2		
			**War Pictures — see Phillips*	Ha.504-8		

SECTION II

FOREIGN CIGARETTE CARDS

INDEX OF BRANDS

Admiral Cigarettes — see National Cigarette & Tobacco Co.
Albert Cigarettes — see British American Tobacco Co.
S. Anargyros — see American Tobacco Co.

Between the Acts — see American Tobacco Co.
Big Run Cigarettes — see American Tobacco Co.
Black Spot Cigarettes — see Scerri
British Consuls — see Macdonald
Broadleaf Cigarettes — see American Tobacco Co.

Cairo Monopol Cigarettes — see American Tobacco Co.
Carolina Brights — see American Tobacco Co.
Copain Cigarettes — see British American Tobacco Co.
Coronet Cigarettes — see Sniders & Abrahams
Cycle Cigarettes — see American Tobacco Co.

Derby Little Cigars — see American Tobacco Co.
Domino Cigarettes — see British American Tobacco Co.

Egyptienne Luxury — see American Tobacco Co.
Emblem Cigarettes — see American Tobacco Co.

Fez Cigarettes — see American Tobacco Co.
Fume Emblem — see Westminster Tobacco Co.

Gold Coin Tobacco — see Buchner

Hassan Cigarettes — see American Tobacco Co.
Havelock Cigarettes — see Wills
Helmar Cigarettes — see American Tobacco Co.
Herbert Tareyton Cigarettes — see American Tobacco Co.
Hindu Cigarettes — see American Tobacco Co.
Hoffman House Magnums — see American Tobacco Co.
Honest Long Cut — see Duke or American Tobacco Co.
Hustler Little Cigars — see American Tobacco Co.

Islander, Fags, Specials, Cubs — see Bucktrout

Jack Rose Little Cigars — see American Tobacco Co.
Just Suits Cut Plug — see American Tobacco Co.

Kopec Cigarettes — see American Tobacco Co.

Lennox Cigarettes — see American Tobacco Co.
Le Roy Cigars — see Miller
Lifeboat Cigarettes — see United Tobacco Co.
Lotus Cigarettes — see United Tobacco Co.
Lucky Strike Cigarettes — see American Tobacco Co.
Luxury Cigarettes — see American Tobacco Co.

Magpie Cigarettes — see Schuh
Mascot Cigarettes — see British American Tobacco Co.
Mecca Cigarettes — see American Tobacco Co.
Milo Cigarettes — see Sniders & Abrahams

AFRICAN CIGARETTE CO. LTD, Egypt

Size	*Number in set*		*Price per card*	*Complete set*
	50	Actresses ALWICS (c1905)	£9.00	—
L	25	Auction Bridge (c1925)	£7.00	—

AFRICAN TOBACCO MANUFACTURERS, South Africa

A CARD ISSUES

L	29	All Blacks South African Tour (1928)	£11.00	—
	60	Animals (c1920):		
		A Cut Outs	£3.50	—
		B Not Cut Out	£3.25	—
	25	The Arcadia Fair (1924)	£6.50	—
MP	48	British Aircraft (1932)	£3.50	—
	50	Chinese Transport (1930)	£3.25	—
MP	48	Cinema Artistes (1930)	£3.25	—
	50	Cinema Stars "OMBI" Officers Mess Issue 1st Series (1921)	£1.80	£90.00
	50	Cinema Stars "OMBI" Officers Mess Issue 2nd Series (1921)	£1.80	£90.00
M	50	Famous and Beautiful Women (1938)	£1.80	—
L	50	Famous and Beautiful Women (1938)	£1.40	—
	33	Houses of Parliament (c1920)	£6.00	—
	58	Miniatures (c1925)	£6.00	—
MP	48	National Costume (1930)	£3.25	—
K	53	Playing Cards MP-SA Virginia Cigarettes (c1930)	£1.60	—
K	53	Playing Cards, OK Cigarettes (c1930)	£1.60	—
K	53	Playing Cards, Scotts Cigarettes (c1930)	£1.60	—
MP	48	Popular Dogs (1930)	£3.80	—
M	100	Postage Stamps, Rarest Varieties (1929)	£1.50	£150.00
M	80	Prominent NZ and Australian Rugby Players and Springbok 1937 Touring Team (1937)	£1.80	—
L	80	Prominent NZ and Australian Rugby Players and Springbok 1937 Touring Team (1937)	£1.80	—
	25	The Racecourse (1924)	£8.00	—
M	132	S. African Members of the Legislative Assembly (1921)	£22.00	—
M	100	The World of Sport (1938)	£2.50	—
L	100	The World of Sport (1938)	£2.50	—

B SILK ISSUES

M	30	Some Beautiful Roses (c1925)	£8.00	—
M	25	Types of British Birds (c1925)	£8.00	—
M	20	Types of British Butterflies (c1925)	£8.00	—
M	25	Types of Railway Engines (c1925)	£22.00	—
M	25	Types of Sea Shells (c1925)	£11.00	—

ALLEN & GINTER, USA

ALL SERIES ISSUED 1885-95

	?	Actors and Actresses (sepia photographic)	£4.00	—
	?	Actresses and Beauties (coloured)	£8.00	—
	50	American Editors	£22.00	—
L	50	American Editors	£28.00	—
	50	Arms of All Nations	£17.00	—
	50	Birds of America	£10.00	£500.00
L	50	Birds of America	£18.00	—
	50	Birds of the Tropics	£12.00	£600.00
L	50	Birds of the Tropics	£22.00	—
	50	Celebrated American Indian Chiefs	£20.00	—
	50	City Flags	£10.00	—
	50	Fans of the Period	£18.00	—

ALLEN & GINTER, USA *(continued)*

Size	*Number in set*		*Price per card*	*Complete set*
	50	Fish from American Waters	£10.00	—
L	50	Fish from American Waters	£22.00	—
	50	Flags of All Nations (series title curved)	£6.50	£325.00
	48	Flags of All Nations (series title in straight line)	£6.50	£325.00
	50	Flags of All Nations, 2nd series	£7.50	£375.00
	47	Flags of the States and Territories	£9.00	—
	50	Fruits	£16.00	—
	50	Game Birds	£10.00	£500.00
L	50	Game Birds	£22.00	—
	50	General Government and State Capitol Buildings	£10.00	—
	50	Great Generals	£25.00	—
	50	Natives in Costume	£22.00	—
	50	Naval Flags	£11.00	£550.00
	50	Parasol Drill	£18.00	—
	50	Pirates of the Spanish Main	£24.00	—
	50	Prize and Game Chickens	£15.00	—
	50	Quadrupeds	£12.00	—
L	50	Quadrupeds	£22.00	—
	50	Racing Colors of the World:		
		A Front with white frame	£16.00	—
		B Front without white frame	£16.00	—
	50	Song Birds of the World	£10.00	£500.00
L	50	Song Birds of the World	£22.00	—
	50	Types of All Nations	£16.00	—
	50	Wild Animals of the World	£12.00	—
	50	The World's Beauties, 1st series	£16.00	—
	50	The World's Beauties, 2nd series	£16.00	—
	50	The World's Champions, 1st series	£20.00	—
	50	The World's Champions, 2nd series	£22.00	—
L	50	The World's Champions, 2nd series	£40.00	—
	50	The World's Decorations	£11.00	£550.00
L	50	The World's Decorations	£22.00	—
	50	World's Dudes	£16.00	—
	50	The World's Racers	£18.00	—
	50	World's Smokers	£13.00	£650.00
	50	World's Sovereigns	£22.00	—

ALLEN TOBACCO CO., USA

L	?	Views and Art Studies (c1910)	£4.00	—

THE AMERICAN CIGARETTE CO. LTD, China

	25	Beauties Group 1 (c1900)	£16.00	—
	? 15	Beauties Group 2 (c1900)	£18.00	—
	50	Flowers (c1900)	£12.00	—

THE AMERICAN TOBACCO COMPANY, USA

ALL SERIES ISSUED 1890-1902

A TYPESET BACK IN BLACK

	28	Beauties Domino Girls	£16.00	—
	25	Beauties Group 1 RB18/4	£4.00	—
	? 1	Beauties Group 2 RB18/20	—	—
	25	Beauties Group 3 RB18/25	£4.00	—
	27	Beauties Group 3 RB18/26	£4.00	£110.00
	25	Beauties Group 3 RB18/27	£4.00	—

Size	*Number in set*		*Price per card*	*Complete set*
	25	Beauties Group 3 RB18/29	£4.00	—
		Beauties Group 4 RB18/36:		
	50	a Coloured	£4.00	£200.00
	? 50	b Sepia	£15.00	—
	52	Beauties PC Inset	£7.00	£365.00
	25	Beauties — Star Girls	£13.00	—
	25	Dancers	£9.00	—
	50	Dancing Women	£14.00	—
	50	Fancy Bathers	£14.00	—
	36	Japanese Girls	£35.00	—
	25	Military Uniforms RB18/101	£11.00	—
	25	Military Uniforms RB18/102	£11.00	—
	27	Military Uniforms RB18/103	£6.00	—
	50	Musical Instruments	£12.00	—
	50	National Flag and Arms	£8.00	—
	25	National Flag and Flowers — Girls	£16.00	—
	50	Savage Chiefs and Rulers	£18.00	—
B		***NET DESIGN BACK IN GREEN***		
	25	Beauties — black background RB18/62	£8.00	—
	25	Beauties — Curtain Background RB18/65	£7.00	£175.00
	25	Beauties Flower Girls RB18/67	£7.00	—
	25	Beauties Group 1 RB18/1	£4.00	—
	27	Beauties Group 1 RB18/2	£4.00	—
	25	Beauties Group 1 RB18/3	£4.00	—
	24	Beauties Group 1 RB18/4	£4.00	—
	25	Beauties Group 1 RB18/5	£4.00	—
	25	Beauties Group 1 RB18/6	£4.00	—
	50	Beauties Group 1 RB18/10	£4.00	—
	25	Beauties Group 2 RB18/16	£4.00	—
	25	Beauties Group 2 RB18/17	£4.00	—
	? 24	Beauties Group 2 RB18/18	£4.00	—
	25	Beauties Group 2 RB18/19	£4.00	—
	25	Beauties Group 2 RB18/20	£4.00	—
	25	Beauties Group 2 RB18/21	£5.00	—
	36	Beauties Group 2 RB18/22	£6.00	—
	25	Beauties Group 3 RB18/25	£4.00	—
	? 10	Beauties Group 3 RB18/28	—	—
	25	Beauties Group 3 RB18/30	£4.00	—
	25	Beauties Group 3 RB18/31	£8.00	—
	25	Beauties Group 3 RB18/32	£4.00	—
	50	Beauties Marine and Universe Girls	£18.00	—
	25	Beauties Palette Girls	£7.50	—
	25	Beauties Star Girls	£14.00	—
	25	Beauties — stippled background RB18/78	£8.00	—
	20	Beauties — thick border RB18/79	£22.00	—
	52	Beauties with Playing Card inset Set 1 RB18/85	£7.50	—
	52	Beauties with Playing Card inset Set 2 RB18/86	£7.50	£375.00
	25	Boer War Series II — Series A:		
		a) numbered	£4.00	£100.00
		b) unnumbered	£5.00	—
		c) unnumbered and untitled "series A"	£6.00	—
	22	Boer War Series II — Series B	£6.00	—
	25	Chinese Girls	£9.00	—
	25	Fish from American Waters	£6.00	—
	25	International Code of Signals	£8.00	—
	27	Military Uniforms numbered	£5.00	—

Size	*Number in set*		*Price per card*	*Complete set*
	25	Military Uniforms unnumbered	£10.00	—
	50	National Flags and Arms	£10.00	—
	25	Old and Ancient Ships 1st Series	£4.00	£100.00
	25	Old and Ancient Ships 2nd Series	£6.00	£150.00
	25	Star Series — Beauties	£12.00	—
C		***NET DESIGN BACK IN BLUE***		
		Actresses:		
P	? 300	A Large Letter Back	£4.00	—
P	? 300	B Small Letter Back	£5.00	—
	25	Beauties blue frameline:		
		A Matt	£20.00	—
		B Varnished	£20.00	—
	28	Beauties — Domino Girls	£16.00	—
	28	Beauties Group 1 dull backgrounds	£8.00	—
	23	Beauties Group 1 vivid coloured backgrounds set 1	£8.00	—
	25	Beauties Group 1 vivid coloured backgrounds set 2	£8.00	—
	25	Beauties:		
		A Front in black and white	£18.00	—
		B Front in mauve	£12.00	—
	24	Beauties — orange framelines	£25.00	—
		Beauties — playing cards:		
	52	A Inscribed 52 subjects	£7.50	—
	53	B Inscribed 53 subjects	£7.50	—
	32	Celebrities	£4.50	—
	25	Comic Scenes	£7.50	—
P	? 149	Views	£3.00	—
D		***"OLD GOLD" BACK***		
	25	Beauties Group 1 RB18/1	£4.00	—
	27	Beauties Group 1 RB18/2	£4.00	—
	25	Beauties Group 1 RB18/3	£4.00	—
	24	Beauties Group 1 RB18/4	£4.00	—
	25	Beauties Group 1 RB18/5	£4.00	—
	25	Beauties Group 1 RB18/6	£4.00	—
	? 47	Beauties Group 2 RB18/16, 17, 18	£4.00	—
	25	Beauties Group 2 RB18/22	£4.00	—
	25	Beauties Group 3 RB18/25	£4.00	—
	27	Beauties Group 3 RB18/26	£4.00	—
	25	Beauties Group 3 RB18/27	£4.00	—
	25	Beauties Group 3 RB18/28	£4.00	—
	25	Beauties Group 3 RB18/30	£4.00	—
	25	Flowers Inset on Beauties	£6.00	£150.00
	25	International Code of Signals:		
		A With series title	£6.00	£150.00
		B Without series title	£6.00	£150.00
E		***LABELS BACK***		
	35	Beauties Group 1 RB18/2-3	£4.00	—
	25	Beauties Group 2 1st Set RB18/15	£4.00	—
	25	Beauties Group 2 2nd Set RB18/16	£4.00	—
		Beauties Group 3 RB18/25-26:		
	27	A Old Gold Label	£4.00	—
	26	B Brands Label	£4.00	—
F		***OTHER BACKS WITH NAME OF FIRM***		
P	100	Actresses RB18/91	£4.00	—
	44	Australian Parliament	£4.00	£170.00

Size	Number in set		Price per card	Complete set
	25	Battle Scenes	£8.00	—
	1	Columbian and Other Postage Stamps (1892)	—	£12.00
	50	Congress of Beauty — Worlds Fair	£18.00	—
	50	Fish from American Waters	£9.00	—
	50	Flags of All Nations	£10.00	—
	25	Flower Inset on Beauties	£6.00	£150.00
	25	International Code of Signals	£6.00	£150.00
	25	Songs A (1896):		
		A Thicker board size 70 × 39mm	£9.00	—
		B Thinner board size 67 × 39mm	£9.00	£225.00
	25	Songs B:		
		A Size 70 × 39mm	£9.00	£225.00
		B Size 67 × 39mm	£9.00	—
	25	Songs C 1st series	£6.00	—
	25	Songs C 2nd series	£9.00	—
	25	Songs D	£6.00	£150.00
	27	Songs E	£9.00	—
	25	Songs F	£9.00	—
	25	Songs G	£7.00	—
	25	Songs H	£13.00	—
	25	Songs I	£18.00	—
ISSUES 1903-1940				
	50	Actors	£5.00	—
	85	Actress Series	£6.00	—
	50	Actresses	£8.00	—
		Animals:		
	40	A Descriptive back	£1.60	—
	40	B Non descriptive back	£1.60	—
	25	Arctic Scenes	£2.80	—
	15	Art Gallery Pictures	£5.00	—
	50	Art Reproductions	£5.00	—
	21	Art Series	£15.00	—
	18	Ask Dad	£12.00	—
	50	Assorted Standard Bearers of Different Countries	£5.00	—
	25	Auto-drivers	£12.00	—
	50	Automobile Series	£12.00	—
	50	Baseball Folder series (T201) (1911)	£16.00	—
	121	Baseball series (T204)	£35.00	—
	208	Baseball series (T205) (1911)	£16.00	—
	522	Baseball series (T206)	£16.00	—
	200	Baseball series (T207) (1910)	£25.00	—
	565	Baseball series (T210)	£20.00	—
	75	Baseball series (T211)	£20.00	—
	426	Baseball series (T212)	£20.00	—
	180	Baseball series (T213)	£25.00	—
	90	Baseball series (T214)	£60.00	—
	100	Baseball series (T215)	£20.00	—
	76	Baseball Triple Folders (T202) (1912)	£30.00	—
		Bird series:		
	50	A With white borders	£2.00	—
	50	B With gold borders	£2.00	—
	30	Bird Series with Fancy Gold Frame	£2.50	—
	360	Birthday Horoscopes	£1.80	—
	24	British Buildings "Tareyton" issue	£2.50	—
	42	British Sovereigns "Tareyton" issue	£2.20	—
	50	Butterfly Series	£4.00	—

Size	*Number in set*		*Price per card*	*Complete set*
L	153	Champion Athlete & Prize Fighter series (size 73 × 64mm)	£4.50	—
L	50	Champion Athlete and Prize Fighter series (size 83 × 63 mm)	£10.00	—
L	50	Champion Pugilists	£15.00	—
EL	100	Champion Women Swimmers	£6.00	—
M	150	College series	£1.70	—
M	50	Costumes and Scenery for All Countries of the World	£3.00	—
L	49	Cowboy series	£5.00	—
M	38	Cross Stitch	£9.00	—
M	17	Embarrassing Moments or Emotional Moments	£14.00	—
M	50	Emblem Series	£2.50	—
L	100	Fable Series	£2.25	—
LP	53	Famous Baseball Players, American Athletic Champions and Photoplay Stars	£25.00	—
	50	Fish Series inscribed "1 to 50" — 1st 50 subjects	£2.00	—
	50	Fish Series inscribed "1 to 100" — 2nd 50 subjects	£2.00	—
	200	Flags of All Nations	£1.25	—
M	100	Flags of All Nations	£8.00	—
	50	Foreign Stamp Series	£5.00	—
L	505	Fortune Series	£1.60	—
M	79	Henry "Tareyton" issue	£1.80	—
L	50	Heroes of History	£5.00	—
M	50	Historic Homes	£3.00	—
L	25	Historical Events Series	£5.00	—
M	25	Hudson — Fulton Series	£6.00	—
L	50	Indian Life in the 60s (1910)	£5.00	—
L	221	Jig Saw Puzzle Pictures	£5.00	—
L	50	Light House Series	£4.00	—
L	50	Men of History	£5.00	—
	100	Military Series white borders	£4.00	—
	50	Military Series gilt borders	£4.50	—
	50	Military Series "Recruit" issue:		
		A Uncut cards	£4.00	—
		B Die-cut cards	£4.00	—
	50	Movie Stars	£4.50	—
L	100	Movie Stars	£4.00	—
	33	Moving Picture Stars	£16.00	—
EL	50	Murad Post Card Series	£7.00	—
	100	Mutt & Jeff Series (black and white)	£4.00	—
	100	Mutt & Jeff Series (coloured)	£4.00	—
EL	16	National League and American League Teams	£25.00	—
	50	Pugilistic Subjects	£15.00	—
EL	18	Puzzle Picture Cards	£12.00	—
M	200	Riddle Series	£2.30	—
EL	60	Royal Bengal Souvenir Cards	£6.00	—
M	150	Seals of the United States and Coats of Arms	£1.50	—
L	25	Series of Champions	£20.00	—
L	50	Sights and Scenes of the World	£3.00	—
L	50	Silhouettes	£6.00	—
L	25	Song Bird Series	£8.00	—
	39	Sports Champions	£20.00	—
	45	Stage Stars	£6.00	—
	25	State Girl Series	£5.00	—
L	50	Theatres Old and New Series	£5.50	—
M	50	Toast Series	£5.50	—
M	550	Toast Series	£2.00	—
L	25	Toasts	£9.00	—

THE AMERICAN TOBACCO COMPANY, USA *(continued)*

Size	Number in set		Price per card	Complete set
	50	Types of Nations:		
		A Without series title	£2.20	—
		B With series title	£2.20	—
		C Anonymous back	£2.20	—
L	25	Up to Date Baseball Comics	£15.00	—
L	25	Up to Date Comics	£7.00	—
P	340	World Scenes and Portraits	£3.00	—
	250	World War I Scenes	£2.00	—
L	50	World's Champion Athletes	£9.00	—
L	25	The World's Greatest Explorers	£3.00	—

THE AMERICAN TOBACCO CO. OF NEW SOUTH WALES LTD, Australia

	25	Beauties Group 1 RB18/8 (c1900)	£10.00	—
	25	Beauties Group 2 (c1900)	£10.00	—

THE AMERICAN TOBACCO CO. OF VICTORIA LTD, Australia

	? 98	Beauties Group 2 (c1900)	£10.00	—

ATLAM CIGARETTE FACTORY, Malta

M	65	Beauties back in blue (c1925)	£2.30	—
	150	Beauties back in brown (c1925)	£4.50	—
M	519	Celebrities (c1925)	£1.20	—
L	50	Views of Malta (c1925)	£4.50	—
M	128	Views of the World (c1925)	£4.50	—

BANNER TOBACCO CO., USA

L	25	Girls (c1890)	£25.00	—

THOMAS BEAR & SONS LTD

	50	Aeroplanes (1926)	£3.40	—
	50	Cinema Artistes Set 2 (c1935)	£3.50	—
	50	Cinema Artistes Set 4 (c1935)	£3.50	—
	50	Cinema Stars coloured (1930)	£1.80	£90.00
	50	Do You Know (1923)	£1.50	£75.00
	270	Javanese series 1 blue background (c1925)	£1.20	—
	100	Javanese series 4 yellow background (c1925)	£8.00	—
	50	Stage and Film Stars (1926)	£3.00	—

AUG BECK & CO. USA

	? 34	Picture Cards (c1890)	£50.00	—

J. & F. BELL LTD, Denmark

	60	Rigvaabner (Arms of Countries) (c1925)	£30.00	—
	60	Women of Nations (1924)	£30.00	—

BENSON & HEDGES (CANADA) LTD

	48	Ancient and Modern Fire Fighting Equipment (1947)	£5.00	—

BRITISH AMERICAN TOBACCO CO. LTD

Size	Number in set		Price per card	Complete set
A	***WITH MAKER'S NAME NET DESIGN IN GREEN (ISSUES 1902-05)***			
	25	Beauties Art series RB18/61	£8.00	—
	25	Beauties — black background RB18/62	£8.00	—
	25	Beauties — Blossom Girls RB18/63	£35.00	—
	25	Beauties — Flower Girls RB18/67	£6.00	—
	25	Beauties — Fruit Girls RB18/68	£10.00	—
	25	Beauties — Girls in Costumes RB18/69	£9.00	—
	20	Beauties Group 1 RB18/9	£7.00	—
	25	Beauties — Lantern Girls RB18/70	£6.00	£150.00
	50	Beauties — Marine and Universe Girls RB18/71	£8.00	—
	25	Beauties — Palette Girls RB18/74:		
		A Plain border to front	£8.00	—
		B Red border to front	£12.00	—
	24	Beauties — Smoke Girls RB18/75	£14.00	—
	25	Beauties — Star Girls RB18/76	£14.00	—
	25	Beauties — stippled background RB18/78	£6.00	£150.00
	25	Beauties — Water Girls RB18/80	£6.00	£150.00
	50	Buildings RB18/131	£8.00	—
	25	Chinese Girls 'A' RB18/111	£8.00	—
	25	Chinese Girls 'B' RB18/112:		
		A Background plain	£8.00	—
		B Background with Chinese letters	£8.00	—
	25	Chinese Girls 'C' RB18/113	£8.00	—
	25	Chinese Girls 'D' RB18/114	£8.00	—
	25	Chinese Girls 'E' RB18/115	£8.00	—
	25	Chinese Girls 'F' Set 1 RB18/116	£8.00	—
	25	Chinese Girls 'F' Set 2 RB18/116:		
		A Yellow border	£8.00	—
		B Gold border	£10.00	—
	50	Chinese Girls 'F' Set 3:		
		A Plain background	£8.00	—
		B Chinese characters background	£9.00	—
	40	Chinese Trades	£6.00	—
B	***WITH MAKER'S NAME NET DESIGN IN BLUE (ISSUES 1902-05)***			
	25	Beauties — numbered	£16.00	—
	53	Beauties — Playing Cards	£6.00	—
C	***WITH MAKER'S NAME OTHER BACKS***			
MP	50	Beauties (1925)	£1.70	£85.00
MP	40	Beauties (1926)	£1.70	—
M	50	Birds, Beasts and Fishes (1925)	£1.70	£85.00
	50	Danish Athletes (1905)	£10.00	—
	28	Dominoes (1905)	£5.50	—
	48	Fairy Tales (1926)	£3.00	—
	48	A Famous Picture — The Toast (c1930)	£3.00	—
	25	New York Views (c1908)	£8.50	—
	53	Playing Cards (1905)	£8.50	—
M	50	Wild Animals (c1930)	£1.30	—
D	***SERIES WITH BRAND NAMES***			
ALBERT CIGARETTES				
M	50	Aeroplanes (Civil) (1935)	£5.00	—
	50	Artistes de Cinema Nd 1-50 (1932)	£2.00	—
	50	Artistes de Cinema Nd 51-100 (1933)	£2.00	—
	50	Artistes de Cinema Nd 101-150 (1934)	£2.00	—
MP	? 67	Beauties (c1928)	£4.00	—
M	75	Belles Vues de Belgique (c1930)	£2.20	—
M	50	Birds, Beasts & Fishes (c1930)	£4.00	—

BRITISH AMERICAN TOBACCO CO. LTD *(continued)*

Size	*Number in set*		*Price per card*	*Complete set*
M	50	Butterflies (Girls) (1926)	£4.00	—
M	50	Cinema Stars (brown photogravure) (c1927)	£2.25	—
M	100	Cinema Stars (numbered, coloured) (c1928)	£2.00	—
M	208	Cinema Stars (unnumbered, coloured) (c1929)	£2.00	—
M	100	Circus Scenes (c1930)	£2.50	—
M	100	Famous Beauties (1916)	£3.50	—
M	50	L'Afrique Equitoriale de l'Est a l'Ouest (c1930)	£2.25	—
M	100	La Faune Congolaise (c1930)	£1.20	—
M	50	Les Grandes Paquebots du Monde (1924)	£4.50	—
M	50	Merveilles du Monde (1927)	£3.50	—
M	50	Women of Nations (Flag Girls) (1922)	£3.50	—
ATLAS CIGARETTES				
	50	Buildings (1907)	£4.50	—
	25	Chinese Beauties (1912)	£2.20	—
	50	Chinese Trades Set IV (1908)	£2.20	—
	85	Chinese Trades Set VI (1912)	£2.20	—
BATTLE AX CIGARETTES				
M	100	Famous Beauties (1916)	£4.00	—
M	50	Women of Nations (Flag Girls) (1917)	£4.50	—
COPAIN CIGARETTES				
	52	Birds of Brilliant Plumage (1927)	£5.50	—
DOMINO CIGARETTES				
	25	Animaux et Reptiles (1961)	16p	£4.00
	25	Corsaires et Boucaniers (1961)	15p	£2.50
	25	Figures Historiques 1st series (1961)	15p	£3.00
	25	Figures Historiques 2nd series (1961)	50p	£12.50
	25	Fleurs de Culture (1961)	15p	£2.50
	25	Les Oiseaux et l'Art Japonais (1961)	70p	£17.50
	25	Les Produits du Monde (1961)	15p	£2.50
	50	Voitures Antiques (1961)	£1.00	—
EAGLE BIRD CIGARETTES				
	50	Animals and Birds (1909)	£2.00	—
	50	Aviation series (1912)	£2.50	—
	25	Birds of the East (1912)	£1.80	£45.00
	25	China's Famous Warriors (1911)	£2.40	£60.00
	25	Chinese Beauties 1st series (1908):		
		A Vertical back	£3.00	—
		B Horizontal back	£3.00	—
	25	Chinese Beauties 2nd series (1909):		
		A Front without framelines	£2.00	—
		B Front with framelines	£2.00	—
	50	Chinese Trades (1908)	£2.00	£100.00
	25	Cock Fighting (1911)	£5.00	—
	60	Flags and Pennons (1926)	£1.20	£72.00
	50	Romance of the Heavens (1929)	£2.00	—
	50	Siamese Alphabet (1922)	£1.20	£60.00
	50	Siamese Dreams and Their Meanings (1923)	£1.10	£55.00
	50	Siamese Horoscopes (c1915)	£1.10	£55.00
	50	Siamese Play-Inao (c1915)	£1.30	£65.00
	50	Siamese Play-Khun Chang Khun Phaen 1st series (c1915)	£1.20	£60.00
	50	Siamese Play-Khun Chang Khun Phaen 2nd series (c1915)	£1.20	£60.00
	36	Siamese Play-Phra Aphaiu 1st series (c1918)	£1.25	£45.00
	36	Siamese Play-Phra Aphaiu 2nd series (1919)	£1.25	£45.00
	150	Siamese Play — Ramakien I (c1913)	£1.20	—
	50	Siamese Play — Ramakien II (1914)	£1.20	£60.00
	50	Siamese Uniforms (1915)	£1.80	£90.00

Size	*Number in set*		*Price per card*	*Complete set*
	50	Views of Siam (1928)	£1.20	£60.00
	50	Views of Siam (Bangkok) (1928)	£1.20	£60.00
	30	War Weapons (1914)	£2.00	£60.00
KONG BENG CIGARETTES				
	60	Animals (cut-outs) (1912)	£4.50	—
MASCOT CIGARETTES				
	100	Cinema Stars (Nd 201-300) (1931)	£3.00	—
M	208	Cinema Stars unnumbered (1924)	£2.00	—
MILLBANK CIGARETTES				
	60	Animals (cut-outs):		
		A '1516' at base of back (1922)	£1.00	—
		B '3971' at base of back (1923)	80p	£48.00
NASSA CIGARETTES				
M	50	Birds, Beasts and Fishes (1924)	£4.00	—
PEDRO CIGARETTES (see also Imperial Tobacco Co. of India)				
	50	Actors and Actresses (c1905)	£3.50	—
	40	Nautch Girls. Coloured (1905)	£2.00	—
	37	Nautch Girls. Red border (c1905)	£1.75	—
PINHEAD CIGARETTES				
	50	Chinese Modern Beauties (1912)	£1.30	—
	33	Chinese Heroes Set 1 (1912)	£1.50	—
	50	Chinese Heroes Set 2 (1913)	£1.50	—
	50	Chinese Trades Set III (1908)	£1.30	£65.00
	50	Chinese Trades Set IV (1909)	£1.30	£65.00
	50	Chinese Trades Set V (1910)	£1.30	£65.00
	50	Types of the British Army (1909)	£2.50	—
RAILWAY CIGARETTES (see also Imperial Tobacco Co. of India)				
	37	Nautch Girls series (1907)	£2.00	—
TEAL CIGARETTES				
	30	Chinese Beauties (c1915)	£4.00	—
	50	Cinema Stars (1930):		
		A Back in blue	£1.50	—
		B Back in red brown	£1.50	—
	30	Fish series (1916)	£1.80	£55.00
	50	War Incidents (1916)	£1.80	£90.00
TIGER CIGARETTES				
	52	Nautch Girls series (1911):		
		A Without frameline to front	£2.40	—
		B With frameline to front:		
		i With crossed cigarettes on back	£1.60	—
		ii Without crossed cigarettes on back	£2.00	—
E PRINTED ON BACK NO MAKER'S NAME OR BRAND				
(See also Imperial Tobacco Co. of Canada Ltd and United Tobacco Companies (South) Ltd)				
		Actresses 'ALWICS' (c1905):		
	175	A Portrait in black	£2.50	—
	50	B Portrait in red	£4.00	—
	50	Aeroplanes (1926)	£1.80	£90.00
	50	Aeroplanes of Today (1936)	80p	£40.00
	25	Angling (1930)	£3.00	£75.00
	50	Arms and Armour (1910)	£3.50	—
	25	Army Life (c1910)	£5.00	—
	50	Art Photogravures (1913)	£1.00	—
	1	Australia Day (1915)	—	£12.00
	22	Automobielen (c1925)	£6.00	—
	75	Aviation (1910)	£2.50	—

BRITISH AMERICAN TOBACCO CO. LTD *(continued)*

Size	*Number in set*		*Price per card*	*Complete set*
	50	Aviation series (1911):		
		A With album clause	£3.00	—
		B Without album clause	£2.50	—
		Beauties Set I (1925):		
P	50	A Black and white	£1.30	£65.00
MP	50	B Coloured	£1.50	—
P	50	Beauties 2nd series (1925):		
		A Black and white	£1.30	£65.00
		B Coloured	£2.00	—
P	50	Beauties 3rd series (1926)	£1.30	£65.00
	50	Beauties red tinted (c1906)	£1.80	—
		Beauties tobacco leaf back (c1908):		
	52	A With PC inset	£2.50	£130.00
	50	B Without PC inset	£3.60	£180.00
P	50	Beauties of Great Britain (1930):		
		A Non-stereoscopic	60p	£30.00
		B Stereoscopic	£1.20	—
P	50	Beautiful England (1928)	50p	£25.00
MP	60	La Belgique Monumentale et Pittoresque (c1925)	£3.00	—
	50	Best Dogs of Their Breed (1916)	£3.40	—
	50	Billiards (1929)	£1.25	—
	50	Birds, Beasts and Fishes (1937)	50p	£25.00
M	50	Birds, Beasts and Fishes (1929)	£1.20	£60.00
	24	Birds of England (1924)	£2.20	£55.00
	50	Boy Scouts (1930) — without album clause	£1.80	£90.00
	50	Britain's Defenders (1915):		
		A Blue grey fronts	£1.60	—
		B Mauve fronts	£1.40	£70.00
	50	British Butterflies (1930)	£1.00	£50.00
	50	British Empire series (1913)	£2.50	—
	25	British Trees and Their Uses (1930)	£1.80	£45.00
	50	British Warships and Admirals (1915)	£2.50	—
	50	Butterflies and Moths (1911):		
		A With album case	£2.50	—
		B Without album case	£1.40	—
	50	Butterflies (Girls) (1928)	£4.50	£225.00
M	50	Butterflies (Girls) (1928)	£4.50	£225.00
M	50	Celebrities of Film and Stage (1930):		
		A Title on back in box	£1.30	£65.00
		B Title on back not in box	£1.30	£65.00
LP	48	Channel Islands Past and Present (1939):		
		A Without '3rd Series'	£1.20	—
		B With '3rd Series'	30p	£15.00
	40	Characters from the Works of Charles Dickens (1919):		
		A Complete set	—	£45.00
		B 38 different (— Nos 33, 39)	60p	£23.00
	50	Cinema Artistes, black and white set 1 (Nd 1-50) (c1928)	£1.00	£50.00
	50	Cinema Artistes black and white set 4 (Nd 101-150) (c1928)	£1.00	£50.00
		Cinema Artistes brown set 1 (c1930):		
	60	A With 'Metro Golden Mayer'	£1.00	£60.00
	50	B Without 'Metro Golden Mayer'	£1.20	—
	50	Cinema Artistes brown set 2 (c1931):		
		A Oblong panel at top back	£1.00	£50.00
		B Oval panel at top back	£1.20	£60.00
L	48	Cinema Artistes set 3 (c1931)	£1.25	£60.00
	48	Cinema Celebrities (C) (1935)	80p	£40.00

BRITISH AMERICAN TOBACCO CO. LTD *(continued)*

Size	*Number in set*		*Price per card*	*Complete set*
L	48	Cinema Celebrities (C) (1935)	90p	£45.00
L	56	Cinema Celebrities (D) (1936)	£2.50	—
	50	Cinema Favourites (1929)	£2.20	£110.00
	50	Cinema Stars Set 2 (Nd 1-50) (1928)	80p	£40.00
	50	Cinema Stars Set 3 (Nd 51-100) (1929)	90p	—
	50	Cinema Stars Set 4 (Nd 101-150) (1930)	80p	—
	100	Cinema Stars 'BAMT' (coloured) (1931)	£1.40	£140.00
P	50	Cinema Stars Set 1 (c1928)	90p	—
P	50	Cinema Stars Set 2 (c1928)	80p	£40.00
P	50	Cinema Stars Set 3 (c1928)	£1.00	—
MP	52	Cinema Stars Set 4 (c1928)	£1.30	—
MP	52	Cinema Stars Set 5 (c1928)	£1.30	—
MP	52	Cinema Stars Set 6 (c1928)	£1.75	—
LP	48	Cinema Stars Set 7 (c1928)	£2.00	—
P	50	Cinema Stars Set 8 (Nd 1-50) (c1928)	£1.00	£50.00
P	50	Cinema Stars Set 9 (Nd 51-100) (c1928)	£1.00	£50.00
P	50	Cinema Stars Set 10 (Nd 101-150) (c1928)	£1.00	£50.00
P	50	Cinema Stars Set 11 (Nd 151-200) (c1928)	£1.00	£50.00
	25	Derby Day series (1914)	£7.50	—
	50	Do You Know? (1923)	45p	£22.50
	50	Do You Know? 2nd series (1931)	45p	£22.50
	25	Dracones Posthistorici (c1930)	£6.00	—
	25	Dutch Scenes (1928)	£2.40	£60.00
	50	Engineering Wonders (1930)	50p	£25.00
	40	English Costumes of Ten Centuries (1919)	£1.25	£50.00
P	25	English Cricketers (1926)	£2.60	£65.00
	26	Etchings (of Dogs) (1926)	£1.75	£45.00
P	50	Famous Bridges (1935)	60p	£30.00
	50	Famous Footballers Set 1 (1923)	£2.50	—
	50	Famous Footballers Set 2 (1924)	£2.50	—
	50	Famous Footballers Set 3 (1925)	£2.50	—
	25	Famous Racehorses (1926)	£2.40	£60.00
	25	Famous Railway Trains (1929)	£1.80	£45.00
	50	Favourite Flowers (c1925)	70p	£35.00
	50	Film and Stage Favourites (c1925)	£1.30	£65.00
	75	Film Favourites (1928)	£1.20	£90.00
	50	Flags of the Empire (1928)	70p	£35.00
	50	Foreign Birds (1930)	60p	£30.00
	50	Game Birds and Wild Fowl (1929)	£1.40	£70.00
LP	45	Grace and Beauty (Nos 1-45) (1938)	35p	£16.00
LP	45	Grace and Beauty (Nos 46-90) (1939)	30p	£13.50
LP	48	Guernsey, Alderney and Sark Past and Present 1st series (1937)	30p	£15.00
LP	48	Guernsey, Alderney and Sark Past and Present 2nd series (1938)	30p	£15.00
L	80	Guernsey Footballers Priaulx League (1938)	40p	£32.00
P	52	Here There and Everywhere:		
		A Non stereoscopic (1929)	40p	£20.00
		B Stereoscopic (1930)	60p	£30.00
	25	Hints and Tips for Motorists (1929)	£2.20	£55.00
P	50	Homeland Events (1928)	60p	£30.00
	50	Horses of Today (1906)	£4.50	—
	32	Houses of Parliament (red back) (1912)	£1.75	—
	32	Houses of Parliament (brown backs with verse) (1912)	£7.50	—
	50	Indian Chiefs (1930)	£7.00	—
	50	Indian Regiment series (1912)	£8.00	—
	50	International Airliners (1937)	70p	£35.00
	25	Java Scenes (1929)	£7.50	—

BRITISH AMERICAN TOBACCO CO. LTD *(continued)*

Size	*Number in set*		*Price per card*	*Complete set*
LP	48	Jersey Then and Now 1st series (1935)	60p	£30.00
LP	48	Jersey Then and Now 2nd series (1937)	30p	£15.00
	50	Jiu Jitsu (1911)	£2.50	—
	50	Keep Fit (1939)	80p	£40.00
	50	Leaders of Men (1929)	£2.20	—
	50	Life in the Tree Tops (1931)	50p	£25.00
	50	Lighthouses (1926)	£1.20	£60.00
	40	London Ceremonials (1929)	£1.25	£50.00
	50	London Zoo (1927)	70p	£35.00
	50	Lucky Charms (1930)	£1.50	£75.00
	25	Marvels of the Universe series (c1925)	£2.20	£55.00
	45	Melbourne Cup Winners (1906)	£5.00	—
	50	Merchant Ships of the World (1925)	£3.00	—
	25	Merchant Ships of the World (1925)	£3.00	—
	25	Military Portraits (1917)	£2.20	—
	36	Modern Beauties 1st series (1938)	75p	£27.00
	36	Modern Beauties 2nd series (1939)	60p	£22.00
MP	54	Modern Beauties 1st series (1937)	80p	£45.00
MP	54	Modern Beauties 2nd series (1938)	80p	£45.00
MP	36	Modern Beauties 3rd series (1938)	£1.25	£45.00
MP	36	Modern Beauties 4th series (1939)	80p	£30.00
ELP	36	Modern Beauties 1st series (1936)	£1.00	£36.00
ELP	36	Modern Beauties 2nd series (1936)	60p	£22.00
ELP	36	Modern Beauties 3rd series (1937)	75p	£27.00
ELP	36	Modern Beauties 4th series (1937)	75p	£27.00
ELP	36	Modern Beauties 5th series (1938)	40p	£15.00
ELP	36	Modern Beauties 6th series (1938)	40p	£15.00
ELP	36	Modern Beauties 7th series (1938)	50p	£18.00
LP	36	Modern Beauties 8th series (1939)	75p	£27.00
LP	36	Modern Beauties 9th Series (1939)	£1.00	£36.00
LP	36	Modern Beauties (1939)	£1.00	£36.00
	50	Modern Warfare (1936)	70p	£35.00
M	48	Modern Wonders (1938)	£3.00	—
	25	Modes of Conveyance (1928)	£1.60	£40.00
	48	Motor Cars green back (1926)	£3.00	—
	36	Motor Cars brown back (1929)	£3.50	—
	50	Motorcycles (1927)	£3.20	—
	50	Native Life in Many Lands (1932)	50p	£25.00
	50	Natural and Man Made Wonders of the World (1937)	50p	£25.00
	50	Nature Studies stereoscopic (1928)	50p	£25.00
	48	Nature Studies stereoscopic (1930)	70p	£35.00
	50	Naval Portraits (1917)	£2.20	—
	25	Notabilities (1917)	£2.20	£55.00
	25	Past and Present (1929)	£1.80	£45.00
	48	Pictures of the East (1930):		
		A 'A Series of 48' 17mm long	50p	£25.00
		B 'A Series of 48' 14mm long	50p	£25.00
M	48	Picturesque China (c1925):		
		A With 'P' at left of base	£1.25	£60.00
		B Without 'P' at left of base	£1.25	£60.00
M	53	Playing Cards Ace of Hearts Back (c1935)	22p	£11.00
K	53	Playing Cards designed back (c1935):		
		A Blue back	70p	—
		B Red back	70p	—
	36	Popular Stage, Cinema and Society Celebrities (c1928)	£2.50	—
	25	Prehistoric Animals (1931)	£2.40	£60.00

BRITISH AMERICAN TOBACCO CO. LTD *(continued)*

Size	Number in set		Price per card	Complete set
	50	Prominent Australian and English Cricketers (1911)	£30.00	—
	25	Puzzle series (1916)	£4.00	—
	50	Railway Working (1927)	£1.20	£60.00
	10	Recruiting Posters (1915)	£6.50	—
	33	Regimental Pets (1911)	£4.50	—
	50	Regimental Uniforms (1936)	£1.30	£65.00
	50	Romance of the Heavens (1929)	60p	£30.00
P	50	Round the World in Pictures stereoscopic (1931)	60p	£30.00
	50	Royal Mail (1912)	£3.00	—
P	50	Royal Navy (1930)	£2.00	—
	27	Rulers of the World (1911)	£5.00	—
	40	Safety First (1931)	80p	£32.00
	25	Ships' Flags and Cap Badges 1st series (1930)	£1.80	£45.00
	25	Ships' Flags and Cap Badges 2nd series (1930)	£1.80	£45.00
P	50	Ships and Shipping (1928)	70p	£35.00
	50	Signalling series (1913)	£2.20	—
	100	Soldiers of the World (tobacco leaf back) (c1902)	£9.00	—
	50	Speed (1938)	60p	£30.00
	25	Sports and Games in Many Lands (1930)	£4.00	£100.00
	50	Stage and Film Stars (1926)	£1.20	—
M	50	Stars of Filmland (1927)	£2.00	—
	48	Transport Then and Now (1940)	45p	£22.00
	32	Transport of the World (1917)	—	—
	20	Types of North American Indians (c1930)	£9.00	—
P	50	Types of the World (1936)	60p	£30.00
P	270	Views of the World stereoscopic (1908)	£3.00	—
	25	Warriors of All Nations (gold panel) (1937)	£1.20	£30.00
	50	War Incidents (brown back) (1915)	£1.40	£70.00
	50	War Incidents (blue back) (1916)	£1.40	£70.00
	50	Warships (1926)	£2.60	—
	25	Whaling (1930)	£1.80	£45.00
P	50	Who's Who in Sport (1926)	£2.50	£125.00
	50	Wild Animals of the World (tobacco leaf back) (1902)	£6.00	—
	25	Wireless (1923)	£2.50	—
	50	Wonders of the Past (1930)	70p	£35.00
	50	Wonders of the Sea (1929)	70p	£35.00
	25	Wonders of the World (c1928)	70p	£17.50
	40	World Famous Cinema Artistes (1933)	£1.00	£40.00
M	40	World Famous Cinema Artistes (1933)	£1.00	£40.00
	50	World's Products	50p	£25.00
P	50	The World of Sport (1927)	£2.00	£100.00
P	50	Zoo (1935)	60p	£30.00
	50	Zoological Studies (1928):		
		A Brown back	50p	£25.00
		B Black back	£1.50	—
F		***PLAIN BACKS***		
	50	Actors and Actresses 'WALP' (c1905):		
		A Portraits in black and white, glossy	£1.80	£90.00
		B Portraits flesh tinted, matt	£1.80	£90.00
	50	Actresses 'ALWICS' (c1905)	£2.00	—
	50	Actresses, four colours surround (c1905)	£1.80	£90.00
	30	Actresses unicoloured (c1910):		
		A Fronts in purple brown	90p	£27.00
		B Fronts in light brown	90p	£27.00
	50	Animals and Birds (1912)	£1.80	£90.00
	60	Animals — cut-outs (1912)	£1.10	—

Size	*Number in set*		*Price per card*	*Complete set*
	50	Art Photogravures (1912)	£1.40	—
	50	Aviation series (1911)	£2.50	—
	40	Beauties — brown tinted (1913)	£2.20	—
	50	Beauties with backgrounds (1911)	£2.20	—
	32	Beauties Picture Hats I with borders (1914)	£2.50	—
	45	Beauties Picture Hats II without borders (1914)	£2.50	—
	30	Beauties and Children (c1910)	£5.00	—
	30	Beauties 'Celebrated Actresses' (c1910)	£3.00	—
	52	Birds of Brilliant Plumage — PC inset (1914)	£2.20	—
	25	Bonzo series (1923):		
		A With series title	£3.40	—
		B Without series title	£3.40	—
	30	Boy Scouts Signalling (c1920):		
		A Captions in English	£2.50	£75.00
		B Captions in Siamese	£2.50	£75.00
	50	British Man of War series (1910)	£8.00	—
	50	Butterflies and Moths (1910)	£1.40	—
	50	Cinema Artistes (c1928)	£1.00	—
	50	Cinema Stars RB21/259 (c1930):		
		A Front matt	90p	£45.00
		B Front glossy	£1.00	—
	50	Cinema Stars RB21/260 (Nd 1-50) (c1930)	80p	—
	50	Cinema Stars RB21/260 (Nd 51-100) (c1930)	80p	—
	50	Cinema Stars RB21/260 (Nd 101-150) (c1930)	80p	—
	100	Cinema Stars RB21/260 (Nd 201-300) (c1930)	80p	£80.00
	50	Cinema Stars 'FLAG' (c1930)	80p	—
	27	Dancing Girls (1913)	£1.30	—
	32	Drum Horses (1910)	£4.50	—
	50	English Period Costumes	70p	£35.00
	50	Flag Girls of All Nations (1911)	£1.60	—
		Flags, Pennons and Signals (c1910):		
	70	A Numbered 1-70	60p	—
	70	B Unnumbered	60p	—
	50	C Numbered 71-120	60p	—
	45	D Numbered 121-165	70p	—
	20	Flowers (1915)	90p	£18.00
	50	Girls of All Nations (1908)	£1.60	—
	30	Heroic Deeds (1913)	£1.60	—
	25	Hindou Gods (1909)	£5.50	—
	32	Houses of Parliament (1914)	£3.00	—
	25	Indian Mogul Paintings (1909)	£7.00	—
	53	Jockeys and Owners Colours — PC inset (c1914)	£2.75	—
	30	Merrie England Female Studies (1922)	£5.00	—
	36	Modern Beauties 1st series (1938)	£2.50	—
	36	Modern Beauties 2nd series (1939)	£2.00	—
	48	Movie Stars (c1930)	£1.30	—
	50	Music Hall Celebrities (1911):		
		A Blue border	£2.20	—
		B Gilt border	£2.00	—
		C Red border	£2.20	—
		D Yellow border	£4.00	—
	50	New Zealand, Early Scenes and Maori Life (c1928)	£1.50	—
	50	Poultry and Pidgeons (c1926)	£4.00	—
	25	Products of the World (1914)	£1.00	£25.00
	50	Royal Mail (1912)	£5.00	—
	36	Ships and Their Pennants (1913)	£2.00	—

BRITISH AMERICAN TOBACCO CO. LTD *(continued)*

Size	*Number in set*		*Price per card*	*Complete set*
	75	Soldiers of the World (c1902)	£7.50	-
	30	Sporting Girls (1913)	£3.50	-
	50	Sports of the World (1917):		
		A Brown front	£3.50	-
		B Coloured front	£3.00	-
M	50	Stars of Filmland (1927)	£1.80	-
	32	Transport of the World (1917)	£1.20	-
	50	Types of the British Army (1908):		
		A Numbered	£1.80	-
		B Unnumbered	£1.80	-
P	50	Types of the World (1936)	£1.60	-
P	50	Units of the British Army and RAF (c1930)	£1.60	-
M	50	Women of Nations (Flag Girls) (1922)	£2.50	-
G	***PAPER BACKED SILKS ISSUED 1910-1917***			
M	25	Arabic Proverbs	£11.00	-
M	50	Arms of the British Empire:		
		A Back in blue	£3.00	-
		B Back in brown	£4.00	-
M	50	Australian Wild Flowers	£3.00	-
M	50	Best Dogs of their Breed	£5.50	-
	110	Crests and Badges of the British Army	£2.50	-
M	108	Crests and Badges of the British Army	£2.00	-
M	50	Crests and Colours of Australian Universities, Colleges and Schools	£2.25	-

BRITISH AMERICAN TOBACCO COMPANY (CHINA) LTD

	32	Sectional Picture — 'Beauties of Old China' (1934)	£5.00	-

BRITISH AMERICAN TOBACCO CO. LTD, Switzerland

	30	Series Actrices (1921)	£6.00	-

BROWN & WILLIAMSON TOBACCO CORP, USA (Wings Cigarettes)

M	50	Modern American Airplanes (c1938):		
		A Inscribed 'Series A'	£3.00	-
		B Without 'Series A'	£2.00	£100.
M	50	Modern American Airplanes 'Series B' (c1938)	£2.00	£100.
M	50	Modern American Airplanes 'Series C' (c1938)	£2.00	£100.
	50	Movie Stars (1940)	£5.00	-

D. BUCHNER & CO., USA

	48	Actors (c1890)	£20.00	-
L	50	Actresses (c1890)	£22.00	-
	144	Baseball Players (c1890)	£65.00	-
L	28	Butterflies and Bugs (c1890)	£50.00	-
L	52	Morning Glory Maidens (c1890)	£36.00	-
L	23	Musical Instruments (c1890)	£45.00	-
L	21	Yacht Club Colours (c1890)	£45.00	-

BUCKTROUT & CO. LTD, Guernsey, Channel Islands

M	416	Around the World (1926):		
		A Inscribed 'Places of Interest' Nd. 1-104	50p	£52.
		B Inscribed 'Around the World' Nd. 105-208	50p	£52.
		C Inscribed 'Around the World' Nd. 209-312	50p	£52.
		D Inscribed 'Around the World' Nd. 313-416	50p	£52.

BUCKTROUT & CO. LTD, Guernsey, Channel Islands *(continued)*

Size	*Number in set*		*Price per card*	*Complete set*
	24	Birds of England (1923)	£3.00	£75.00
	50	Cinema Stars, 1st series (1921)	£1.60	£80.00
	50	Cinema Stars, 2nd series (1922)	£1.80	£90.00
M	50	Football Teams (1924)	£2.40	£120.00
M	22	Football Teams of the Bailiwick (1924)	70p	£15.00
	123	Guernsey Footballers (c1925)	£2.00	—
	20	Inventors Series (1924)	80p	£16.00
	25	Marvels of the Universe Series (1923)	£2.20	£55.00
M	53	Playing Cards (1928)	70p	£35.00
	25	Sports and Pastimes (1925)	£3.40	—

CALCUTTA CIGARETTE CO., India

	25	Actresses — 'ALWICS' (c1905):		
		A Fronts in blue	£20.00	—
		B Fronts in chocolate	£25.00	—

A. G. CAMERON & SIZER, USA (including Cameron & Cameron)

	25	The New Discovery (1889):		
		A Without overprint	£25.00	—
		B With overprint	£25.00	—
	24	Occupations for Women (1890)	£45.00	—
		Photographic Cards (c1890):		
	? 3	Actresses	£17.00	—
	? 2	Actresses	£20.00	—
	343	Framed Paintings	£5.00	—

. CAMILLERI, Malta

MP	104	Popes of Rome (1922):		
		A Nd. 1-52	£1.50	£75.00
		B Nd. 53-104	£1.50	£75.00

CAMLER TOBACCO COY, Malta

	? 247	Footballers (c1925)	£4.50	—
M	96	Maltese Families Coats of Arms:		
		A Thick board (c1925)	£1.20	—
		B Thin board (1958)	£1.20	—

CARRERAS LTD, Australia & Canada

M	20	Canadian Wild Animals (1984):		
		A Complete set	—	—
		B 15 Different	20p	£3.00
	72	Film Star Series (1933)	£1.30	—
	72	Football Series (1933)	£1.30	—
	24	Personality Series (1933)	£1.50	—
	72	Personality Series Film Stars (1933)	£1.30	—
	72	Personality Series Footballers (1933)	£1.30	—

CHING & CO., Jersey, Channel Islands

	24	Around and About in Jersey, 1st series (1964)	30p	£7.50
	24	Around and About in Jersey, 2nd series (1964)	80p	£20.00
7	25	Do You Know? (1962)	15p	£2.25

CHING & CO., Jersey, Channel Islands *(continued)*

Size	*Number in set*		*Price per card*	*Complete set*
	48	Flowers (1962)	80p	£40.00
L	24	Jersey Past and Present, 1st series (1960)	20p	£5.00
L	24	Jersey Past and Present, 2nd series (1962)	25p	£6.00
L	24	Jersey Past and Present, 3rd series (1963)	20p	£5.00
	25	Ships and Their Workings (1961)	15p	£2.25
	50	Veteran and Vintage Cars (1960)	35p	£17.50

W.A. & A.C. CHURCHMAN, Channel Islands

(All cards without ITC clause)

M	48	Air Raid Precautions (1938)	£1.50	—
M	48	Holidays in Britain (sepia) (1937)	£1.50	—
M	48	Holidays in Britain (coloured) (1938)	£1.50	—
M	48	Modern Wonders (1938):		
		A ITC clause blocked out in silver	£5.00	—
		B Reprinted without ITC clause	£1.50	—
M	48	The Navy at Work (1937)	£1.50	—
M	48	The RAF at Work (1939)	£1.50	—
M	48	Wings Over the Empire (1939)	£1.50	—

THE CIGARETTE COMPANY, Jersey, Channel Islands

	72	Jersey Footballers (c1910)	£5.00	—

LA CIGARETTE ORIENTAL DE BELGIQUE, Belgium

L	100	Famous Men Throughout the Ages (c1940)	15p	£15.00

C. COLOMBOS, Malta

MP	200	Actresses (c1900)	£3.00	—
MP	59	Actresses (c1900)	£15.00	—
	50	Actresses (coloured) (c1900)	£10.00	—
MP	57	Celebrities (c1900)	£15.00	—
P	136	Dante's Divine Comedy (c1914)	£1.80	—
		Famous Oil Paintings (c1910):		
MP	72	1 Series A	£1.00	—
MP	108	2 Series B	£1.00	—
MP	240	3 Series C	£1.00	—
MP	100	4 Series D	£1.00	—
LP	91	5 Large size	£6.00	—
MP	100	Life of Napoleon Bonaparte (c1914)	£2.00	—
MP	70	Life of Nelson (c1914)	£2.00	—
MP	70	Life of Wellington (c1914)	£2.00	—
MP	100	National Types and Costumes (c1910)	£2.20	—
MP	30	Opera Singers (c1900)	£30.00	—
	120	Paintings and Statues (c1912)	65p	£80.00
M	112	Royalty and Celebrities (c1910)	£2.40	—

D. CONDACHI & SON, Malta

	? 15	Artists & Beauties (c1905)	£16.00	—

CONSOLIDATED CIGARETTE CO., USA

		Ladies of the White House (c1895):		
	14	A Size 73 × 43mm, white borders	£30.00	—
	25	B Size 70 × 38mm, no borders	£25.00	—

COPE BROS. & CO. LTD

Size	*Number in set*		*Price per card*	*Complete set*
A		***INDIAN ISSUE***		
	30	Flags of Nations (c1903)	£50.00	—
B		***DANISH ISSUES***		
	50	Jordklodens Hunde (1912)	£30.00	—
	30	Scandinavian Actors and Actresses (1910)	£40.00	—
	35	Speider Billeder I Hver Pakke (1910)	£30.00	—
	25	Uniformer A F Fremragende Britiske Regimenter (1908)	£25.00	—
	25	Vilde Dyr Og Fugle (1907)	£35.00	—

A.G. COUSIS & CO., Malta

		Actors and Actresses (c1910):		
P	100	A Back with framework	£2.00	—
KP	100	B Back without framework	£2.00	—
K	254	Actors and Actresses (c1925)	70p	—
KP	100	Actresses Series I (c1910)	£1.50	—
KP	80	Actresses Series II (c1910)	£1.50	—
P	100	Actresses (c1910):		
		A Series I	£1.50	—
		B Series II	£1.50	—
		C Series III	£1.50	—
		D Series IV	£1.50	—
		E Series V	£1.50	—
		F Series VI	£1.50	—
		G Series VII	£1.50	—
		H Series VIII	£1.50	—
		I Series IX	£1.50	—
		J Series X	£1.50	—
		K Series XI	£1.50	—
		L Series XII	£1.50	—
		M Series XIII	£1.50	—
		N Series XIV	£1.50	—
		O Series XV	£1.50	—
		P Series XVI	£1.50	—
		Q Series XVII	£1.50	—
		R Series XVIII	£1.50	—
		S Series XIX	£1.50	—
		Actresses (c1910):		
KP	2281	A Miniature size 50 × 30mm	70p	—
	1283	B Small size 58 × 39mm	80p	—
MP	325	Actresses, Celebrities and Warships (c1910)	£9.00	—
		Actresses, Partners and National Costumes (c1910):		
KP	200	A Miniature size 50 × 30mm	£1.70	—
	100	B Small size 60 × 39mm	£1.70	—
MP	50	Beauties, Couples and Children (c1908):		
		A Back inscribed 'Collection No. 1'	£2.50	—
		B Back inscribed 'Collection No. 2'	£2.50	—
		C Back inscribed 'Collection No. 3'	£2.50	—
	50	Beauties, Couples and Children (red back) (c1925)	£2.00	—
	402	Celebrities Numbered Matt (c1910):		
		A Front inscribed 'Cousis' Dubec Cigarettes', Nd. 1-300	£1.00	—
		B Front inscribed 'Cousis' Cigarettes', Nd. 301-402	£1.25	—
	2162	Celebrities Unnumbered (c1910):		
		A Miniature size 50 × 30mm	80p	—
		B Small size 59 × 39mm	80p	—

A.G. COUSIS & CO., Malta *(continued)*

Size	*Number in set*		*Price per card*	*Complete set*
MP	72	Grand Masters of the Order of Jerusalem (c1910)	£2.30	—
P	100	National Costumes (c1910)	£2.00	—
MP	? 57	Paris Exhibition 1900 (c1901)	£25.00	—
MP	102	Paris Series (1902)	£25.00	—
		Popes of Rome (c1910):		
MP	182	A Back inscribed 'A.G. Cousis' Dubec Cigarettes'	£1.50	—
MP	81	B Back inscribed 'Cousis' Dubec Cigarettes'	£2.50	—
P	100	Statues and Monuments (c1910):		
		A Numbered	£1.50	—
		B Unnumbered	£1.50	—
KP	127	Views of Malta (c1910)	£2.00	—
P	115	Views of Malta Numbered (c1910)	90p	—
MP	127	Views of Malta Numbered (c1910)	90p	—
MP	? 65	Views of Malta Unnumbered (c1910)	90p	—
P	559	Views of the World (c1910):		
		A Small size 59 × 39mm	£1.00	—
		B Medium size 65 × 45mm	£1.00	—
P	99	Warships, white border (c1910)	£2.40	—
		Warships, Liners and Other Vessels (c1904):		
MP	105	A 'Cousis' Dubec Cigarettes'	£3.50	—
MP	22	B 'Cousis' Excelsior Cigarettes'	£3.50	—
MP	40	C 'Cousis' Superior Cigarettes'	£4.00	—
MP	851	D 'Cousis' Cigarettes'	£1.20	—
KP	851	E 'Cousis' Cigarettes'	90p	—

CROWN TOBACCO CO., India

	? 15	National Types, Costumes and Flags (c1900)	£30.00	—

DIXSON, Australia

	50	Australian MPs and Celebrities (c1900)	£12.00	—

DOMINION TOBACCO CO., Canada

	50	The Smokers of the World (c1905)	£40.00	—

DOMINION TOBACCO CO. LTD, New Zealand

	50	Coaches and Coaching Days (c1928)	£1.50	—
	50	People and Places Famous in New Zealand History (c1928)	£1.80	—
	50	Products of the World (c1928)	£1.00	£50.00
	50	USS Co's Steamers (c1928)	£2.40	—

DUDGEON & ARNELL, Australia

K	16	1934 Australian Test Team (1934)	£5.50	£90.00
K	55	Famous Ships (1933)	£2.50	—

W. DUKE, SONS & CO., USA

ALL SERIES ISSUED 1885-95

	50	Actors and Actresses Series No. 1	£12.00	—
	50	Actors and Actresses Series No. 2	£12.00	—
	25	Actresses RB18/27	£11.00	—
EL	25	Albums of American Stars	£38.00	—
EL	25	Battle Scenes	£26.00	—

Size	*Number in set*		*Price per card*	*Complete set*
EL	25	Breeds of Horses	£26.00	—
EL	25	Bridges	£22.00	—
EL	50	Coins of All Nations	£12.00	—
EL	25	Comic Characters	£22.00	—
EL	25	Cowboys Scenes	£28.00	—
EL	50	Fairest Flowers in the World	£22.00	—
	50	Fancy Dress Ball Costumes	£12.00	—
EL	50	Fancy Dress Ball Costumes	£23.00	—
	50	Fishers and Fish	£12.00	£600.00
EL	25	Flags and Costumes	£24.00	—
	50	Floral Beauties and Language of Flowers	£12.00	—
EL	25	French Novelties	£22.00	—
EL	25	Gems of Beauty	£22.00	—
	50	Great Americans	£16.00	—
	25	Gymnastic Exercises	£25.00	—
EL	25	Habitations of Man	£22.00	—
	50	Histories of Generals (Booklets)	£25.00	—
	50	Histories of Poor Boys who have become rich and other famous people	£22.00	—
	50	Holidays	£12.00	£600.00
EL	25	Illustrated Songs	£23.00	—
EL	25	Industries of the States	£26.00	—
	50	Jokes	£13.00	—
EL	25	Lighthouses (die cut)	£24.00	—
EL	25	Miniature Novelties	£22.00	—
	50	Musical Instruments	£16.00	—
	36	Ocean and River Steamers	£22.00	—
M	240	Photographs from Life RB23/D76-84	£6.00	—
	53	Playing Cards	£11.00	—
	50	Popular Songs and Dancers	£17.00	—
	50	Postage Stamps	£13.00	—
		Rulers, Flags and Coats of Arms:		
EL	50	A Thick card type	£22.00	—
EL	50	B Thin folders	£13.00	—
	50	Scenes of Perilous Occupations	£17.00	—
EL	25	Sea Captains	£28.00	—
	50	Shadows	£12.00	£600.00
EL	25	Snap Shots from Puck	£22.00	—
EL	25	Stars of the Stage, 1st series:		
		A With Duke	£22.00	£550.00
		B Inscribed '3rd Series'	£22.00	—
EL	25	Stars of the Stage, 2nd series	£22.00	—
EL	25	Stars of the Stage, 3rd series	£22.00	£550.00
EL	25	Stars of the Stage, 4th series (die cut)	£22.00	—
L	48	State Governors' Coats of Arms	£22.00	—
L	48	State Governors' Coats of Arms (folders)	£13.00	—
	50	The Terrors of America and Their Doings	£13.00	—
L	50	The Terrors of America and Their Doings	£22.00	—
	50	Tinted Photos:		
		A Standard size	£17.00	—
		B Die cut to shape	£17.00	—
L	25	Types of Vessels (die cut)	£23.00	—
	50	Vehicles of the World	£18.00	—
	50	Yacht Colors of the World	£12.00	—

PHOTOGRAPHIC CARDS

	340	Actors and Actresses, 'Cross-Cut Cigarettes' with number and caption in design, Group 1	£4.00	—

W. DUKE, SONS & CO., USA *(continued)*

Size	*Number in set*		*Price per card*	*Complete set*
	260	Actors and Actresses, 'Cross-Cut Cigarettes' in design, number and caption at base, Group 2	£4.00	—
	?	Actors and Actresses, 'Cross-Cut Cigarettes' and all wording at base, Group	£4.00	—
	148	Actors and Actresses, 'Dukes Cameo Cigarettes' in design, number and caption at base, Group 4	£4.00	—
	?	Actors and Actresses, 'Dukes Cameo Cigarettes', number and caption at base, Group 5	£4.00	—
	?	Actors and Actresses, 'Dukes Cigarettes' in design, number and caption at base, Group 6	£4.00	—
	?	Actors and Actresses, 'Dukes Cigarettes' and all wording at base, Group 7	£4.00	—
	?	Actors, Actresses and Celebrities, printed back:		
		1 Horizontal 'Dukes Cameo Cigarettes' back	£4.00	—
		2 Vertical 'Sales 1858' back	£4.00	—
		3 Horizontal 'Dukes Cigarettes' back	£4.00	—
EL	?	Actors, Actresses, Celebrities etc	£4.00	—

H. ELLIS & CO., USA

	25	Breeds of Dogs (c1890)	£37.00	—
	25	Costumes of Women (c1890)	£50.00	—
	25	Generals of the Late Civil War (c1890)	£65.00	—
	25	Photographic Cards — Actresses (c1887)	£7.00	—

FOH CHONG, China

M	10	Chinese Series (c1930)	—	£20.00

G.W. GAIL & AX., USA

EL	25	Battle Scenes (c1890)	£28.00	—
EL	25	Bicycle and Trick Riders (c1890)	£35.00	—
EL	25	French Novelties (c1890)	£26.00	—
EL	25	Industries of the States (c1890)	£26.00	—
EL	25	Lighthouses (die cut) (c1890)	£24.00	—
EL	25	Novelties (die cut) (c1890)	£27.00	—
EL	?	Photographic Cards (c1890)	£5.00	—
EL	25	Stars of the Stage (c1890)	£26.00	—

GENERAL CIGAR COMPANY, Montreal, Canada

		Northern Birds:		
EL	24	A With series title Nd. 1-24 (1968)	£1.20	—
EL	12	B Without series title, Nd. 25-36 (1977)	£1.40	—

GOODWIN & CO, USA

	15	Beauties — 'PAC' (c1888)	£55.00	—
	50	Champions (c1888)	£27.00	—
	50	Dogs of the World (c1888)	£17.00	—
	50	Flowers (c1888)	£17.00	—
	50	Games and Sports Series (c1888)	£22.00	—
	50	Holidays (c1888)	£23.00	—
	50	Occupations for Women (c1888)	£55.00	—
		Photographic Cards (c1888):		
	?	Actors and Actresses	£5.00	—
	?	Baseball Players	£50.00	—
	?	Celebrities and Prizefighters	£25.00	—

ɜOODWIN & CO, USA *(continued)*

ɜize	*Number in set*		*Price per card*	*Complete set*
	50	Vehicles of the World (c1888)	£23.00	—

ɜUERNSEY TOBACCO CO., Channel Islands

		A Famous Picture:		
	49	A And When Did You Last See Your Father? (1934)	£1.50	—
	48	B The Laughing Cavalier (1935)	£1.50	—
	48	C The Toast (1936)	£1.50	—
	52	Miniature Playing Cards (1933)	80p	—

'HOS. H. HALL, USA

	4	Actresses RB23/-H6-1 (1880)	£60.00	—
	14	Actresses RB23/-H6-2 (c1885)	£16.00	—
	140	Actors and Actresses RB23/-H6-3 (c1885)	£16.00	—
	112	Actresses and Actors RB23/-H6-4 (c1885)	£16.00	—
	?	Actresses and Actors RB23/-H6-5 (c1885)	£16.00	—
	? 158	Actresses and Actors RB23/-H6-6 (c1885)	£16.00	—
	52	Actresses RB23/-H6-7 (c1885)	£18.00	—
	12	Actresses RB23/-H6-8 (c1885)	£28.00	—
	25	Actresses RB23/-H6-9 (c1885)	£22.00	—
	11	Actresses RB23/-H6-10 (c1885)	£60.00	—
	12	Athletes RB23/-H6-3 (1881)	£60.00	—
	4	Presidential Candidates RB23/-H6-1 (1880)	£60.00	—
	22	Presidents of the United States RB23/-H6-11 (c1888)	£28.00	—
	25	Theatrical Types RB23/-H6-12 (c1890)	£28.00	—

IGNETT BROS. & CO., New Zealand

P	50	Beauties, Set 1 (1926):		
		A Back without framelines, no brand mentioned	£1.30	—
		B Back with framelines, 'Chess Cigarettes'	£1.00	£50.00
P	50	Beauties, Set 2 (1927)	£1.00	£50.00

. & J. HILL LTD

	10	Chinese Series (c1912)	£70.00	—

HE HILSON CO., USA

	25	National Types (c1900)	£22.00	—

IPERIAL TOBACCO COMPANY OF CANADA LTD, Canada

WITH FIRM'S NAME

	25	Beauties — Girls in Costume (c1903)	£40.00	—
	24	Beauties — Smoke Girls (c1903)	£45.00	—
	50	Birds, Beasts and Fishes (1923)	£1.60	£80.00
	100	Birds of Canada (1924)	£2.50	—
	100	Birds of Canada (Western Canada) (1925)	£5.00	—
	50	British Birds (1923)	70p	£35.00
	48	Canadian History Series (1926)	£1.10	—
	50	Children of All Nations (1924)	80p	£40.00
	23	Dogs Series (1924)	£1.20	£28.00
	50	Dogs, 2nd series (1925)	£1.00	£50.00
	50	Famous English Actresses (1924)	£1.00	£50.00

IMPERIAL TOBACCO COMPANY OF CANADA LTD, Canada *(continued)*

Size	*Number in set*		*Price per card*	*Compl*
	50	Film Favourites (1925):		
		A English Issue:		
		i Numbered	£2.80	
		ii Unnumbered	£3.20	
		B French Issue:		
		i Numbered	£6.00	
		ii Unnumbered	£6.00	
	50	Fish and Bait (1924)	£1.20	£60.
	50	Fishes of the World (1924)	£1.20	£60
	50	Flower Culture in Pots (1925)	60p	£30.
	30	Game Bird Series (1925)	£1.00	£30
	50	Gardening Hints (1923)	60p	£30
M	25	Heraldic Signs and Their Origins (1925)	£1.20	£30.
	50	How to Play Golf (1925)	£6.00	
	50	Infantry Training (1915):		
		A Glossy card	£2.20	
		B Matt card	£2.20	
L	48	Mail Carriers and Stamps (1903)	£22.00	
	50	Merchant Ships of the World (1924)	90p	£45.
	25	Military Portraits (1914)	£2.20	
	50	Modern War Weapons, 'Sweet Caporal' issue (1914)	£3.50	
	56	Motor Cars (1924)	£1.50	
	50	Naval Portraits (1914)	£2.20	
	25	Notabilities (1914)	£2.20	
	53	Poker Hands (1924)	90p	
	53	Poker Hands, New Series (1925)	90p	
	25	Poultry Alphabet (1924)	£1.80	
	50	Railway Engines (1924):		
		A With 'Wills' blanked out	£1.20	
		B Without 'Wills'	90p	£45
	50	The Reason Why (1924)	£1.00	£50
	127	Smokers Golf Cards (1925)	£4.50	
B	***WITHOUT FIRM'S NAME***			
	50	Arms of the British Empire (1911)	£2.20	
	50	Around the World (c1910)	£3.50	
	90	Baseball Series (1912)	£25.00	
	30	Bird Series (c1910)	£2.00	
	50	Boy Scouts (1911) — with album clause	£4.50	
	50	Canadian Historical Portraits (1913)	£6.00	
	50	Canadian History Series (1914)	£1.20	
	50	Fish Series (c1910)	£2.20	
	50	Fowls, Pigeons and Dogs (1911)	£2.80	
	45	Hockey Players (1912)	£9.00	
	36	Hockey Series (coloured) (1911)	£9.00	
	50	How To Do It (c1910)	£2.50	
	100	Lacrosse Series, Leading Players (c1910)	£4.00	
	100	Lacrosse Series (coloured) (c1910)	£4.00	
	50	Lacrosse Series (black and white) (c1910)	£4.00	
	50	L'Historie du Canada (1926)	£1.20	
	50	Movie Stars (c1930)	£1.20	
L	50	Pictures of Canadian Life (c1910):		
		A Brown front	£7.00	
		B Green front	£6.00	
	50	Prominent Men of Canada (c1910)	£3.00	
	50	Tricks and Puzzles (c1910)	£7.00	
	50	Types of Nations (c1910)	£3.00	

IPERIAL TOBACCO COMPANY OF CANADA LTD, Canada *(continued)*

ze Number in set		Price per card	Complete set
25	Victoria Cross Heroes (blue back) (1915)	£2.40	£60.00
45	Views of the World (c1910)	£6.00	—
25	The World's Dreadnoughts (1910)	£2.60	—
	SILKS ISSUED 1910-25		
55	Animals with Flags	£2.60	—
50	Canadian History Series	£11.00	—
121	Canadian Miscellany	£3.50	—
55	Garden Flowers of the World	£2.50	—
55	Orders and Military Medals	£2.50	—
55	Regimental Uniforms of Canada	£3.50	—
50	Yachts, Pennants and Views	£6.00	—

HE IMPERIAL TOBACCO CO. OF INDIA LTD, India

25	Indian Historical Views (1915):		
	A Set 1, First Arrangement	£2.00	—
	B Set 2, Second Arrangement	£2.00	—
40	Nautch Girl Series:		
	A 'Pedro Cigarettes' (c1905)	£2.00	—
	B 'Railway Cigarettes' (c1907)	£2.00	—
52	Nautch Girl Series, PC inset:		
	A 'Pedro Cigarettes' (c1905)	£2.00	—
	B 'Railway Cigarettes' (c1907)	£2.00	—
53	Playing Cards, red back (1919)	£1.50	—
52	Playing Cards, blue back (1933)	£1.00	—

IE JERSEY TOBACCO CO. LTD, Channel Islands

53	Miniature Playing Cards (1933)	90p	—

JST SO, USA

?	Actresses (c1890)	£10.00	—

ENTUCKY TOBACCO PTY. LTD, South Africa

120	The March of Mankind (1940)	£1.20	—

M. S. KIMBALL & CO., USA

	L SERIES ISSUED 1885-95		
? 33	Actresses	£55.00	—
72	Ancient Coins	£26.00	—
48	Arms of Dominions	£16.00	—
50	Ballet Queens	£17.00	—
52	Beauties with Playing Card Insets	£17.00	—
20	Beautiful Bathers	£25.00	—
50	Butterflies	£20.00	—
50	Champions of Games and Sports	£28.00	—
50	Dancing Girls of the World	£16.00	—
50	Dancing Women	£16.00	—
50	Fancy Bathers	£16.00	—
50	Goddesses of the Greeks & Romans	£18.00	—
25	Household Pets	£25.00	—
?	Photographic Actresses RB23/K26-15-2	£5.00	—

WM. S. KIMBALL & CO., USA *(continued)*

Size	Number in set		Price per card	Compl.
EL	20	Pretty Athletes	£25.00	
	50	Savage and Semi Barbarous Chiefs and Rulers	£24.00	

KINNEY BROS, USA

ALL SERIES ISSUED 1885-95

	25	Actresses Group 1 Set 1 RB18/1	£7.50	
	25	Actresses Group 1 Set 2 RB18/2	£11.00	
	25	Actresses Group 1 Set 3 RB18/3	£13.00	
	25	Actresses Group 1 Set 4	£15.00	
	25	Actresses Group 1 Set 5	£15.00	
	25	Actresses Group 2 RB18/15	£6.00	
	25	Actresses Group 2 RB18/16:		
		A Subjects named	£6.00	
		B Subjects unnamed	£6.00	
	25	Actresses Group 3 RB18/26	£6.00	
	25	Actresses Group 3 RB18/29	£6.00	
	50	Actresses Group 4 RB18/36	£6.00	
	150	Actresses Group 4	£6.00	
	25	Animals	£16.00	
	10	Butterflies of the World. Light background	£16.00	
	50	Butterflies of the World. Gold background	£13.00	
	25	Famous Gems of the World	£16.00	
	52	Harlequin Cards 1st series	£16.00	
	53	Harlequin Cards 2nd series (1889)	£16.00	
L	50	International Cards	£32.00	
K	24	Jocular Oculars	£36.00	
	25	Leaders:		
		A Standard size	£17.00	£425
		B Narrow card — officially cut	£17.00	£425
	50	Magic Changing Cards (1881)	£18.00	
	622	Military series	From £4.50	
	50	National Dances:		
		A Front with white border	£12.00	£600
		B Front without border	£16.00	
	25	Naval Vessels of the World	£17.00	
	50	New Year 1890 (1889)	£18.00	
	25	Novelties Type 1. Thick circular, no border	£22.00	
	50	Novelties Type 2. Thin circular with border	£9.00	
		Novelties Type 3. Die cut:		
	25	A Inscribed '25 Styles'	£6.50	
	50	B Inscribed '50 Styles'	£6.50	
	75	C Inscribed '75 Styles'	£6.50	
	50	Novelties Type 5. Standard size cards	£9.00	
	14	Novelties Type 6. Oval	£26.00	
		Photographic Cards:		
	?	A Actors and Actresses. Horizontal back with Kinney's name	£4.00	
	?	B Actors and Actresses. Vertical, Sweet Caporal backs	£4.00	
	45	C Famous Ships	£9.00	
		Racehorses:		
	25	1 American Horses:		
		A Back with series title 'Famous Running Horses'	£18.00	
		B Back 'Return 25 of these small cards' 11 lines of text	£16.00	
	25	2 English Horses 'Return 25 of these cards' with 6 lines of text	£15.00	
	25	3 Great American Trotters	£20.00	
	50	Surf Beauties	£18.00	

INNEY BROS, USA *(continued)*

ize	Number in set		Price per card	Complete set
	52	Transparent Playing Cards	£14.00	—
	25	Types of Nationalities (folders)	£23.00	—

RAMERS TOBACCO CO. (PTY) LTD, South Africa

	50	Badges of South African Rugby Football Clubs (1933)	£6.00	—

AMBERT & BUTLER

	50	Actors and Actresses — 'WALPS' (1905)	£2.60	—
	250	Actresses — 'ALWICS' (1905):		
		A Portraits in black, border in red	£2.60	—
		B Portraits and border in black	£6.50	—
	50	Beauties red tinted (1908)	£2.80	—
	83	Danske Byvaabner (c1915)	£14.00	—
	26	Etchings of Dogs (1926)	£25.00	—
	25	Flag Girls of All Nations (1908)	£12.00	—
	50	Homeland Events (1928)	£1.20	£60.00
	50	London Zoo (1927)	£1.20	—
	50	Merchant Ships of the World (1924)	£2.00	—
	30	Music Hall Celebrities (1916)	£4.00	—
	50	Popular Film Stars (1926):		
		A Series title in one line, no brand quoted	£1.20	£60.00
		B Series title in two lines, inscribed 'Varsity Cigarettes'	£1.80	—
		C Series title in two lines, no brand quoted	£1.20	£60.00
	50	The Royal Family at Home and Abroad (1927)	£1.20	£60.00
	100	Royalty, Notabilities and Events in Russia, China, Japan and South Africa (1902)	£10.00	—
	100	Russo Japanese series (1905)	£4.00	—
	50	Types of Modern Beauty (1927)	90p	£45.00
	50	Who's Who in Sport (1926)	£2.50	£125.00
	50	The World of Sport (1927)	£1.60	£80.00

EWIS & ALLEN CO. USA

	? 120	Views and Art Studies (c1910)	£5.50	—

ONE JACK CIGARETTE CO. USA

	50	Language of Flowers (1888)	£24.00	—

. LORILLARD CO., USA

LL SERIES ISSUED 1885-98

	25	Actresses RB23/L70-4-3	£22.00	—
	25	Actresses RB23/L70-5	£22.00	—
L	25	Actresses RB23/L70-6:		
		A 'Red Cross' long cut	£22.00	—
		B 'Sensation Cut Plug' front and back	£22.00	—
		C 'Sensation Cut Plug' front only	£22.00	—
L	25	Actresses RB23/L70-8	£22.00	—
L	25	Actresses in Opera Roles RB23/L70-9	£35.00	—
	25	Ancient Mythology Burlesqued RB23/L70-10	£22.00	—
	50	Beautiful Women RB23/L70-11:		
		A '5c Ante' front and back	£22.00	—
		B 'Lorillard's Snuff' front and back	£22.00	—
		C 'Tiger' front and back	£22.00	—

P. LORILLARD CO., USA *(continued)*

Size	*Number in set*		*Price per card*	*Complete set*
EL	25	Circus Scenes	£55.00	–
EL	50	Prizefighters	£65.00	–
M	25	Types of the Stage	£22.00	–

W.C. MACDONALD INC., Canada

	?	Aeroplanes and Warships (c1940)	70p	–
M	53	Playing Cards (different designs) (1926-47)	60p	–

B. & J.B. MACHADO, Jamaica

	25	British Naval series (1916)	£15.00	–
	50	The Great War — Victoria Cross Heroes (1916)	£14.00	–
P	50	Popular Film Stars (1926)	£5.00	–
P	50	The Royal Family at Home and Abroad (1927)	£5.00	–
P	52	Stars of the Cinema (1926)	£5.00	–
P	50	The World of Sport (1928)	£5.00	–

MACLIN-ZIMMER-MCGILL TOB. CO., USA

EL	53	Playing Cards — Actresses (c1890)	£22.00	–

H. MANDELBAUM, USA

	20	Types of People (c1890)	£50.00	–

MARBURG BROS, USA

	48	National Costume Cards (c1890)	£50.00	–

P.H. MAYO & BROTHER, USA

	25	Actresses RB23/M80-1 (c1890)	£22.00	–
M	25	Actresses RB23/M80-3 (c1890)	£22.00	–
L	12	Actresses RB23/M80-4 (c1890)	£50.00	–
	? 39	Actresses RB23/M80-5 (c1890)	£22.00	–
	40	Baseball Players (c1890)	£70.00	–
	20	Costumes and Flowers (c1890)	£24.00	–
	25	Head Dresses of Various Nations (c1890)	£26.00	–
M	25	National Flowers (Girl and Scene) (c1890)	£25.00	–
	20	Naval Uniforms (c1890)	£24.00	–
	35	Prizefighters (c1890)	£35.00	–
	20	Shakespeare Characters (c1890)	£25.00	–

M. MELACHRINO & CO., Switzerland

	52	Peuples Exotiques 1st series (c1925)	80p	£40.00
	52	Peuples Exotiques 2nd series (c1925)	80p	£40.00
	52	Peuples Exotiques 3rd series (c1925)	80p	£40.00

MIFSUD & AZZOPARDI, Malta

KP	59	First Maltese Parliament (1922)	£5.50	–

L. MILLER & SONS, USA

M	25	Battleships (c1900)	£23.00	–

L. MILLER & SONS, USA *(continued)*

Size	*Number in set*		*Price per card*	*Complete set*
M	25	Generals and Admirals (Spanish War) (c1900)	£24.00	—
M	24	Presidents of US (c1900)	£20.00	—
L	50	Rulers of the World (c1900)	£18.00	—

CHAS. J. MITCHELL & CO., Canada

	26	Actresses — 'FROGA A' (1900):		
		A Backs in brown	£24.00	—
		B Backs in green	£24.00	—

MITSUI & CO., Japan

	?	Japanese Women (c1908)	£5.00	—

MOORE & CALVI, USA

EL	53	Playing Cards — Actresses (c1890):		
		A 'Trumps Long Cut' back	£22.00	—
		B 'Hard-A-Port' with maker's name	£18.00	—
		C 'Hard-A-Port' without maker's name	£18.00	—

MURAI BROS & CO., Japan

	50	Actresses — 'ALWICS' (c1905)	£9.00	—
	100	Beauties — 'THIBS' (c1900)	£24.00	—
	50	Beauties Group 1 (c1902)	£12.00	—
	54	Chinese Girls Set 3 (c1905)	£7.50	—
	25	Chinese Beauties 1st series Peacock issue (c1910)	£2.60	£65.00
	25	Chinese Beauties 3rd series Peacock issue (c1910)	£4.00	—
	50	Chinese Beauties, back in red (c1908)	£5.00	—
	50	Chinese Children's Games without border Peacock issue (c1910)	£2.40	£120.00
	20	Chinese Children's Games with border Peacock issue (c1910)	£2.60	—
	50	Chinese Pagodas Peacock issue (c1910)	£2.60	—
	30	Chinese Series Peacock issue (c1910)	£2.50	£75.00
	40	Chinese Trades 1, back in black (c1905)	£4.50	—
	50	Dancing Girls of the World (c1900)	£28.00	—

NATIONAL CIGARETTE AND TOBACCO CO., USA

L	13	Art Miniatures (1892)	£24.00	—
L	?	Cabinet Pictures (c1890)	£24.00	—
	25	National Types (c1890)	£22.00	—
	44	National Types (c1890)	£22.00	—

PHOTOGRAPHIC CARDS

	?	Actresses (c1888):		
		A Plain back	£5.00	—
		B Printed back	£7.00	—

OGDENS LTD

	51	Actresses, black and white Polo issue (1906)	£3.00	—
	30	Actresses, unicoloured Polo issue (1908):		
		A Tin foil at back white	£2.50	£75.00
		B Tin foil at back shaded	£3.00	£90.00
	17	Animals Polo issue (1916)	£11.00	—

OGDENS LTD *(continued)*

Size	*Number in set*		*Price per card*	*Complete set*
	60	Animals — cut-outs:		
		A Ruler issue (1912)	£2.50	—
		B Tabs issue (1913):		
		i With captions	£2.50	—
		ii Without captions	£4.50	—
	50	Aviation series Tabs issue (1912):		
		A Ogdens at base	£6.00	—
		B Ogdens England at base	£6.00	—
		Beauties green net design back 1901:		
	? 66	A Front black & white	£12.00	—
	? 98	B Front coloured	£22.00	—
	45	Beauties Picture Hats Polo issue (1911)	£5.50	—
	50	Best Dogs of Their Breed Polo issue (1916):		
		A Back in red	£7.00	—
		B Back in blue	£7.00	—
	52	Birds of Brilliant Plumage Ruler issue (1914):		
		A Fronts with framelines	£3.00	—
		B Fronts without framelines	£3.00	—
	25	British Trees and Their Uses, Guinea Gold issue (1927)	£1.80	£45.00
	25	China's Famous Warriors, Ruler issue (1913)	£4.50	—
	25	Famous Railway Trains, Guinea Gold issue (1928)	£2.40	£60.00
	20	Flowers, Polo issue (1915):		
		A Without Eastern inscription	£5.50	—
		B With Eastern inscription	£5.50	—
	25	Indian Women, Polo issue (1919):		
		A Framework in apple green	£5.00	—
		B Framework in emerald green	£5.00	—
K	52	Miniature Playing Cards, Polo issue (1922)	£13.00	—
		Music Hall Celebrities (1911):		
	30	A Polo issue	£5.00	—
	50	B Tabs issue	£5.00	—
	50	Riders of the World, Polo issue (1911)	£4.00	—
	50	Russo-Japanese series (1905)	£22.00	—
	36	Ships and Their Pennants, Polo issue (1911)	£5.50	—
	32	Transport of the World, Polo issue (1917)	£5.50	—

OLD FASHION, USA

L	? 200	Photographic Cards — Actresses (c1890)	£7.00	—

PENINSULAR TOBACCO CO. LTD, India

	50	Animals and Birds (1910)	£1.80	—
	52	Birds of Brilliant Plumage (1916):		
		A Back with single large packings	£3.00	—
		B Back with two small packings	£3.00	—
	25	Birds of the East, 1st series (1912)	£1.80	—
	25	Birds of the East, 2nd series (1912)	£1.80	£45.00
	25	China's Famous Warriors:		
		A Back 'Monchyr India'	£2.60	£65.00
		B Back 'India' only	£2.40	£60.00
	25	Chinese Heroes (1913)	£2.00	£50.00
	50	Chinese Modern Beauties (1912)	£4.50	—
	50	Chinese Trades (1908):		
		A Back with 'Monchyr'	£3.00	—
		B Back without 'Monchyr'	£3.00	—

PENINSULAR TOBACCO CO. LTD, India *(continued)*

Size	Number in set		Price per card	Complete set
	30	Fish series (1916)	£2.50	—
	25	Hindoo Gods (1909)	£2.00	£50.00
	37	Nautch Girl series (1910)	£4.50	—
	25	Products of the World (1915)	£1.80	£45.00

PLANTERS' STORES & AGENCY CO. LTD, India

	? 47	Actresses — 'FROGA' (1900)	£30.00	—
	25	Beauties 'FECKSA' (1900)	£32.00	—

JOHN PLAYER & SONS

A CHANNEL ISLANDS ISSUES (WITHOUT ITC CLAUSE)

	50	Aircraft of the Royal Air Force (1938)	£1.00	£50.00
	50	Animals of the Countryside (1939)	70p	£35.00
	50	Birds and Their Young (1937)	70p	£35.00
	50	Coronation series Ceremonial Dress (1937)	70p	£35.00
	50	Cricketers (1938)	£1.40	£70.00
	50	Cycling (1939)	£1.20	£60.00
L	25	Famous Beauties (1937)	£2.00	£50.00
	50	Film Stars 3rd series (1938)	£1.10	£55.00
L	25	Golf (1939)	£7.00	—
	50	International Air Liners (1936)	70p	£35.00
	50	Military Uniforms of the British Empire Overseas (1938):		
		A Adhesive backs	£1.20	£60.00
		B Non-adhesive backs	£1.30	£65.00
	50	Modern Naval Craft (1939)	80p	£40.00
	50	Motor Cars 1st series (1936)	£1.60	£80.00
	50	Motor Cars 2nd series (1937)	£1.60	£80.00
	50	National Flags and Arms (1936)	70p	£35.00
L	25	Old Hunting Prints (1938)	£3.20	—
L	25	Old Naval Prints (1936)	£3.20	—
L	25	Racing Yachts (1938)	£4.00	—
	50	RAF Badges (1937)	90p	£45.00
	50	Sea Fishes (1935)	70p	£35.00
L	25	Types of Horses (1939)	£4.00	—
L	25	Zoo Babies (1937)	£2.00	—

B GENERAL OVERSEAS ISSUES

	50	Aeroplane series (1926)	£2.00	—
	50	Arms and Armour (1926)	£2.60	£130.00
MP	50	Beauties 1st series (1925):		
		A Black and white fronts	£1.40	£70.00
		B Coloured fronts	£1.50	£75.00
MP	50	Beauties 2nd series (1925)	£1.40	£70.00
	52	Birds of Brilliant Plumage (1927)	£3.50	—
	25	Bonzo Dogs (1923)	£4.20	—
	50	Boy Scouts (1924)	£2.00	—
M	25	British Live Stock (1924)	£6.00	—
	50	Butterflies (Girls) (1928)	£4.50	—
	25	Dogs (Heads) (1927)	£1.00	£25.00
	32	Drum Horses (1911)	£6.50	—
	25	Flag Girls of All Nations (1908)	£6.50	—
	50	Household Hints (1928-29)	90p	£45.00
	50	Lawn Tennis (1928)	£2.80	—
	50	Leaders of Men (1925)	£1.60	£80.00
	48	Pictures of the East (1931)	£1.80	£90.00

JOHN PLAYER & SONS *(continued)*

Size	*Number in set*		*Price per card*	*Complete set*
	25	Picturesque People of the Empire (1928)	£2.00	£50.00
M	53	Playing Cards (1929)	£1.20	—
	50	Pugilists in Action (1928)	£3.00	—
	50	Railway Working (1926)	£1.60	£80.00
P	50	The Royal Family at Home and Abroad (1927)	£2.00	—
	50	Ships Flags and Cap Badges (1930)	£1.40	£70.00
	50	Signalling series (1926)	£1.30	—
	25	Whaling (1930)	£2.40	£60.00

POLICANSKY BROS, South Africa

	50	Beautiful Illustrations of South African Fauna (1925)	£7.50	—

RICHMOND CAVENDISH CO. LTD

	28	Chinese Actors and Actresses (1922)	£4.00	—
P	50	Cinema Stars (1926)	£3.00	—

RUGGIER BROS, Malta

M	50	Story of the Knights of Malta (c1925)	£5.00	—

SCERRI, Malta

		Beauties and Children (c1930):		
	150	A Black and white, no borders	80p	—
	? 86	B Black and white, white border	£9.00	—
	45	C Coloured	£1.30	—
MP	50	Beautiful Women (c1935)	£1.40	£70.00
MP	480	Cinema Artists (c1935)	£1.60	—
MP	180	Cinema Stars (c1935)	£1.80	—
MP	50	Famous London Buildings (c1935)	£3.00	—
MP	60	Film Stars 1st series Nos 1-60 (c1935)	£1.80	—
MP	60	Film Stars 2nd series Nos 61-120 (c1935)	£1.80	—
	52	Interesting Places of the World (c1936)	50p	£26.00
P	25	International Footballers (c1935)	£8.00	—
M	401	Malta Views (c1930)	60p	—
M	51	Members of Parliament — Malta (c1930)	44p	£22.00
	146	Prominent People (c1930)	90p	—
MP	100	Scenes from Films (c1935)	£1.50	—
LP	100	Talkie Stars (c1930)	£1.80	—
M	100	World's Famous Buildings (c1930)	55p	£55.00

J.J. SCHUH TOBACCO CO. PTY LTD, Australia

ALL SERIES ISSUED 1920-25

	60	Australian Footballers series A (half-full length)	£4.00	—
	40	Australian Footballers series B (Rays)	£4.00	—
	59	Australian Footballers series C (oval frame)	£7.50	—
		Australian Jockeys:		
	30	A Numbered	£5.00	—
	30	B Unnumbered	£5.00	—
P	72	Cinema Stars	£1.70	—
	60	Cinema Stars	£2.00	—
L	12	Maxims of Success	£40.00	—
P	72	Official War Photographs	£2.50	—
P	96	Portraits of Our Leading Footballers	£2.50	—

G. SCLIVAGNOTI, Malta

Size	Number in set		Price per card	Complete set
	50	Actresses and Cinema Stars (1923)	£2.00	—
MP	71	Grand Masters of the Orders of Jerusalem (1897)	£9.00	—
P	102	Opera Singers (1897)	£9.00	—
M	100	Opera Singers (1897)	£9.00	—

SIMONETS LTD, Jersey, Channel Islands

MP	36	Beautiful Women (c1925)	£4.50	—
P	24	Cinema Scenes series (c1925)	£5.50	—
P	27	Famous Actors and Actresses (c1925)	£4.50	—
	50	Local Footballers (c1914)	£3.50	—
	25	Picture Series (c1920)	£4.00	—
P	27	Sporting Celebrities (c1930)	£7.00	—
LP	50	Views of Jersey (plain back) (c1940)	£2.00	—

THE SINSOCK & CO., Korea

	20	Korean Girls (c1905)	£12.00	—

SNIDERS & ABRAHAMS PTY LTD, Australia

		Actresses (c1905):		
	30	A Gold background	£6.00	—
	14	B White Borders	£6.00	—
	20	Admirals and Warships of USA (1908)	£6.00	—
	60	Animals (c1912)	£3.00	—
	60	Animals and Birds (c1912):		
		A 'Advertisement Gifts' issue	£2.50	—
		B 'Peter Pan' issue	£3.00	—
	15	Australian Cricket Team (1905)	£35.00	—
	16	Australian Football Incidents in Play (c1906)	£7.00	—
	24	Australian Footballers (full length) series AI with blue framelines (1905)	£7.50	—
	50	Australian Footballers (full length) series AII without framelines (1905)	£7.50	—
	76	Australian Footballers (½ length) series B (1906)	£6.00	—
	76	Australian Footballers (½ length) series C (1907)	£6.00	—
	140	Australian Footballers (head and shoulders) series D (1908)	£4.50	—
	60	Australian Footballers (head in oval) series E (1910)	£4.50	—
	60	Australian Footballers (head in rays) series F (1911)	£4.50	—
	60	Australian Footballers (with pennant) series G (1912)	£4.50	—
	60	Australian Footballers (head in star) series H (1913)	£4.50	—
	60	Australian Footballers (head in shield) series I (1914)	£4.50	—
	56	Australian Footballers (½-¾ length) series J (1910)	£6.50	—
	48	Australian Jockeys, back in blue (1907)	£3.00	—
	83	Australian Jockeys, back in brown (1908)	£3.50	—
	56	Australian Racehorses, horizontal back (1906)	£3.50	—
	56	Australian Racehorses, vertical back (1907)	£3.50	—
	40	Australian Racing Scenes (1911)	£3.50	—
	? 133	Australian VCs and Officers (1917)	£4.50	—
	12	Billiard Tricks (c1910)	£9.00	—
	60	Butterflies and Moths, captions in small letters (c1912)	£1.60	—
	60	Butterflies and Moths, captions in block letters (c1912)	£1.60	—
	60	Cartoons and Caricatures (c1908)	£5.50	—
	12	Coin Tricks (c1910)	£8.00	—
	64	Crests of British Warships (1915)	£4.50	—
	40	Cricketers in Action (1906)	£40.00	—
	12	Cricket Terms (c1906)	£25.00	—

SNIDERS & ABRAHAMS PTY LTD, Australia *(continued)*

Size	*Number in set*		*Price per card*	*Complete set*
	32	Dickens series (c1910)	£4.00	—
	16	Dogs (c1910):		
		A 'Standard' issue	£7.00	—
		B 'Peter Pan' issue:		
		1 White panel	£7.00	—
		2 Gilt panel	£7.00	—
		C 'Coronet' issue	£7.00	—
	6	Flags (shaped metal) (c1910)	£3.00	—
	6	Flags (shaped card) (c1910)	£3.00	—
	60	Great War Leaders and Warships (c1915):		
		A Front in green	£3.00	—
		B Front in sepia brown	£3.00	—
	30	How to Keep Fit (c1908)	£4.50	—
	60	Jokes (c1906):		
		A 'Aristocratica' issue	£3.50	—
		B 'Standard' issue	£3.50	—
	12	Match Puzzles (c1910)	£8.00	—
	48	Medals and Decorations (c1915)	£4.50	—
M	48	Melbourne Buildings (c1915)	£6.00	—
	25	Natives of the World (c1906)	£12.00	—
	12	Naval Terms (c1906)	£6.00	—
	29	Oscar Ashe, Lily Brayton and Lady Smokers (1911)	£4.50	—
	40	Shakespeare Characters (c1908)	£4.50	—
	30	Signalling — Semaphore and Morse (c1916)	£6.00	—
	14	Statuary (c1906)	£8.00	—
	60	Street Criers in London, 1707 (c1916)	£7.00	—
	32	Views of Victoria in 1857 (c1908)	£8.00	—
P	250	Views of the World 1908	£2.40	—

STAR TOBACCO CO., India

	52	Beauties (PC inset) (c1898)	£22.00	—
	52	Indian Native Types (PC inset) (c1898)	£22.00	—

TEOFANI & CO. LTD

LP	50	Teofani's Icelandic Employees (1930)	£6.00	—

TOBACCO PRODUCTS CORPORATION, USA

	220	Movie Stars (1915)	£2.50	—

TOBACCO PRODUCTS CORPORATION OF CANADA LTD

	? 45	Canadian Sports Champions (c1920)	£10.00	—
	60	Do You Know (1924)	£5.50	—
	60	Hockey Players (1926)	£15.00	—
	120	Movie Stars (c1920)	£2.50	—
	? 163	Movie Stars Set 4 (c1920)	£2.50	—

TUCKETT LIMITED, Canada

	25	Autograph series (c1913)	£26.00	—
	? 106	Beauties and Scenes (c1910)	£8.00	—
	25	Boy Scout series (c1915)	£18.00	—
P	100	British Views without Tucketts on front (c1912)	£1.80	—

TUCKETT LIMITED, Canada *(continued)*

Size	*Number in set*		*Price per card*	*Complete set*
P	? 224	British Views with Tucketts on front (c1912)	£1.80	—
P	80	British Warships (c1915)	£7.50	—
P	50	Canadian Scenes (c1912)	£1.70	—
	53	Playing Card Premium Certificates (c1930)	£7.50	—
	52	Tucketts Aeroplane series (1930)	£3.50	—
	52	Tucketts Aviation series (1929)	£3.50	—
	52	Tucketts Auction Bridge series (1930)	£5.00	—

UNITED TOBACCO COMPANIES (SOUTH) LTD, South Africa

A WITH FIRM'S NAME

	50	Aeroplanes of Today (1936):		
		A 'Box 78 Capetown'	£1.30	£65.00
		B 'Box 1006 Capetown'	£1.30	£65.00
	50	Animals and Birds Koodoo issue (1923)	£5.50	—
L	24	Arms and Crests of Universities and Schools of South Africa (1930)	£1.20	£30.00
L	52	Boy Scouts, Girl Guide and Voortrekker Badges (1932)	£1.50	£80.00
L	62	British Rugby Tour of South Africa (1938)	£1.30	£80.00
	50	Children of All Nations (1928)	90p	—
	50	Cinema Stars 'Flag Cigarettes' (1924)	£1.80	£90.00
	60	Do You Know? (1929)	60p	£36.00
	50	Do You Know 2nd series (1930)	60p	£30.00
	50	Do You Know 3rd series (1931)	60p	£30.00
K	28	Dominoes 'Ruger Cigarettes' (1934)	£6.00	—
L	50	Exercises for Men and Women (1932)	£1.00	£50.00
	48	Fairy Tales 1st series Flag issue (1928)	£1.30	—
	48	Fairy Tales 2nd series Flag issue (1928)	£1.30	—
	24	Fairy Tales (1926) (booklets)	£10.00	—
L	120	Farmyards of South Africa (1934)	40p	£50.00
M	50	Household Hints (1926)	£2.00	—
	25	Interesting Experiments (1930)	£1.40	£35.00
L	100	Medals and Decorations of the British Commonwealth of Nations (1941)	80p	—
	50	Merchant Ships of the World (1925)	£1.00	£50.00
	50	Motor Cars (1923)	£3.20	—
L	100	Our Land (1938)	22p	£22.00
L	200	Our South Africa Past and Present (1938)	15p	£30.00
L	24	Pastel Plates (1938)	£1.20	£30.00
L	88	Philosophical Sayings (1938)	£1.20	—
	25	Picturesque People of the Empire (1929)	£1.40	£35.00
K	53	Playing Cards 'Flag' Cigarettes	£1.80	—
K	53	Playing Cards 'Lifeboat' Cigarettes (1934)	£1.60	—
M	53	Playing Cards 'Lotus Cigarettes' (1934)	£2.00	—
L	53	Playing Cards 'Loyalist Cigarettes' (1934)	£2.00	—
K	53	Playing Cards 'MP Cigarettes' (1934)	£2.00	—
K	53	Playing Cards 'Rugger Cigarettes' (1934)	£3.00	—
L	50	Racehorses South Africa Set 1 (1929)	£1.50	—
L	52	Racehorses South Africa Set 2 (1930):		
		A Inscribed 'a series of 50'	£1.50	—
		B Inscribed 'a series of 52'	£1.50	—
	50	Regimental Uniforms (1937)	£1.50	£75.00
	50	Riders of the World (1931)	£1.20	£60.00
L	52	S. A. Flora (1935):		
		A With 'CT Ltd'	50p	—
		B Without 'CT Ltd'	40p	£22.00
	25	South African Birds 1st series (1927)	£1.40	—
	25	South African Birds 2nd series (1927)	£1.40	—

Size	*Number in set*		*Price per card*	*Complete set*
L	52	South African Butterflies (1937)	80p	£42.00
L	52	South African Coats of Arms (1931)	50p	£26.00
L	65	South African Rugby Football Clubs (1933)	£1.00	£65.00
L	52	Sports and Pastimes in South Africa (1936)	£1.30	£65.00
L	47	Springbok Rugby and Cricket Teams (1931)	£2.40	—
L	28	1912-13 Springboks (1913)	£35.00	—
	25	Studdy Dogs (1925)	£3.50	—
L	40	Views of South African Scenery 1st series (1918):		
		A Text back	£4.50	—
		B Anonymous plain back	£4.50	—
L	36	Views of South African Scenery 2nd series (1920)	£4.50	—
	25	Wild Flowers of South Africa 1st series (1925)	£1.20	—
	25	Wild Flowers of South Africa 2nd series (1926)	£1.20	—
	50	The World of Tomorrow (1938)	80p	£40.00
B	***WITHOUT FIRM'S NAME***			
	50	African Fish (1937)	£1.20	£60.00
	50	British Aeroplanes (1933)	£1.40	—
EL	25	Champion Dogs (1934)	£3.00	—
	30	Do You Know (1933)	70p	£21.00
	50	Eminent Film Personalities (1930)	£1.80	—
	50	English Period Costumes (1932)	90p	£45.00
	25	Famous Figures from South African History (1932)	£1.80	—
L	100	Famous Works of Art (1939)	22p	£22.00
	25	Flowers of South Africa (1932)	£1.80	—
M	50	Humour in Sport (1929)	£2.20	—
L	100	Our Land (1938)	30p	—
M	150	Our South African Birds (1942)	27p	£40.00
L	150	Our South African Birds (1942)	22p	£33.00
M	100	Our South African Flora (1940)	17p	£17.00
L	100	Our South African Flora (1940)	17p	£17.00
M	100	Our South African National Parks (1941)	18p	£18.00
L	100	Our South African National Parks (1941)	16p	£16.00
L	50	Pictures of South Africa War Effort (1942)	30p	£15.00
	50	Riders of the World (1931)	£1.20	£60.00
	50	Safety First (1936)	80p	£40.00
	40	Ships of All Times (1931)	£1.60	—
	25	South African Birds 2nd series	£2.40	—
L	17	South African Cricket Touring Team (1929):		
		A Fronts with autographs	£20.00	—
		B Fronts without autographs	£20.00	—
M	100	South African Defence (1939)	23p	£23.00
L	50	South African Places in Interest (1934)	30p	£15.00
P	50	Stereoscopic Photographs Assorted Subjects (1928)	90p	—
P	50	Stereoscopic Photographs of South Africa (1929)	90p	—
	50	The Story of Sand (1934)	90p	£45.00
M	50	Tavern of the Seas (1939)	50p	£25.00
	25	Warriors of All Nations (crossed swords at base) (1937)	£1.60	£40.00
	25	What's This (1929)	£1.60	£40.00
	50	Wild Animals of the World (1932)	£1.20	£60.00
M	40	Wonders of the World (1931)	90p	—
M	100	World Famous Boxers (c1935)	£5.00	—
C	***SILK ISSUES***			
M	20	British Butterflies (c1920)	£9.00	—
M	30	British Roses (c1920)	£9.00	—
M	65	Flags of All Nations (c1920)	£3.00	—

UNITED TOBACCO COMPANIES (SOUTH) LTD, South Africa *(continued)*

Size	*Number in set*		*Price per card*	*Complete set*
M	25	Old Masters (c1920)	£8.00	—
M	50	Pottery Types (c1920)	£6.50	—
M	50	South African Flowers Nd 1-50 (c1920)	£3.50	—
M	50	South African Flowers Nd 51-100 (c1920)	£3.50	—

UNIVERSAL TOBACCO CO. PTY LTD, South Africa

	835	Flags of All Nations (1935)	90p	—

S.W. VENABLE TOBACCO CO., USA

EL	?	Actresses (c1890)	£27.00	—

WESTMINSTER TOBACCO CO. LTD

A *CARD ISSUES*

M	332	Adamsons Oplevelser (1930)	£17.00	—
M	50	Beauties (1924)	£2.60	—
MP	100	Beautiful Women (1915)	£2.30	—
M	50	Birds, Beasts and Fishes (1923)	£2.30	—
		British Beauties (1915):		
M	102	A Coloured	£2.70	—
M	86	B Uncoloured	£4.00	—
	48	British Royal and Ancient Buildings (1925)	£1.00	£50.00
M	50	Butterflies and Moths (1920)	£2.20	—
	36	Canada 1st series (1926)	£1.00	£36.00
	36	Canada 2nd series (1928)	£1.00	£36.00
	30	Celebrated Actresses (1921)	£5.00	—
	100	Cinema Artistes green back (1929-33)	£3.00	—
	50	Cinema Artistes grey back (1929-33)	£3.00	—
	48	Cinema Celebrities (1935)	£3.00	—
	50	Cinema Stars (1926)	£2.20	—
MP	50	Cinema Stars black and white (1930)	£2.50	—
MP	50	Cinema Stars (1930) hand coloured	£2.50	—
M	27	Dancing Girls (1917)	£5.50	—
	50	Do You Know (1922)	£2.50	—
	24	Fairy Tale (booklets) (1926)	£5.00	—
M	100	Famous Beauties (1916):		
		A Captions in brown	£2.00	—
		B Captions in blue	£2.00	—
MP	52	Film Favourites (1927):		
		A Uncoloured	£3.50	—
		B Coloured	£3.50	—
M	50	Film Personalities (1931)	£3.00	—
M	50	Garden Flowers of the World (1917)	£2.50	—
	40	The Great War Celebrities (1914)	£6.00	—
	48	Indian Empire 1st series (1925)	£1.00	£50.00
	48	Indian Empire 2nd series (1926)	£1.00	£50.00
P	50	Islenzkar Eimskipamyndir (1931)	£2.20	£110.00
P	50	Islenzkar Landslagmyndir (1928)	£2.00	£100.00
P	50	Islenzkar Landslagmyndir 2nd series (1929)	£2.00	£100.00
	40	Merrie England Studies (1914)	£7.00	—
	36	Modern Beauties (1938)	£3.50	—
MP	52	Movie Stars (1925)	£3.00	—
	36	New Zealand 1st series (1928)	£1.00	£36.00

WESTMINSTER TOBACCO CO. LTD *(continued)*

Size	*Number in set*		*Price per card*	*Complete set*
P	36	New Zealand 2nd series (1929)	£1.00	£36.00
K	53	Playing Cards (1934)	£2.00	—
M	55	Playing Cards (1934):		
		A Blue back	£2.00	—
		B Red back	£2.00	—
P	50	Popular Film Stars (1926)	£3.00	—
P	36	South Africa 1st series (1928)	£1.00	£36.00
P	36	South Africa 2nd series (1928)	£1.00	£36.00
M	49	South African Succulents (1936)	25p	£12.50
M	100	Stage and Cinema Stars, captions in grey (1921)	£2.00	—
M	100	Stage and Cinema Stars, captions in black (1921)	£2.20	—
M	50	Stars of Filmland (1927)	£2.80	—
	50	Steamships of the World (1920)	£6.00	—
M	50	Uniforms of All Ages (1917)	£9.00	—
P	50	Views of Malaya (1930)	£5.50	—
	25	Wireless (1923)	£4.50	—
M	50	Women of Nations (1922)	£4.00	—
	50	The World of Tomorrow (1938)	90p	£45.00
B	***SILK ISSUES***			
M	50	Garden Flowers of the World (c1914)	£4.50	—
M	24	Miniature Rugs (c1925)	£16.00	—

W.D. & H.O. WILLS

A	***CHANNEL ISLAND ISSUES (without ITC clause)***			
	50	Air Raid Precautions (1938)	70p	£35.00
	50	Association Footballers (1936)	£1.50	£75.00
	50	Dogs (1937)	70p	£35.00
	50	Garden Flowers by Richard Sudell (1939)	40p	£20.00
	50	Garden Hints (1938)	40p	£20.00
	50	Household Hints (1936)	40p	£20.00
	50	Life in the Royal Navy (1939)	40p	£20.00
	50	Our King and Queen (1937)	50p	£25.00
	50	Railway Equipment (1939)	40p	£20.00
	50	The Sea Shore (1938)	40p	£20.00
	50	Speed (1938)	40p	£20.00
	50	Wild Flowers 1st series (1936)	40p	£20.00
	50	Wild Flowers 2nd series (1937)	40p	£20.00
B	***GENERAL OVERSEAS ISSUES***			
	50	Actors and Actresses, scroll backs in green (c1905) Ref. 32:		
		A Portraits in black and white	£3.50	—
		B Portraits flesh tinted	£2.50	—
	30	Actresses — brown and green (1905) Ref. 116. Scissors issue	£3.30	£100.00
	50	Actresses — four colours surround (c1904) Ref. 117:		
		A Scissors issue	£5.50	—
		B Green scroll back issue	£2.50	—
	30	Actresses — orange/mauve surround (c1915) Scissors issue Ref. 118:		
		A Surround in Orange	£2.50	£75.00
		B Surround in mauve	£1.50	£45.00
	100	Actresses (c1903) Ref. 34:		
		A Capstan issue	£2.50	—
		B Vice Regal issue	£2.50	—
	250	Actresses (c1903) Ref. 33:		
		A Front portrait in black	£2.50	—
		B Front portrait in red	£3.00	—

Size	*Number in set*		*Price per card*	*Complete set*
	25	Actresses — Tabs type numbered Ref. 16 (1902)	£13.00	—
	50	Actresses — Tabs type unnumbered Ref. 119 Scissors issue (c1905)	£12.00	—
	30	Actresses unicoloured 1 (c1908) Ref. 120:		
		A Scissors issue, back in red	£1.50	£45.00
		B Scissors issue, back in purple brown	£2.50	£75.00
	30	Actresses — unicoloured 11 (c1908) Ref. 121 Scissors issue	£2.00	£60.00
	50	Aeroplanes (1925)	£2.50	—
	60	Animals (cut-outs) (1913):		
		A Havelock issue	£1.60	—
		B Wills' Specialities issue	80p	£54.00
	50	Animals and Birds (1912):		
		A With text, without title	£4.00	—
		B Without text, with title	£4.00	—
		C Without text or title	£4.00	—
	50	Arms and Armour (1910):		
		A Capstan issue	£1.40	—
		B Havelock issue	£3.00	—
		C Vice Regal issue	£1.40	—
		D United Service issue	£2.50	£125.00
	50	Arms of the British Empire (1910):		
		A Backs in black	90p	£45.00
		B Wills' Specialities issue	90p	—
		C Havelock issue	£7.00	—
	25	Army Life 1910 Scissors issue	£2.20	£55.00
	50	Art Photogravures 1st series (1913):		
		A Size 67 × 33mm	70p	—
		B Size 67 × 44mm	70p	—
	50	Art Photogravures 2nd series (1913)	70p	—
	42	Australian Club Cricketers (1905) Ref. 59A:		
		A Dark blue backs	£17.00	—
		B Green backs	£17.00	—
		C Pale blue backs	£17.00	—
	25	Australian and English Cricketers (1903) Ref. 59B	£12.00	—
	25	Australian and English Cricketers (1909) Ref. 59C:		
		A Capstan issue:		
		i Framework in scarlet	£12.00	—
		ii Framework in blue	£12.00	—
		B Vice Regal issue:		
		i Framework in scarlet	£12.00	—
		ii Framework in blue	£12.00	—
	60	Australian and South African Cricketers (1910) Ref. 59D:		
		A Capstan issue:		
		i Framework in scarlet	£14.00	—
		ii Framework in blue	£14.00	—
		B Havelock issue:		
		i Framework in scarlet	£35.00	—
		ii Framework in blue	£35.00	—
		C Vice Regal issue:		
		i Framework in scarlet	£14.00	—
		ii Framework in blue	£14.00	—
	100	Australian Scenic series (1928)	75p	—
	50	Australian Wild Flowers (1913):		
		A Wills' Specialities issue, grey-brown back	70p	£35.00
		B Wills' Specialities issue, green back	£2.00	—
		C Havelock issue	£3.50	—

Size	*Number in set*		*Price per card*	*Comple s*
		Aviation (1910):		
	85	A Black backs 'Series of 85':		
		i Capstan issue	£1.60	–
		ii Vice Regal issue	£1.60	–
	75	B Black backs 'Series of 75':		
		i Capstan issue	£1.50	–
		ii Havelock issue	£2.50	–
		iii Vice Regal issue	£1.50	–
	75	C Green back 'Series of 75':		
		i Capstan issue	£1.60	–
		ii Havelock issue	£3.50	–
		iii Vice Regal issue	£1.60	–
	50	Aviation series (1910):		
		A W.D. AND H.O. Wills back	£3.00	–
		B Anonymous backs with album clause	£2.80	–
		C Anonymous backs without album clause	£2.80	–
	? 97	Baseball series (1912) Pirate issue	£100.00	–
	40	Beauties — brown tinted (c1913):		
		A Scissors issue	£1.40	£56.0
		B Star circle and leaves issue	£3.00	–
	30	Beauties — 'Celebrated Actresses' Ref. 140 Scissors issue (1921)	£4.50	–
	52	Beauties — Heads and shoulders set in background Ref. 141 (1911):		
		A Scissors issue:		
		i Background to packets plain	£4.50	–
		ii Background to packets latticework design	£3.00	£160.
		B Star circle and leaves issue	£5.00	–
P	25	Beauties 1st series (1924) Ref. 142	£3.00	–
P	50	Beauties 2nd series (1924) Ref. 143	£3.00	–
	32	Beauties — Picture Hats (c1914) Ref. 144:		
		A Scissors issue	£3.00	£95.0
		B Star circle and leaves issue	£5.00	–
MP	72	Beauties — red star and circle back (c1920) Ref. 145	£11.00	–
	50	Beauties — red tinted (1905) Ref. 146	£1.60	£80.
	30	Beauties and Children (c1910) Ref. 147 Scissors issue	£2.25	£68.
P	50	Beautiful New Zealand (c1928)	32p	£16.
	50	Best Dogs of Their Breed (1916):		
		A Havelock issue	£6.00	–
		B Wills' Specialities issue	£3.50	–
		C Anonymous back, Wills' on front	£7.00	–
	30	Birds and Animals (1911) Ruby Queen issue	£2.20	–
	50	Birds, Beasts and Fishes (c1925)	40p	£20.0
	100	Birds of Australasia (1912):		
		A Green backs:		
		i Capstan issue	£1.00	£100.
		ii Havelock issue	£2.50	–
		iii Vice Regal issue	£1.00	£100.
		B Yellow backs:		
		i Havelock issue	£2.50	–
		ii Wills' Specialities issue	£1.00	–
	52	Birds of Brilliant Plumage:		
		A Four Aces issue (1924)	£2.50	–
		B Pirate Issue:		
		i With border on front (1914)	£4.00	–
		ii Without border on front (1916)	£4.00	–
		C Red star, circle and leaves issue (1914)	£4.50	–
	25	Birds of the East 1st series Ruby Queen issue (1912)	£1.40	£35.

Size	*Number in set*		*Price per card*	*Complete set*
	25	Birds of the East 2nd series Ruby Queen issue (1912)	£1.40	£35.00
	36	Boxers (1911):		
		A Scissors issue	£7.00	—
		B Green star and circle issue	£7.00	—
		Britain's Defenders (1915):		
		A Wills' Specialities issue:		
	50	i Inscribed 'A Series of 50'	£1.40	£70.00
	8	ii Without inscription 'A Series of 50'	£7.00	—
	50	B Havelock issue	£2.50	—
	50	C Scissors issue:		
		i Red upright 'Scissors' packet	£1.30	£65.00
		ii Green upright 'Scissors' packet	£1.40	£70.00
		iii Red slanting 'Scissors' packet	£1.30	£65.00
	50	D Green star and circle issue	£1.70	—
	43	British Army Boxers (1913) Scissors issue	£5.00	—
	50	British Army Uniforms (c1910):		
		A Wild Woodbine issue	£5.00	£250.00
		B Flag issue	£5.00	—
		C Scissors issue	£4.50	£225.00
	101	British Beauties (c1915)	£1.80	—
	50	British Empire series (1913):		
		A Capstan issue	80p	£40.00
		B Havelock issue	£1.60	—
		C Vice Regal issue	80p	£40.00
	48	British Royal and Ancient Buildings (1925)	32p	£16.00
	45	British Rugby Players (1930)	£1.50	—
	50	Chateaux (1925)	£4.00	—
	50	Children of All Nations (1925)	60p	£30.00
	100	China's Famous Warriors (1911) Pirate issue Ref. 357:		
		A First 25 subjects	£1.80	£45.00
		B Second 25 subjects	£1.80	£45.00
		C Third 25 subjects	£1.80	£45.00
		D Fourth 25 subjects	£1.80	£45.00
	28	Chinese Actors and Actresses (1907) Pirate issue Ref. 361	£2.80	—
	25	Chinese Beauties 1st Series (1907) Pirate issue Ref. 362:		
		A Vertical back	£1.40	£35.00
		B Horizontal back	£1.60	£40.00
	25	Chinese Beauties 2nd series (1909) Pirate issue Ref. 363:		
		A With framelines on front	£1.40	£35.00
		B Without framelines on front	£1.40	£35.00
	30	Chinese Children's Games (1911) Ruby Queen issue Ref. 364	£2.00	—
	50	Chinese Costumes Pirate issue (1928) Ref. 365	£3.00	—
	25	Chinese Pagodas (1905-10) Pirate issue Ref. 366	£35.00	—
	50	Chinese Proverbs brown Ref. 367 (1928):		
		A Pirate issue	£1.25	—
		B Ruby Queen issue	£3.00	—
	50	Chinese Proverbs coloured (1914-16) Pirate issue Ref. 368:		
		A Back in blue:		
		i Without overprint	£1.25	—
		ii With overprint	£1.25	—
		B Back in olive green	£1.50	—
	40	Chinese Trades (c1905) Autocar issue	£6.00	—
	50	Chinese Transport (1914) Ref. 370 Ruby Queen issue	£2.50	—
	50	Cinema Stars Four Aces issue (c1926):		
		A Numbered	£1.60	£80.00
		B Unnumbered	£1.80	£90.00

Size	*Number in set*		*Price per card*	*Comple s*
	25	Cinema Stars (c1922) Scissors issue	£2.20	£55.
	50	Coaches and Coaching Days (1925)	£1.40	£70.
		Conundrums (c1900):		
	25	A With album clause	£10.00	–
	25	B Without album clause	£10.00	–
	25	C Without album clause redrawn	£10.00	–
	50	D Without album clause inscribed '50 Different'	£10.00	–
M	68	Crests and Colours of Australian Universities, Colleges and Schools (1922)	60p	£40.
P	63	Cricketers Ref. 59E (c1925)	£7.00	–
	25	Cricketer series Ref. 59F (1902)	£85.00	–
	50	Cricketer series (1901) Ref. 59G	£85.00	–
P	48	Cricket Season 1928-29	£2.50	–
	27	Dancing Girls (1915) Scissors issue:		
		A Inscribed '28 Subjects' (No. 3 not issued)	£2.30	–
		B Inscribed '27 Subjects'	£2.30	–
	25	Derby Day series (1914):		
		A Scissors issue:		
		i With title	£6.00	–
		ii Without title	£8.00	–
		B Star and circle issue	£7.00	–
	50	Dogs — Scenic backgrounds (1925)	70p	£35.
M	20	Dogs — Heads 1st series (1927):		
		A Wills' World Renown Cigarettes issue:		
		i With album clause	£2.60	–
		ii Without album clause	£2.60	–
		B Three Castles and Vice Regal Cigarettes issue	£2.60	–
M	20	Dogs-Heads 2nd series (1927)	£2.60	–
	32	Drum Horses (c1909):		
		A Scissors issue:		
		i Vertical format, open Scissors packet	£8.00	–
		ii Horizontal format, closed Scissors packet	£6.00	£190.
		B United Service issue	£6.00	–
		C Green star, circle and leaves issue	£6.00	–
P	25	English Cricketers (1926)	£2.40	£60.
M	25	English Period Costumes (1928):		
		A White card	£1.80	–
		B Cream card	£1.80	£45
		Etchings (of Dogs) (1925):		
	26	A Small size English language issues:		
		i With 'Gold Flake Cigarettes'	£7.00	–
		ii Without 'Gold Flake Cigarettes'	£1.50	£40.
	26	B Small size Dutch language issues:		
		i With framelines to back	£8.00	–
		ii Without framelines to back	£8.00	–
M	26	C Medium size	£3.00	–
	25	The Evolution of the British Navy (c1915)	£2.60	£65.
		Famous Film Stars (1934):		
	100	A Small size	70p	–
M	100	B Medium size:		
		i White card	£1.60	–
		ii Cream card	£1.60	–
MP	100	Famous Film Stars (c1936)	£2.40	–
	50	Famous Footballers (1914):		
		A Scissors issue	£6.50	–
		B Star and circle issue	£7.00	–
	50	Famous Inventions (without ITC clause) (1927)	70p	£35.

Size	*Number in set*		*Price per card*	*Complete set*
	75	Film Favourites Four Aces issue (1928)	£1.30	—
	50	Fish of Australasia (1912):		
		A Capstan issue	70p	£35.00
		B Havelock issue	£1.30	—
		C Vice Regal issue	70p	£35.00
		Flag Girls of All Nations (1908):		
	50	A Capstan issue	£2.00	—
	50	B Vice Regal issue	£2.00	—
	25	C United Service issue	£2.40	£60.00
	25	D Scissors issue:		
		i Numbered	£10.00	—
		ii Unnumbered	£10.00	—
	25	E Green star, circle and leaves issue	£2.40	£60.00
	8	Flags, shaped metal (1915)	£8.00	—
	126	Flags and Ensigns (1903)	£1.10	—
	25	Flags of the Empire (no ITC clause) (1926)	£5.50	—
		Flowers Purple Mountain issue (1914):		
	20	A Numbered	£11.00	—
	100	B Unnumbered	£11.00	—
	50	Football Club Colours Scissors/Special Army Quality issue (1905)	£6.00	—
	28	Football Club Colours and Flags (1913):		
		A Capstan issue	£3.00	—
		B Havelock issue	£5.00	—
	200	Footballers (1933):		
		A Small size	60p	—
		B Medium size	£1.20	—
	50	Girls of All Nations (1908):		
		A Capstan issue	£2.20	—
		B Vice Regal issue	£2.20	—
		C Green star, circle and leaves issue	£2.50	—
	25	Governors-General of India, Scissors issue (1911)	£6.00	—
M	25	Heraldic Signs and Their Origins (1925)	£1.40	£35.00
	30	Heroic Deeds (1914) Scissors issue	£2.20	£65.00
	50	Historic Events (1912):		
		A Wills' Specialities issue	90p	£45.00
		B Havelock issue	£2.00	—
M	25	History of Naval Dress (1930)	£15.00	—
	50	Homeland Events (1927)	40p	£20.00
	50	Horses of Today (1906):		
		A Capstan issue	£2.20	—
		B Havelock issue	£4.00	—
		C Vice Regal issue	£2.20	—
	50	Household Hints (1927):		
		A With 'Wills' Cigarettes' at top back	50p	—
		B Without 'Wills' Cigarettes' at top back	£1.30	—
		Houses of Parliament (c1912):		
	33	A Pirate issue	£1.20	£40.00
	32	B Star and circle issue	£2.00	£65.00
	50	Indian Regiments (c1912):		
		A Scissors issue	£6.00	—
		B Star and circle issue	£7.50	—
	50	Interesting Buildings (1905)	£1.80	£90.00
	67	International Footballers Season 1909-1910:		
		A Scissors issue (1910)	£7.00	—
		B United Services issue (1910)	£7.00	—
		C Flag issue (1911)	£7.00	—

Size	*Number in set*		*Price per card*	*Complete set*
	50	Jiu-Jitsu (c1910):		
		A Scissors issue	£5.00	—
		B Flag issue	£4.50	—
	53	Jockeys and Owners Colours with PC inset Scissors issue (1914)	£6.00	—
	50	Lighthouses (1925)	£1.20	£60.00
	45	Melbourne Cup Winners (1906)	£6.00	—
	50	Merchant Ships of the World (1925) (without ITC clause)	90p	£45.00
	40	Merrie England Studies (Male) (1916)	£5.50	—
	24	Merveilles du Monde (1927)	£5.50	—
	25	Military Portraits (1917) Scissors issue	£4.00	—
M	25	Miniatures — oval medallions (1914)	£45.00	—
K	52	Miniature Playing Cards Scissors issue (1906)	£11.00	—
	50	Modern War Weapons (1916):		
		A Wills' Specialities issue	£1.40	—
		B Havelock issue	£2.70	—
	25	Modes of Conveyance (1928) Four Aces issue	£1.60	£40.00
	48	Motor Cars (1924)	£1.50	£75.00
P	50	Motor Cars (1928)	£1.00	£50.00
	50	Motor Cycles (1926)	£2.80	£140.00
P	48	Movie Stars (1927)	£3.50	—
	50	Music Hall Celebrities (1911) Scissors issue	£5.50	—
	50	National Flags and Arms (1936)	£1.40	—
M	25	The Nation's Shrines (1928)	£1.40	£35.00
P	50	Nature Studies (1928)	£1.30	—
	50	New Zealand Birds (1925)	60p	£30.00
P	50	New Zealand — Early Scenes and Maori Life (1926)	32p	£16.00
	50	New Zealand Footballers (1928)	60p	£30.00
	50	New Zealand Race Horses (1928):		
		A Cream card	80p	£40.00
		B White card	90p	—
	50	N.Z. Butterflies, Moths and Beetles (1925)	70p	£35.00
	25	Past and Present (1929)	£1.00	£25.00
	50	Past and Present Champions (1908):		
		A Capstan Cigarette issue	£4.50	—
		B Capstan Tobacco issue	£6.00	—
	25	Picturesque People of the Empire (1928)	80p	£20.00
	25	Pirates and Highwaymen (1925)	£1.00	£25.00
	25	Police of the World (1910)	£8.00	—
M	70	Practical Wireless (1923)	£6.00	—
		Products of the World — Maps and Scenes (1913):		
	50	A Pirate issues	£1.20	—
	25	B Green star, circle and leaves issue	£1.60	—
	50	Products of the World — Scenes only (1929)	35p	£17.50
	50	Prominent Australian and English Cricketers (1907) Ref. 59H	£11.00	—
	23	Prominent Australian and English Cricketers (1907) Ref. 59I	£12.00	—
	59	Prominent Australian and English Cricketers (1911) Ref. 59J:		
		A Capstan issue:		
		i 'A Series of 50'	£12.00	—
		ii 'A Series of .../A Series of 59'	£12.00	—
		B Vice Regal issue:		
		i 'A Series of 50'	£12.00	—
		ii 'A Series of .../A Series of 59'	£12.00	—
		C Havelock issue	£35.00	—
	25	Puzzle series (1910) Scissors/United Service issue	£5.00	—
	50	Races of Mankind (1910)	£11.00	—

Size	*Number in set*		*Price per card*	*Complete set*
	50	Railway Engines (1924)	80p	£40.00
	50	Railway Working (1927)	£1.40	£70.00
	50	Regimental Colours and Cap Badges (c1910):		
		A Scissors issue	£1.30	£65.00
		B United Service issue:		
		i Red back	£1.30	£65.00
		ii Blue back	£1.30	£65.00
	33	Regimental Pets (1911) Scissors issue	£5.50	—
	50	Regimental Standards and Cap Badges (1930)	60p	£30.00
	50	Riders of the World:		
		A Capstan/Vice Regal/Pennant/Wills' Specialities issue (1913)	£1.40	—
		B Havelock issue (1913)	£3.00	—
		C Back in red-brown (1925)	80p	£40.00
	50	Romance of the Heavens (1928) (No ITC clause)	£1.40	—
	25	Roses (1912):		
		A Purple Mountain issues:		
		i With Wills' Cigarettes on front	£5.00	—
		ii Without Wills' Cigarettes on front	£5.00	—
		B Plain backs with Wills' Cigarettes on front	£5.00	—
	50	The Royal Family at Home and Abroad (1927)	70p	—
	50	Royal Mail (with Wills' Cigarettes on fronts) (1913):		
		A Capstan issue	£3.00	£150.00
		B Havelock issue	£4.50	—
		C Vice Regal issue	£3.00	£150.00
		D With anonymous backs	£5.50	—
		E With plain back	£5.50	—
	50	The Royal Navy (c1930)	£1.30	£65.00
	100	Royalty, Notabilities and Events in Russia, China and South Africa (1902)	£2.00	—
	27	Rulers of the World (1911)	£6.50	—
		Russo-Japanese series (1905):		
	100	A Fronts in black	£1.50	£150.00
	50	B Fronts in red	£7.00	—
	50	Safety First (1937)	80p	£40.00
P	48	Scenes from the Empire (1939)	£1.60	£80.00
	30	Semaphore Signalling (1910)	£3.00	£90.00
	50	Ships and Shipping (1928)	50p	£25.00
	36	Ships and Their Pennants (1913)	£5.50	—
	50	Ships' Badges (1926)	80p	£40.00
	50	Signalling series (1913):		
		A Capstan issue	£1.00	£50.00
		B Havelock issue	£2.30	—
		C Vice Regal issue	£1.00	£50.00
	40	Sketches in black and white (1905)	£2.30	—
		Soldiers of the World (1903):		
	50	A Numbered	£6.50	—
	75	B Unnumbered	£9.00	—
	99	South African Personalities (1900)	£90.00	—
	30	Sporting Girls (1913) Scissors issue	£7.00	—
	50	A Sporting Holiday in New Zealand (1928):		
		A Small size	60p	£30.00
		B Medium size	70p	£35.00
	25	Sporting Terms (1905):		
		A Capstan issue	£9.00	—
		B Vice Regal issue	£9.00	—
	50	Sports of the World (1917)	£3.50	

Size	*Number in set*		*Price per card*	*Complete set*
	50	Stage and Music Hall Celebrities (1904) (Portrait in oval frame):		
		A Capstan issue	£3.00	—
		B Vice Regal issue	£3.00	—
		C Havelock issue	£4.50	—
	50	Stage and Music Hall Celebrities (1904) (Portrait in oblong frame)	£3.00	—
P	52	Stars of the Cinema (1925):		
		A Text back	£4.50	—
		B Four Aces issue	£3.50	—
	50	Time and Money in Different Countries (1908):		
		A Capstan issue	£1.10	—
		B Havelock issue	£2.20	—
		C Vice Regal issue:		
		i With album clause	£1.10	£55.00
		ii Without album clause	£1.10	£55.00
	50	A Tour Round the World (1907)	£2.20	—
	50	Types of the British Army (1912):		
		A Capstan issue	£2.00	—
		B Vice Regal issue	£2.00	—
	50	Types of the Commonwealth Forces (1910):		
		A Capstan issue	£2.20	—
		B Vice Regal issue	£2.20	—
		C Havelock issue	£4.50	—
	25	United States Warships (1911):		
		A Capstan issue	£2.20	—
		B Havelock issue	£4.00	—
		C Vice Regal issue	£2.20	—
P	50	Units of the British Army and RAF (1928)	50p	£25.00
	50	USS Co's Steamers (1930)	£2.40	—
	50	VCs (1925)	£1.30	£65.00
	25	Victoria Cross Heroes (c1915):		
		A Havelock issue	£4.00	—
		B Wills' Specialities issue	£1.80	£45.00
		C Scissors issue	£2.40	£60.00
	10	Victorian Football Association (c1910):		
		A Capstan on front	£3.50	—
		B Havelock on front	£4.00	—
	19	Victorian Football League (c1910):		
		A Capstan on front	£3.50	—
		B Havelock on front	£4.50	—
	215	Views of the World (1908):		
		A Numbers 1-50 plain backs (anonymous)	80p	—
		B Numbers 51-215 blue back Capstan issue	80p	—
		C Numbers 51-215 green back Vice Regal issue	80p	—
	25	Village Models series (1925):		
		A Small size	£1.20	£30.00
		B Medium size	£5.00	—
	50	War Incidents 1st series (1916):		
		A Wills' Specialities issue	£1.00	—
		B Havelock issue	£1.80	—
		C Scissors issue	£1.50	£75.00
	50	War Incidents 2nd series (1917):		
		A Wills' Specialities issue	£1.00	£50.00
		B Havelock issue	£5.00	—
	50	War Pictures (1915):		
		A Wills' Specialities issue	£1.00	£50.00
		B Havelock issue	£2.20	—

W.D. & H.O. WILLS *(continued)*

Size	Number in set		Price per card	Complete set
	50	Warships (1925)	£1.20	£60.00
	30	What It Means (1916) Scissors issue	£1.20	£36.00
		Wild Animals (c1935):		
	50	A Small size titled 'Wild Animals' heads	60p	£30.00
M	25	B Medium size titled 'Wild Animals'	£1.20	£30.00
	50	Wild Animals of the World (1906):		
		A Bristol and London issue	£10.00	—
		B Celebrated Cigarettes issue	£4.50	£225.00
		C Star, circle and leaves issue	£7.00	—
	25	Wonders of the World (1926)	£1.20	£30.00
	25	The World's Dreadnoughts (1910):		
		A Capstan issue	£1.80	—
		B Vice Regal issue	£1.80	—
		C No ITC clause	£2.20	£55.00
	50	Zoo (1927):		
		A Scissors issue without descriptive back	£4.00	—
		B Wills' issue with descriptive back	30p	£15.00
MP	50	Zoological series (1922)	£1.80	—
C	***SILK ISSUES 1911-17***			
M	50	Arms of the British Empire	£3.00	—
M	50	Australian Butterflies	£3.00	—
M	50	Birds and Animals of Australia	£3.00	—
M	50	Crests and Colours of Australian Universities, Colleges and Schools	£3.00	—
EL	1	Flag	£25.00	—
	28	Flags of 1914-18 Allies:		
		A Backs with letterpress in capitals	£2.00	—
		B Backs with letterpress in small lettering	£2.00	—
	38	Kings and Queens of England	£4.50	—
M	50	Popular Flowers:		
		A Backs inscribed 'Now being inserted in the large packets'	£4.00	—
		B Backs inscribed 'Now being inserted in the 1/- packets'	£4.00	—
M	67	War Medals	£3.00	—

J. WIX & SONS LTD

P	24	Royal Tour in New Zealand (1928)	£12.00	—

GEO. F. YOUNG & BRO., USA

L	?	Actresses (c1890)	£25.00	—

ANONYMOUS SERIES — Chinese Language

M	10	Chinese Beauties (Ref ZE2-11) (c1930)	—	£20.00
M	10	Chinese Series (Ref ZE9-31) (c1930)	—	£20.00
	10	Chinese Views & Scenes (Ref ZE9-49) (c1930)	—	£20.00
	48	Hints on Association Football (Ref ZE3-2) (c1930)	—	£10.00
	30	Safety First (Ref ZE9-41) (c1930)	—	£36.00

SECTION III

REPRINT SERIES

The following are classic series which have been reprinted, and are clearly marked as such on each card.

ALLEN & GINTER/GOODWIN/KIMBALL (USA)

Size	*Printing*	*Number in set*		*Complete set*
A	C	28	Baseball Greats of 1890 (reprinted 1991)	£6.00

ALLEN & GINTER (USA)

A	C	50	Celebrated American Indian Chiefs 1888 (reprinted 1989)	£7.50
A	C	50	Fruits (Children) 1891 (reprinted 1989)	£7.50
A	C	50	Pirates of the Spanish Main 1888 (reprinted 1996)	£7.50

BARBERS TEA LTD

A	C	24	Cinema & Television Stars 1955 (reprinted 1993)	£5.00

FELIX BERLYN

A	C	25	Golfing Series Humorous 1910 (reprinted 1989)	£6.00

ALEXANDER BOGULAVSKY LTD

—	C	12	Big Events on the Turf (133 × 70mm) 1924 (reprinted 1995)	£7.50
A	C	25	Conan Doyle Characters 1923 (reprinted 1996)	£6.00
A	C	25	Winners on the Turf 1925 (reprinted 1995)	£6.00

BRITISH AMERICAN TOBACCO CO. LTD

A	C	50	Motorcycles 1927 (reprinted 1991)	£7.50

CARRERAS LTD

A	C	50	Famous Airmen & Airwomen 1936 (reprinted 1996)	£7.50

W.A. & A.C. CHURCHMAN

A	U	50	Boxing Personalities 1938 (reprinted 1990)	£7.50
A	C	52	Frisky 1935 (reprinted 1994)	£7.50
A	C	50	Landmarks in Railway Progress 1931 (reprinted 1994)	£7.50
A	C	50	Prominent Golfers 1931 (reprinted 1989)	£7.50
B	C	12	Prominent Golfers 1931 (reprinted 1989)	£5.00
A	C	50	Racing Greyhounds 1934 (reprinted 1989)	£7.50
—	C	48	The RAF at Work (68 × 53mm) 1938 (reprinted 1995)	£14.00

CO-OPERATIVE WHOLESALE SOCIETY LTD (C.W.S)

Size	Print-ing	Number in set		Complete set
A	C	25	Parrot Series 1910 (reprinted 1996)	£6.00
A	C	48	Poultry 1927 (reprinted 1996)	£7.50

COPE BROS. & CO. LTD

A	C	50	British Warriors 1912 (reprinted 1996)	£7.50
A	C	50	Cope's Golfers 1900 (reprinted 1983)	£7.50
A	C	50	Dickens Gallery 1900 (reprinted 1989)	£7.50
A	C	50	Shakespeare Gallery 1900 (reprinted 1989)	£7.50
A	C	25	Uniforms of Soldiers and Sailors 1898 (reprinted 1996)	£6.00

ELLIS TOB. (USA)

A	C	25	Generals of the Late Civil War 1890 (reprinted 1991)	£6.00

W. & F. FAULKNER

D2	C	12	Cricket Terms 1898 (reprinted 1991)	—
A	C	25	Prominent Racehorses of the Present day 1923 (reprinted 1993)	£6.00

J. GABRIEL

A	BW	20	Cricketers Series 1901 (reprinted 1992)	£3.50

GALLAHER LTD

A	C	25	Motor Cars 1934 (reprinted 1995)	£6.00
A	C	50	Regimental Colours and Standards 1899 (reprinted 1995)	£7.50
A	C	48	Signed Portraits of Famous Stars 1935 (reprinted 1997)	£7.50
A	C	50	Types of the British Army No. 1-50 1900 (reprinted 1995)	£7.50
A	C	50	Types of the British Army No. 51-100 1900 (reprinted 1996)	£7.50

R. & J. HILL LTD

A	C	25	Battleships and Crests 1901 (reprinted 1995)	£6.00

HUDDEN & CO. LTD

A	C	25	Famous Boxers 1927 (reprinted 1992)	£5.00

IMPERIAL TOBACCO COMPANY OF CANADA LTD

A	C	45	Hockey Players 1912 (reprinted 1987)	£9.00
A	C	36	Hockey Series 1911 (reprinted 1987)	£9.00

JONES BROS., Tottenham

A	BW	18	Spurs Footballers 1912 (reprinted 1986)	£2.00

KINNEY BROS. (USA)

A	C	25	Famous English Running Horses 1889 (reprinted 1996)	£6.00
A	C	25	Leaders 1889 (reprinted 1990)	£6.00

KNIGHT (HUSTLER SOAP)

A	C	30	Regimental Nicknames 1924 (reprinted 1996)	£6.00

LAMBERT & BUTLER

Size	*Printing*	*Number in set*		*Complete set*
A	C	25	Dance Band Leaders 1936 (reprinted 1992)	£6.00
A	C	25	Hints and Tips for Motorists 1929 (reprinted 1994)	£6.00
A	C	50	Horsemanship 1938 (reprinted 1994)	£7.50
A	C	25	London Characters 1934 (reprinted 1992)	£6.00
A	C	25	Motor Cars 1st series 1922 (reprinted 1988)	£4.00
A	C	25	Motor Cars 2nd series 1923 (reprinted 1988)	£4.00
A	C	25	Motor Cars 1934 (reprinted 1992)	£6.00
A	C	50	Motor Cycles 1923 (reprinted 1990)	£7.50
A	C	25	Motors 1908 (reprinted 1992)	£6.00
A	C	50	World's Locomotives 1912 (reprinted 1988)	£7.50

R. J. LEA LTD

A	C	50	Flowers to Grow 1913 (reprinted 1997)	£7.50

STEPHEN MITCHELL & SON

A	C	25	Angling 1928 (reprinted 1993)	£6.00
A	C	25	Regimental Crests, Nicknames and Collar Badges 1900 (reprinted 1993)	£6.00

MURRAY, SONS & CO. LTD

A	BW	20	Cricketers 1912 (reprinted 1991)	£6.00

OGDENS LTD

A	C	50	A.F.C. Nicknames 1933 (reprinted 1996)	£7.50
A	C	50	Jockeys 1930 (reprinted 1990)	£7.50
A	C	50	Modern Railways 1936 (reprinted 1996)	£7.50
A	C	50	Motor Races 1931 (reprinted 1993)	£7.50
A	C	50	Soldiers of the King 1909 (reprinted 1993)	£7.50
A	C	50	The Story of the Life Boat 1940 (reprinted 1989)	—

GODFREY PHILLIPS LTD

A	C	25	Railway Engines 1924 (reprinted 1997)	£6.00
A	C	25	Types of British Soldiers 1900 (reprinted 1997)	£6.00

JOHN PLAYER & SONS

A	C	50	Aeroplanes (Civil) 1935 (reprinted 1990)	£7.50
A	C	50	Aircraft of The Royal Air Force 1938 (reprinted 1990)	£7.50
A	C	50	Aviary & Cage Birds 1933 (reprinted 1989)	£7.50
B	C	25	Aviary and Cage Birds 1935 (reprinted 1987)	£7.50
B	C	24	Cats 1936 (reprinted 1986)	£7.50
A	C	25	Characters from Dickens 1912 (reprinted 1990)	£6.00
A	C	25	Characters from Dickens 2nd series 1914 (reprinted 1990)	£6.00
A	C	50	Cricketers 1934 (reprinted 1990)	£7.50
A	C	50	Cricketers Caricatures by "Rip" 1926 (reprinted 1993)	£7.50
A	C	50	Derby and Grand National Winners 1933 (reprinted 1988)	£7.50
A	C	50	Dogs' Heads (silver-grey backgrounds) 1940 (reprinted 1994)	£7.50
A2	C	25	England's Naval Heroes 1898 descriptive (reprinted 1987)	£10.00
A	C	50	Film Stars 3rd series 1938 (reprinted 1989)	£7.50
A	C	50	Fire-Fighting Appliances 1930 (reprinted 1991)	£7.50
B	C	25	Game Birds and Wild Fowl 1928 (reprinted 1987)	£7.50
A	C	50	Gilbert & Sullivan 2nd series 1927 (reprinted 1990)	£7.50
B	C	25	Golf 1939 (reprinted 1986)	£7.50

OHN PLAYER & SONS *(continued)*

ize	*Printing*	*Number in set*		*Complete set*
A	C	25	Highland Clans 1908 (reprinted 1997)	£6.00
A	C	50	Kings & Queens 1935 (reprinted 1990)	£7.50
A	C	50	Military Series 1900 (reprinted 1983)	£7.50
A	C	50	Motor Cars 1st series 1936 (reprinted 1990)	£7.50
A	C	25	Napoleon 1916 (reprinted 1989)	£6.00
A	C	50	Old England's Defenders 1898 (reprinted 1987)	—
B	C	25	Old Hunting Prints 1938 (reprinted 1989)	£7.50
B	C	25	Old Naval Prints 1936 (reprinted 1989)	£7.50
A	C	50	Poultry 1931 (reprinted 1993)	£7.50
B	C	25	Racing Yachts 1938 (reprinted 1987)	£7.50
A	C	50	Regimental Standards & Cap Badges 1930 (reprinted 1993)	£7.50
A	C	50	Regimental Uniforms Nd. 51-100 1914 (reprinted 1995)	£7.50
	C	24	Treasures of Britain 1931 (reprinted 1996)	£7.50
	C	50	Uniforms of the Territorial Army 1939 (reprinted 1990)	£7.50

EEVES LTD

	C	25	Cricketers 1912 (reprinted 1993)	£8.00

ALMON & GLUCKSTEIN LTD

	C	15	Billiard Terms 1905 (reprinted 1997)	£5.00

OHN SINCLAIR LTD

	C	50	British Sea Dogs 1926 (reprinted 1997)	£7.50

INGLETON & COLE LTD

	BW	35	Famous Boxers 1930 (reprinted 1992)	£6.00

& J. SMITH

	C	25	Cinema Stars 1920 (reprinted 1987)	£6.00
	C	25	Prominent Rugby Players 1924 (reprinted 1992)	£8.00

ADDY & CO.

	C	20	Clowns & Circus Artists 1920 (reprinted 1991)	£6.00
	BW	238	County Cricketers 1907 (reprinted 1987)	£27.50
			Individual Counties of the above set:	
		15	Derbyshire	£2.00
		15	Essex	£2.00
		16	Gloucestershire	£2.00
		15	Hampshire	£2.00
		15	Kent	£2.00
		15	Lancashire	£2.00
		14	Leicestershire	£2.00
		15	Middlesex	£2.00
		15	Northamptonshire	£2.00
		14	Nottinghamshire	£2.00
		15	Somersetshire	£2.00
		15	Surrey	£2.00
		15	Sussex	£2.00
		15	Warwickshire	£2.00
		14	Worcestershire	£2.00
		15	Yorkshire	£2.00

TADDY & CO. *(continued)*

Size	*Print-ing*	*Number in set*		*Comple se*
A	C	25	Famous Jockeys 1910 (reprinted 1996)	£6.0
A	BW	15	Prominent Footballers Aston Villa 1907 (reprinted 1992)	£2.0
A	BW	15	Prominent Footballers Leeds 1907 (reprinted 1992)	£2.0
A	BW	15	Prominent Footballers Liverpool 1907 (reprinted 1992)	£2.0
A	BW	15	Prominent Footballers Manchester Utd 1907 (reprinted 1992)	£2.0
A	BW	15	Prominent Footballers Newcastle Utd 1907 (reprinted 1992)	£2.0
A	BW	15	Prominent Footballers Queens Park Rangers 1907 (reprinted 1992)	£2.0
A	BW	15	Prominent Footballers Woolwich Arsenal 1907 (reprinted 1992)	£2.0
A	BW	15	South African Cricket Team 1907 (reprinted 1992)	£4.5
A	C	25	Territorial Regiments 1908 (reprinted 1996)	£6.0
A	C	25	Thames Series 1903 (reprinted 1996)	£6.0
A	C	20	Victoria Cross Heroes (Nos 1-20) 1900 (reprinted 1996)	£6.0
A	C	20	Victoria Cross Heroes (Nos 21-40) 1900 (reprinted 1996)	£6.0
A	C	25	Victoria Cross Heroes (Nos 101-125) 1905 (reprinted 1996)	£6.0

D. C. THOMSON

A	C	24	Motor Bike Cards 1929 (reprinted 1993)	£6.0
A	C	20	Motor Cycles 1923 (Wizard Series) (reprinted 1993)	£6.0

W.D. & H.O. WILLS

EL	C	4	Advert Postcards of Packings 1902 (reprinted 1988)	£5.0
A	C	50	Cricketers 1896 (reprinted 1982)	£7.5
A	C	50	Cricketers 1901 (reprinted 1983)	–
B	C	25	Dogs 1914 (reprinted 1987)	£7.5
B	C	25	Famous Golfers 1930 (reprinted 1987)	£7.5
A	C	50	Fish & Bait 1910 (reprinted 1990)	£7.5
B	C	25	Lawn Tennis 1931 (reprinted 1988)	£7.5
A	C	50	Life in the Hedgerow 1950 (reprinted 1991, Swan Vestas)	£7.5
A	C	50	Military Aircraft (unissued c1967) (reprinted 1991)	£8.5
A	C	50	Military Motors 1916 (reprinted 1994)	£7.5
A	C	58	Musical Celebrities 2nd series including 8 substituted cards 1914 (reprinted 1987)	£8.5
A	C	50	Naval Dress &Badges 1909 (reprinted 1997)	£7.5
A	C	50	Old English Garden Flowers 2nd Series 1913 (reprinted 1994)	£7.5
B	C	40	Puppies by Lucy Dawson (unissued) (reprinted 1990)	£12.5
A	C	50	Railway Engines 1924 (reprinted 1995)	£7.5
A	C	50	Railway Engines 1936 (reprinted 1992)	£7.5
A	C	50	Railway Equipment 1939 (reprinted 1993)	£7.5
A	C	50	Railway Locomotives 1930 (reprinted 1993)	£7.5
A	C	12	Recruiting Posters 1915 (reprinted 1987)	£3.0
B	C	25	Rigs of Ships 1929 (reprinted 1987)	£7.5
A	C	50	Roses 1st series 1912 (reprinted 1994)	£7.5
A	C	50	Rugby Internationals 1929 (reprinted 1996)	£7.5
A	C	50	Waterloo 1915 (reprinted 1987)	£10.0
A	C	50	Wild Flowers 1st series 1936 (reprinted 1993)	–
A	C	25	World's Dreadnoughts 1910 (reprinted 1994)	£6.0

W.D. & H.O. WILLS (Australia)

A	C	50	Types of the British Army 1912 (reprinted 1995)	£7.5
A	C	50	War Incidents 2nd Series 1917 (reprinted 1995)	£7.5

W.H. & J. WOODS LTD

A	C	25	Types of Volunteers & Yeomanry 1902 (reprinted 1996)	£6.0

ILLUSTRATIONS

47 Carreras, History of Naval Uniforms
48 Carreras, Flags of All Nations
49 Wills, Gems of Belgium Architecture
50 Amalgamated Tobacco, Famous British Ships 2nd Series
51 Wills, World of Firearms
52 R.J. Hill, Views of Interest 1st Series
53 R.J. Hill, Views of Interest 3rd Series
54 Lambert & Butler, Wonders of Nature
55 Players, R.A.F. Badges
56 Gallaher, Sporting Personalities
57 Ogden, Actors' Natural & Character Studies
58 Players, Football Caricatures by Mac
59 Players, Cycling
60 G. Phillips, Coronation of Their Majesties
61 J. Sinclair, Well Known Footballers — Scottish
62 R. Lloyd, Cinema Stars Nos. 28-54
63 Players, War Decorations & Medals
64 R.J. Hill, Nautical Songs
65 Churchman, Association Footballers 1st Series
66 G. Phillips, Soldiers of the King
67 Lewis, Horoscopes
68 Ogden, Shots from the Films
69 Ogden, Air Raid Precautions
70 R.J. Lea, Coronation Souvenir
71 Players, Motor Cars 2nd Series
72 Wills, Garden Hints
73 Players, Birds and Their Young 1st Series (Unissued)
74 Drapkin, Girls of Many Lands
75 Ardath, Figures of Speech
76 Gallaher, Art Treasures of the World
77 Players, Golden Age of Steam
78 G. Phillips, Flower Studies
79 Gallaher, Dogs (Series of 24)
80 Wills, Pond & Aquarium 1st Series
81 Gallaher, British Birds
82 Gerard, Modern Armaments
83 Murray, Story of Ships
84 Carreras, Famous Airmen & Airwomen
85 Morris, At the London Zoo Aquarium
86 Wills, Army Life (Overseas Issue)
87 R. Lloyd, Zoo Series
88 Co-operative Wholesale Society, Wayside Flowers (Grey Back)
89 Ardath, Famous Scots
90 Players, Military Uniforms of the British Empire Overseas
91 Players, Gilbert & Sullivan 2nd Series
92 Marcovitch, Beauties
93 Allman, Pin Up Girls 1st Series
94 Wills, Garden Flowers 1939
95 Players, Characters from Dickens 1923
96 G. Phillips, British Birds and Their Eggs
97 Gallaher, Film Episodes

98 Wills, Alpine Flowers
99 Players, Tennis
100 G. Phillips, Famous Crowns
101 Players, Association Cup Winners
102 Churchman, Treasure Trove
103 G. Phillips, Bird Painting
104 Anstie, Places of Interest
105 Wills, Household Hints 1st Series
106 Churchman, Well Known Ties 2nd Series
107 Gallaher, Stars of Screen and Stage
108 Wills, Radio Celebrities 2nd Series
109 Wills, Life in the Tree Tops
110 United Kingdom Tobacco, British Orders of Chivalry & Valour
111 Churchman, Boxing Personalities
112 Players, Uniforms of the Territorial Army
113 G. Phillips, Personalities of To-day
114 Players, Coronation Series Ceremonial Dress
115 Wills, Famous Inventions
116 Wills, Air Raid Precautions
117 Teofani, Past and Present Weapons of War
118 Players, International Air Liners
119 Mitchell, Famous Crosses
120 Bucktrout, Inventors Series
121 G. Phillips, Sportsmen Spot the Winner
122 Gallaher, Army Badges
123 R.J. Lea, Flowers to Grow
124 Millhoff, Things to Make
125 Carreras, School Emblems
126 Wills, The Reign of H.M. King George V
127 Ogden, Prominent Racehorses of 1933
128 Taddy, Motor Cars
129 Cope, Castles
130 Wills, Railway Engines 1936
131 Wills, Old English Garden Flowers 1st Series
132 Mitchell, Money
133 Carreras, Celebrities of British History 1935
134 G. Phillips, Famous Minors
135 Ogden, Poultry 1st Series
136 Players, Animals of the Countryside
137 Wills, Safety First
138 Churchman, World Wonders Old and New
139 Gallaher, Champions of Screen & Stage
140 Gallaher, Champions 2nd Series
141 Ogden, Steeplechase Trainers' and Owners' Colours
142 Rothman, Landmarks in Empire History
143 Players, Dogs Pairs and Groups
144 Players, British Naval Craft

1

2

3

4

5

6

7

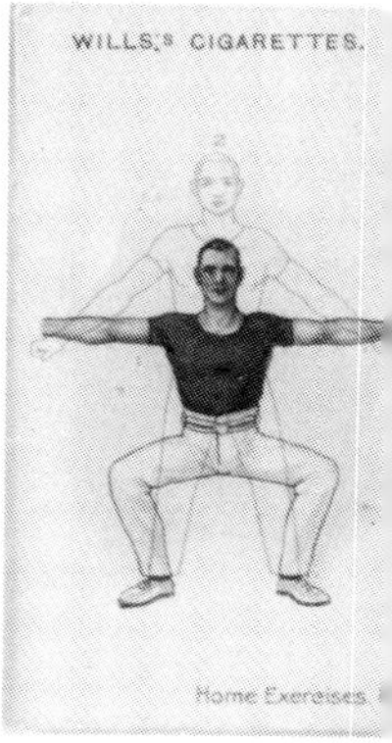

8

9

10

11

12

LAMBERT & BUTLER'S
CIGARETTES
CANTERING
ON RIGHT LEG

18
ENGLISH SETTER.
RINGERS
CIGARETTES

The S.S. United States

14

Henry

17

20

21

22

23

24

25

26

27

28

29

30

31

2

33

34

35

6

37

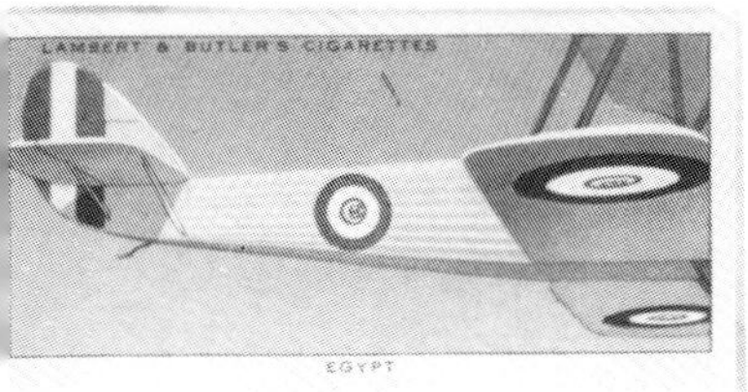

8

39

0

41

42

43

44

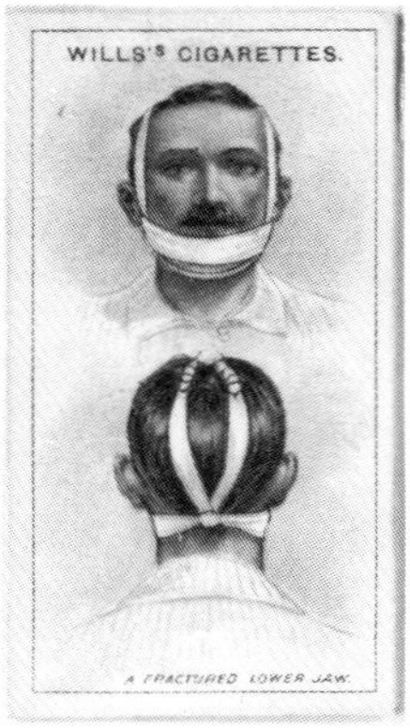

45

46

47

48

49

50

51

52

53

55

56

57

59

60

61

63

64

65

66

67

68

69

70

71

72

73

74

75

76

78

CAIRN TERRIER

WILLS'S CIGARETTES
A
B
C
D
FOUR COMMON FISHES

80

BLUE TIT

NAVAL ANTI-AIRCRAFT GUN

82

THE TRANSIT, 1800

CODY CATHEDRAL

84

BROWN TROUT

WATERING HORSES

86

87

88

89

90

91

92

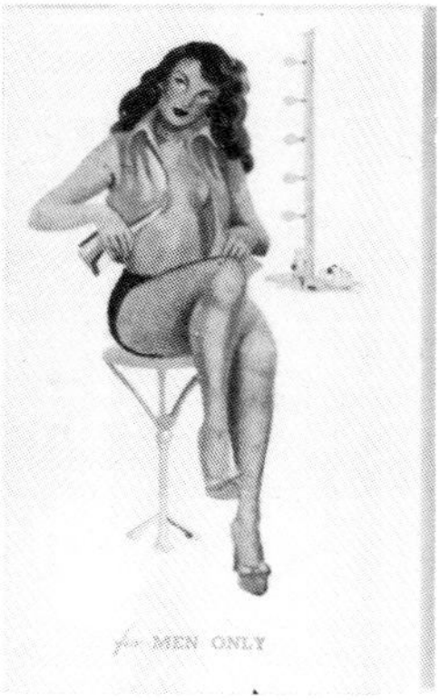

93

94

95

96

97

98

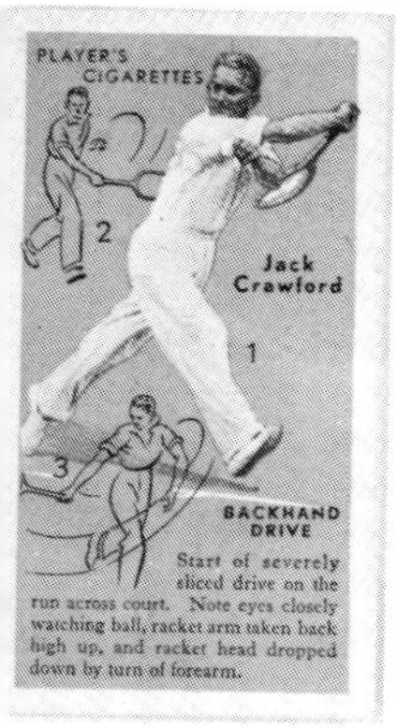

9

100

101

102

3

104

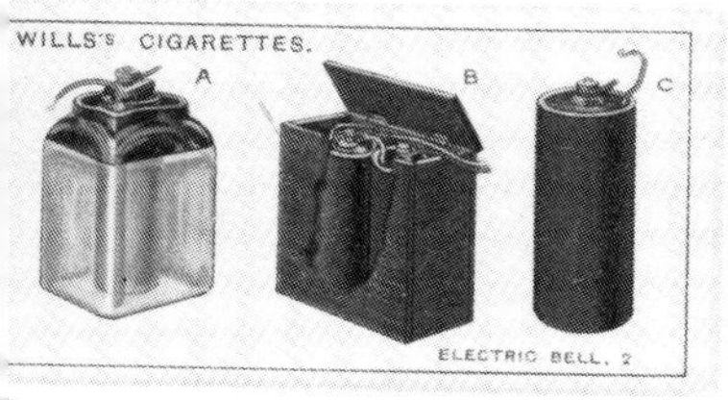

5

106

108

109

110

111

112

113

114

115

116

117

118

119

120

121

122

124

125

126

128

130

132

133

134

135

136

137

138

139

140

141

142

143

144